SECONDARY V

536

BOOK 1

GUY BRETON

Claude Delisle

André Deschênes

Antoine Ledoux

Claire Bourdeau

Benoît Côté

W&L

Wilson & Lafleur ltée
40, rue Notre-Dame Est
Montréal H2Y 1B9
(514) 875-6326

Mathematical Reflections 536, Book 1
English version of Réflexions Mathématiques 536
© 1998 Les Éditions CEC inc.
Material subsidized by the Ministère de l'Éducation
du Québec

Publishing Director
Suzanne Légaré

Production Manager
Lucie Plante-Audy

Production Coordinator
Diane Karneyeff

Translation
Services d'édition Guy Connolly

Graphic Design and Layout
Productions Fréchette et Paradis inc.

Illustrations
Marius Allen
Dan Allen

Computer Graphics
Dan Allen

Cover Design
Matteau Parent Graphistes inc.

© 1999 Wilson & Lafleur ltée
40, rue Notre-Dame Est
Montréal, Québec
H2Y 1B9

Legal deposit: 3rd quarter 1999
Bibliothèque nationale du Québec
National Library of Canada
ISBN 2-89127-470-9

Printed in Canada
1 2 3 4 5 03 02 01 00 99

Acknowledgements

The authors and the publisher wish to thank the
following people who participated in the
development of this project as consultants:

Sonya Bracken
> Mathematics Teacher
> Laurentian Regional High School

Donald Craig
> Former Mathematics Teacher
> Three Rivers High School

Cathrine Le Maistre, PhD
> Professor, Faculty of Education
> McGill University

TABLE OF CONTENTS

GLOSSARY OF MASTER KEYS

 **INVESTMENT 1**

The *Investment* is a series of exercises or problems aimed at immediate application of the newly acquired basic concepts.

 **THINK TANK**

The *Think Tank* is a forum for discussion, sharing ideas, developing your understanding and incorporating new material.

 *Math Express 1*

The *Math Express* section offers a theoretical analysis of the previously covered topics. It brings together the main mathematical concepts to be retained.

 **WORKOUT 1**

The *Workout* is a series of problems and exercises aimed at reinforcing your knowledge. The colours of the keys each have specific meanings:

: Basic problems and exercises.

: Applied problems and strategies.

: Problems that develop inductive and deductive reasoning.

: Problems that make connections and relate to real-life applications of mathematics.

: Problems that integrate the use of calculators.

 **POP QUIZ**

The *Pop Quiz* allows you to check what you have learned. Your knowledge is checked in accordance with the required objectives.

 *Interview with...*

Interview with . . . invites you to get to know those who contributed to the progress of mathematics over the centuries.

 **MY PROJECTS**

The *My Projects* section invites you to participate in creative activities that apply the mathematical skills you have acquired.

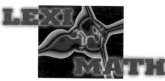 **LEXIMATH**

The *LexiMath* is a mathematical glossary. It lists useful definitions of mathematical terms and lists the key skills to be acquired during the chapter.

 **WORKSHEET 1**

This indicates that this page is found in the *Teacher's Guide* and can be reproduced.

FOREWORD

Your fifth and final year of secondary school brings you to a crossroads: you will soon be choosing the direction of your future career. This is an important choice. *Mathematical Reflections 536* is designed to give you a solid background to help prepare you for a career in the sciences. The authors have worked hard to come up with scenarios that capture your attention and pique your interest. You will come to realize the enormous impact of mathematics on every aspect of daily life.

The concepts in this book will cover a variety of areas. You will start by focusing on functions, from constant functions right through to exponential, logarithmic and trigonometric functions. You will continue to develop your deductive reasoning by studying vectors and the different metric relationships within circles and right triangles. The study of conics will open the door to more advanced scientific studies. You will develop the ability to make decisions by analysing situations in optimization and gathering statistical data on various subjects.

The problem scenarios, which your teacher will guide you through and evaluate, begin the learning process. The *Investments* will help reinforce your knowledge. The *Think Tanks* will allow you to express yourself, assimilate these new concepts, and exchange ideas with your fellow students as you work together to find novel solutions to problems. The *Workouts* will enable you to hone your skills, discover applications for these skills and develop effective problem-solving tools.

Mathematical Reflections 536 also introduces you to the men and women who have contributed to the ongoing progress of mathematical science. Perhaps someday you will contribute your share! In *My Projects*, we challenge you to follow the lead of these innovators and organize mathematically-oriented projects that will allow you to build the self-confidence needed by tomorrow's leaders.

You are now holding the right tools to complete this last stage of your high school education. Put them to work as you strive to meet your career and life objectives. If you persevere in your endeavours, you will realize your full potential. The world needs you!

Guy Breton

Reflection 1

FUNCTIONS IN THE DOMAIN OF REAL NUMBERS

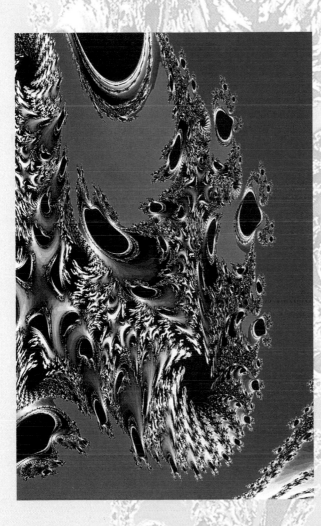

THE MAIN IDEAS

- ▶ Concept of a function
- ▶ Properties of functions
- ▶ Transforming functions
- ▶ Linear functions
- ▶ Quadratic functions
- ▶ Absolute value functions
- ▶ Square root functions
- ▶ Step functions
- ▶ Rational functions

TERMINAL OBJECTIVE

- ▶ To solve problems using functions involving real variables as models for given situations.

INTERMEDIATE OBJECTIVES

- ▶ **To represent** a situation with a function involving real variables.
- ▶ **To determine** the properties of a function involving real variables.
- ▶ **To determine** the relationships between the parameters in the rule of a function involving real variables and the corresponding Cartesian graph.
- ▶ **To graph** and **to describe** characteristics of certain real functions.
- ▶ **To determine** the rules of certain functions involving real variables, given sufficient algebraic or graphical data.
- ▶ **To determine** the sum, difference, product, quotient or composite of two functions in the domain of real numbers, given their graphs or rules.

FUNCTIONS

PROPERTIES OF FUNCTIONS

Fly the friendly skies with functions

While seated comfortably in flight, passengers can read flight information displayed on monitors in the cabin. This information, which is updated frequently during take-off, is updated less frequently as the flight progresses.

Elapsed time: 2 min Flight speed: 507 km/h Remaining distance: 5531 km Altitude: 2444 m Temperature: 6 °C	Elapsed time: 3 min Flight speed: 513 km/h Remaining distance: 5528 km Altitude : 2910 m Temperature: 1 °C	Elapsed time: 4 min Flight speed: 540 km/h Remaining distance: 5524 km Altitude : 3292 m Temperature: -2 °C
Elapsed time: 5 min Flight speed: 600 km/h Remaining distance: 5518 km Altitude : 3686 m Temperature: -3 °C	Elapsed time: 6 min Flight speed: 670 km/h Remaining distance: 5508 km Altitude : 4205 m Temperature: -10 °C	Elapsed time: 9 min Flight speed: 800 km/h Remaining distance: 5450 km Altitude : 5490 m Temperature: -28 °C
Elapsed time: 12 min Flight speed: 900 km/h Remaining distance: 5420 km Altitude : 8802 m Temperature: -41 °C	Elapsed time: 15 min Flight speed: 950 km/h Remaining distance: 5375 km Altitude : 9100 m Temperature: -45 °C	Elapsed time: 60 min Flight speed: 957 km/h Remaining distance: 4732 km Altitude : 10 100 m Temperature: -55 °C

The earth's atmosphere is divided into four main layers. In the lowest layer, known as the troposphere (from 0 to 10 km), the average temperature drops approximately 6°C for every kilometre increase in altitude.

a) What do these facts represent?

b) Can these facts be considered to be variables? Justify your answer.

c) Are these facts interrelated? If so, describe some of the connections between them.

Identifying a connection between two variables creates a **relation,** which translates into sets of ordered pairs.

A set of ordered pairs represents a **relation.** More specifically, a **relation between two variables** is a **function** when each value of the independent variable has **no more than one corresponding value** of the dependent variable.

d) Below are the Cartesian graphs of different relations for in-flight information. Which of them represent functions?

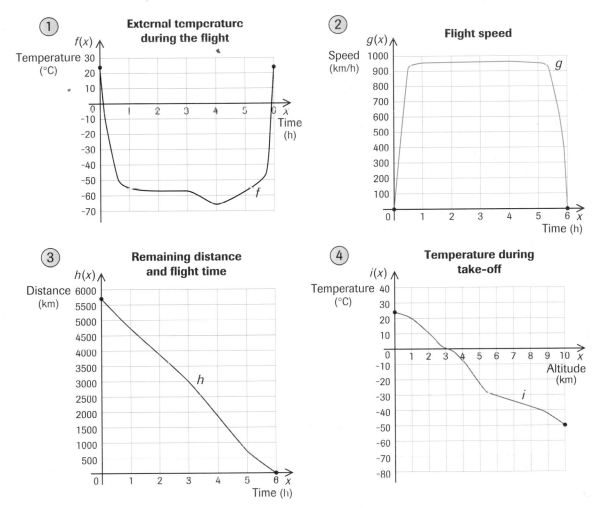

1. External temperature during the flight
2. Flight speed
3. Remaining distance and flight time
4. Temperature during take-off

The graph of a function is a set of points or a curve that **cannot have more than one point in common** with any vertical line in the same plane.

e) What must happen to the airplane in the function relating altitude (dependent variable) to elapsed time (independent variable) for the relation not to be a function?

f) Is the inverse of the previous function— that is, the relation between the altitude (independent variable) and elapsed time (dependent variable)—a function? Justify your answer using a graph.

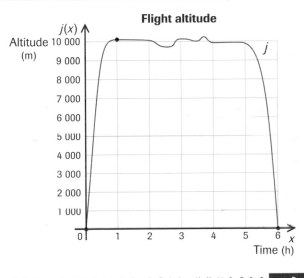

Flight altitude

A function is a relation **from** a source set **to** a target set. Usually, the **source set** and **target set** are composed of real numbers. Sometimes, especially in real-life situations, these sets are restricted to subsets of IR such as IR_+, IR_-, $\mathbb{Z}$, IN, etc. The source and target sets are usually identified in the definition of a function.

$$f: IR \longrightarrow IR \qquad\qquad g: IR_+ \longrightarrow IR \qquad\qquad h: IN \longrightarrow \mathbb{Z}$$

Since it is not necessary that each element in a function's source set should have an image, the domain is not always the same as the source set. Similarly, it is not necessary that each of the elements in the target set should be **images.**

The source set whose elements have images is called the **domain** of the function; the target set whose elements have images is called the **range** (or codomain) of the function.

The **domain** is the set of values assigned to the independent variable:

$$\text{dom } f = \{x \in IR \,|\, (x, f(x)) \in f\}.$$

The **range** or **codomain** is the set of values assigned to the dependent variable:

$$\text{ran } f = \{f(x) \in IR \,|\, (x, f(x)) \in f\}.$$

g) Determine the approximate domain and range of the functions in *d*).

As values in the domain of a function increase, if their images also increase, the function is said to be **increasing.** If their images decrease, the function is said to be **decreasing.**

This is written:

A function *f* is **increasing** over a given interval [a, b] of its domain if:

$$\forall x_1, x_2 \in [a, b] : x_1 < x_2 \implies f(x_1) \leq f(x_2).$$

A function *f* is **decreasing** over a given interval [a, b] of its domain if:

$$\forall x_1, x_2 \subset [a, b] : x_1 < x_2 \implies f(x_1) > f(x_2).$$

We can also speak of strictly increasing or strictly decreasing functions by excluding the equivalence of the two images in the previous definitions. A function that is increasing and decreasing at the same time is called a **constant** function.

A function *f* is **constant** over a given interval [a, b] of its domain if:

$$\forall x_1, x_2 \in [a, b] : x_1 \neq x_2 \implies f(x_1) = f(x_2).$$

h) Find the approximate intervals over which the function *f* is increasing and decreasing in question *d*).

Certain values of the domain and range of a function are important. This is especially true for its **zeros, value at *x* = 0** and **extremes,** as these values form the coordinates of critical points on the graph.

The **zeros,** or *x*-intercepts, of a function *f* are the values of the domain that make the function equal 0.

$$\forall x \in \text{dom } f, x \text{ is a zero if and only if } f(x) = 0.$$

The **value at *x* = 0,** or *y*-intercept, of a function *f* is the value of the range when the *x*-coordinate equals zero.

$$\text{If } f(0) \in \text{ran } f, \text{ then } f(0) \text{ is the value at zero.}$$

The **extremes** (maximum or minimum) correspond to the **maximum value** and the **minimum value** of the range, if they exist. Some maximums or minimums are absolute, others are relative.

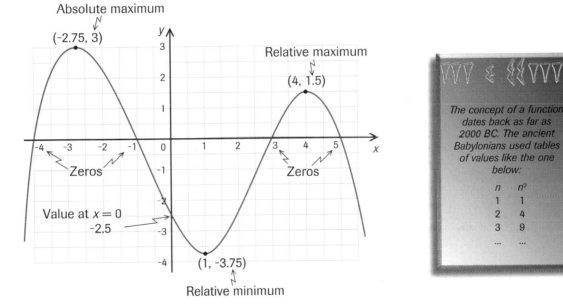

The concept of a function dates back as far as 2000 BC. The ancient Babylonians used tables of values like the one below:

n	n^2
1	1
2	4
3	9
...	...

A function *f* has:

- An **absolute maximum** at x_1 over its domain, if and only if:
$$\forall x \in \text{dom } f, \text{ we have } f(x_1) \geqslant f(x);$$

- An **absolute minimum** at x_1 over its domain, if and only if:
$$\forall x \in \text{dom } f, \text{ we have } f(x_1) \leqslant f(x);$$

- A **relative maximum** at x_1 if for every *x* in the neighbourhood of x_1, we have $f(x_1) \geqslant f(x)$;

- A **relative minimum** at x_1 if for every *x* in the neighbourhood of x_1, we have $f(x_1) \leqslant f(x)$.

i) Find the approximate maximums and minimums (absolute or relative) of the functions in question *d)*.

The images associated with the values of a function's domain can be either strictly positive, zero, or strictly negative. This is referred to as the **sign** of a function.

A function *f* is:

• **Positive** over an interval [a, b] $\Leftrightarrow \forall x \in$ [a, b], where $f(x) \geq 0$;

• **Negative** over an interval [a, b] $\Leftrightarrow \forall x \in$ [a, b], where $f(x) \leq 0$.

A function may also be strictly positive or strictly negative where $f(x) > 0$ or $f(x) < 0$.

j) Find the approximate intervals over which the domain of function *i* in question *d)* is:

1) Positive.   2) Strictly negative.

The main functions used in everyday life conform to different models. Their rules are displayed by their graphs.

k) The main types of functions are shown below. Describe the shape of the graph in each case (horizontal line, oblique line, curved line, parabola, etc.).

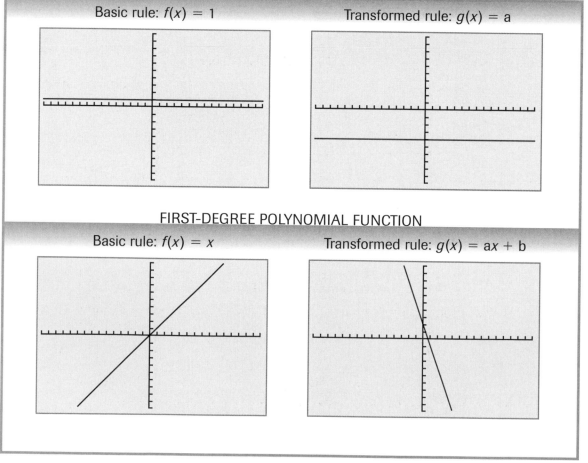

ZERO-DEGREE POLYNOMIAL (OR CONSTANT) FUNCTION

Basic rule: $f(x) = 1$ Transformed rule: $g(x) = a$

FIRST-DEGREE POLYNOMIAL FUNCTION

Basic rule: $f(x) = x$ Transformed rule: $g(x) = ax + b$

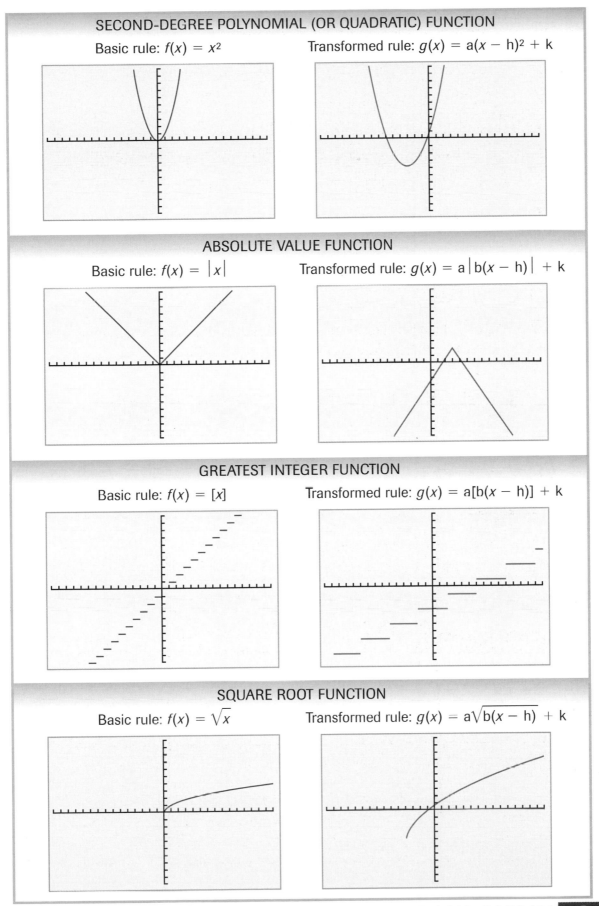

SECOND-DEGREE POLYNOMIAL (OR QUADRATIC) FUNCTION

Basic rule: $f(x) = x^2$

Transformed rule: $g(x) = a(x - h)^2 + k$

ABSOLUTE VALUE FUNCTION

Basic rule: $f(x) = |x|$

Transformed rule: $g(x) = a|b(x - h)| + k$

GREATEST INTEGER FUNCTION

Basic rule: $f(x) = [x]$

Transformed rule: $g(x) = a[b(x - h)] + k$

SQUARE ROOT FUNCTION

Basic rule: $f(x) = \sqrt{x}$

Transformed rule: $g(x) = a\sqrt{b(x - h)} + k$

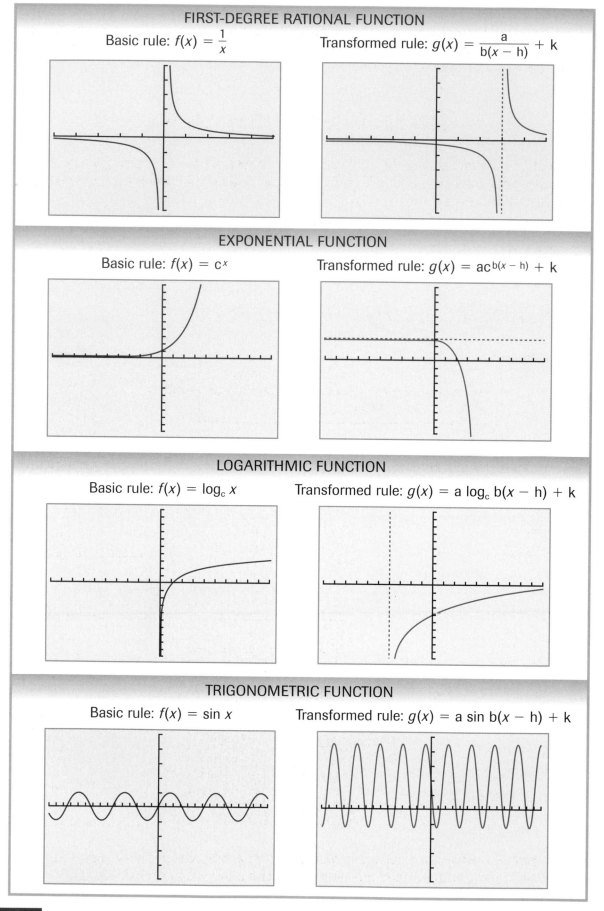

FIRST-DEGREE RATIONAL FUNCTION

Basic rule: $f(x) = \dfrac{1}{x}$

Transformed rule: $g(x) = \dfrac{a}{b(x - h)} + k$

EXPONENTIAL FUNCTION

Basic rule: $f(x) = c^x$

Transformed rule: $g(x) = ac^{b(x - h)} + k$

LOGARITHMIC FUNCTION

Basic rule: $f(x) = \log_c x$

Transformed rule: $g(x) = a \log_c b(x - h) + k$

TRIGONOMETRIC FUNCTION

Basic rule: $f(x) = \sin x$

Transformed rule: $g(x) = a \sin b(x - h) + k$

These types of functions will each be studied in turn. Finding all the properties of a function involves stating its **rule**; drawing and describing its **graph**; determining its **domain, range, zeros** and **extremes**; identifying the **intervals** over which it increases or decreases; and noting the **sign changes** throughout its domain.

THE FUNCTION RULE AND ITS PARAMETERS

A total of four parameters may be introduced into the rule of a basic function, which will generate various transformed functions. Two of these parameters affect the x-coordinates, the other two affect the y-coordinates.

These parameters are represented by the letters **a, b, h** and **k.** It is important to understand the exact role of each of these parameters. To make things clearer, each is introduced into various basic functions below, and different values are assigned to them in each of these functions.

Introducing the parameters!

Role of a:

Let's introduce the first parameter, represented by the letter **a**, into the rule of several basic functions.

a) Determine which coordinate parameter **a** modifies, then describe its effect.

$f\!\!: Y_1 = x$

$g\!\!: Y_2 = 2x$ or $Y_2 = 2Y_1$

$h\!\!: Y_3 = 3x$ or $Y_3 = 3Y_1$

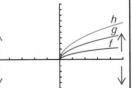

$f\!\!: Y_1 = \sqrt{x}$

$g\!\!: Y_2 = 2\sqrt{x}$ or $Y_2 = 2Y_1$

$h\!\!: Y_3 = 3\sqrt{x}$ or $Y_3 = 3Y_1$

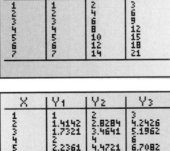

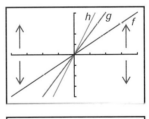

$f\!\!: Y_1 = x^2$

$g\!\!: Y_2 = 2x^2$ or $Y_2 = 2Y_1$

$h\!\!: Y_3 = 3x^2$ or $Y_3 = 3Y_1$

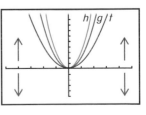

b) For each of the functions defined in a), assign **a** its appropriate value and describe the resulting changes in the corresponding graph. Use a graphing calculator for this problem.

c) Assign a value between 0 and 1 to **a** and describe the resulting changes in the graph for each of the functions defined in *a)*.

d) Here are some ordered pairs of a basic function: (0, 0), (2, 2), (4, 4), (6, 6), (8, 8). Find the corresponding ordered pairs of the transformed function obtained by introducing the following values for parameter **a** into the function rule:

1) 3   2) $\dfrac{1}{2}$ 3) $-\dfrac{3}{2}$

Role of b:

> Let's introduce the second parameter, represented by **b**, into the rule of various basic functions.

e) Determine which coordinate parameter **b** modifies, then describe its effect.

$f\!: Y_1 = \sqrt{x}$

$g\!: Y_2 = \sqrt{2x}$

$h\!: Y_3 = \sqrt{3x}$

X	Y1	Y2	Y3
1	1	1.4142	1.7321
2	1.4142	2	2.4495
3	1.7321	2.4495	3
4	2	2.8284	3.4641
5	2.2361	3.1623	3.873
6	2.4495	3.4641	4.2426
7	2.6458	3.7417	4.5826

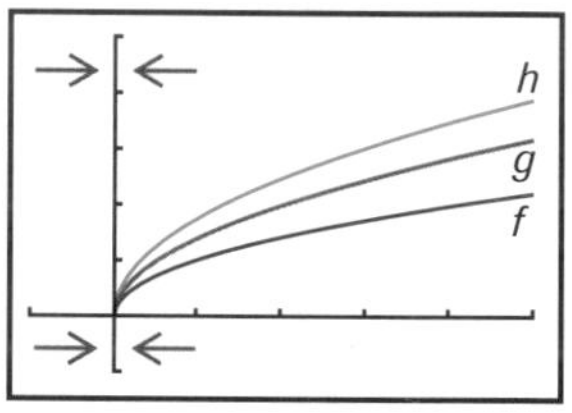

$f\!: Y_1 = \log x$

$g\!: Y_2 = \log 2x$

$h\!: Y_3 = \log 3x$

X	Y1	Y2	Y3
1	0	.30103	.47712
2	.30103	.60206	.77815
3	.47712	.77815	.95424
4	.60206	.90309	1.0792
5	.69897	1	1.1761
6	.77815	1.0792	1.2553
7	.8451	1.1461	1.3222

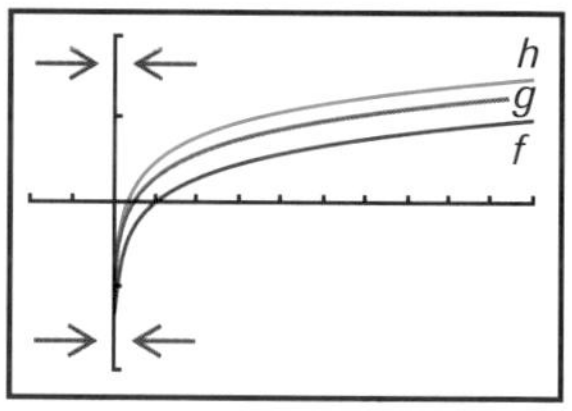

$f\!: Y_1 = \sin x$

$g\!: Y_2 = \sin 2x$

X	Y1	Y2
1	.84147	.9093
2	.9093	-.7568
3	.14112	-.2794
4	-.7568	.98936
5	-.9589	.544
6	-.2794	-.5366
7	.65699	.99061

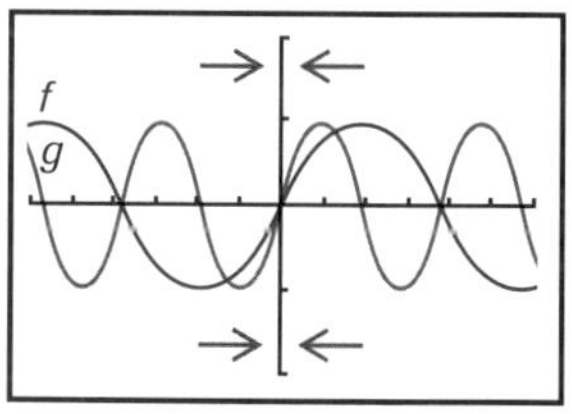

f) Assign the appropriate value to parameter **b** and describe the resulting changes in the graph for each of the functions in *e)*.

g) Assign a value between 0 and 1 to parameter **b** and describe the resulting changes in the graph for each of the functions in *e)*.

h) Here are some ordered pairs of a basic function: (0, 0), (1, 1), (4, 2), (9, 3). Find the corresponding ordered pairs of the transformed function obtained by introducing the following values for parameter **b** into the function rule:

1) 2   2) $\dfrac{1}{3}$ 3) −1

Role of h:

Let's continue by introducing the third parameter, represented by the letter **h**, into the rule of various basic functions.

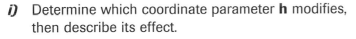

i) Determine which coordinate parameter **h** modifies, then describe its effect.

$f: Y_1 = |x|$

$g: Y_2 = |x - 2|$

$h: Y_3 = |x + 3|$

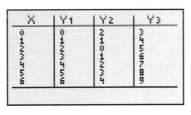
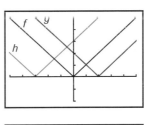

$f: Y_1 = x^2$

$g: Y_2 = (x - 2)^2$

$h: Y_3 = (x + 1)^2$

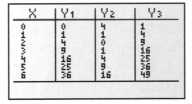
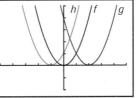

j) Some of the ordered pairs of a basic function are: $\left(-2, -\frac{1}{4}\right)$, $\left(-1, \frac{1}{2}\right)$, (0, 1), (1, 2), (2, 4).

Find the corresponding ordered pairs of the transformed function obtained by introducing the following values for parameter **h** into the function rule:

1) -3   2) $\frac{1}{2}$ 3) 2

Role of k:

Finally, let's introduce the fourth parameter, represented by **k**, into the rule of various basic functions.

k) Determine which coordinate parameter **k** modifies, then describe its effect.

$f: Y_1 = |x|$

$g: Y_2 = |x| + 3$ or $Y_1 + 3$

$h: Y_3 = |x| - 2$ or $Y_1 - 2$

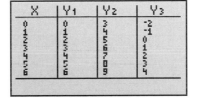
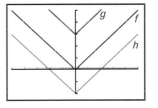

$f: Y_1 = \sqrt{x}$

$g: Y_2 = \sqrt{x} + 3$ or $Y_1 + 3$

$h: Y_3 = \sqrt{x} - 2$ or $Y_1 - 2$

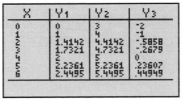
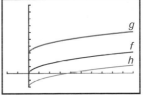

l) Some of the ordered pairs of a basic function are: $\left(\frac{1}{2}, -1\right)$, (1, 0), (2, 1), (4, 2), (8, 3). Find the corresponding ordered pairs of the transformed function obtained by introducing the following values for parameter **k** into the function rule:

1) -4   2) $\frac{1}{2}$ 3) 3

m) Assume that the following ordered pairs belong to a basic function: (-1, 0), (0, 1), (1, 0), (2, -1), (3, 0). Find the corresponding ordered pairs of the transformed function obtained by introducing the following values for the parameters **a, b, h** and **k** respectively, into the function rule: 3, 2, -2 and 1.

Remember:

> • The first parameter, represented by **a,** produces a vertical scale change. The y-coordinates of the ordered pairs in the basic function are multiplied by **a.**
>
> • The second parameter, represented by **b,** produces a horizontal scale change. The x-coordinates of the ordered pairs in the basic function are divided by **b.**
>
> • If they are negative, parameters **a** and **b** produce a reflection across the x-axis and the y-axis, respectively.
>
> • The third parameter, represented by **h,** produces a horizontal translation of **h** units by adding **h** to the x-coordinates of the ordered pairs obtained after the scale changes.
>
> • The fourth parameter, represented by **k,** produces a vertical translation of **k** units by adding **k** to the y-coordinates of the ordered pairs obtained after the scale changes.

The ordered pairs of the transformed function are obtained by taking into account the parameters **a, b, h** and **k,** in that order.

1. The rule of a basic function is given below. Find the rule of the transformed function obtained by introducing the parameters **a, b, h** and **k.**

a) $f(x) = x$ **b)** $g(x) = x^2$ **c)** $h(x) = |x|$ **d)** $i(x) = \sqrt{x}$

e) $j(x) = \cos x$ **f)** $k(x) = \ln x$ **g)** $m(x) = \text{int } x$ **h)** $n(x) = \text{abs } x$

2. Find the value of each of the parameters **a, b, h** and **k** in the given rule.

a) $f(x) = 2 \log (2x + 4) - 3$

b) $g(x) = -3 \sin (2x + \pi) + \frac{\pi}{2}$

c) $h(x) = 2[2x - 6] - 3$

d) $i(x) = -2 \text{ iPart } (2x + 5) - 4$

3. Assume that the ordered pairs below belong to a basic function. The rule of this basic function is transformed by introducing the parameters **a, h** and **k** with the values 2, -3 and 5 respectively. Find the corresponding ordered pairs in the transformed function.

$$\{..., (-3, 4), ..., (-2, 6), ..., (-1, 8), ..., (0, 10), ...\}$$

4. Assume that the ordered pairs below belong to a basic function. The rule of the basic function is transformed by introducing the parameters **b, h** and **k** with the values $\frac{1}{2}$, 3 and -5 respectively. Find the corresponding ordered pairs in the transformed function.

$$\left\{..., (0, 0), ..., \left(\frac{3}{2}, 1\right), ..., \left(\frac{5}{2}, 2\right), ..., \left(\frac{7}{2}, 3\right); ...\right\}$$

Georges Cantor (1845–1918) was the mathematician who defined the function as a set of ordered pairs.

5. The graphs of two basic functions are shown. These functions are transformed by introducing the indicated values for the parameters into their rules. Sketch the graph of each transformed function.

a) a = -1, b = 2 and h = -3

b) a = 2, b = 2, h = 2 and k = 2

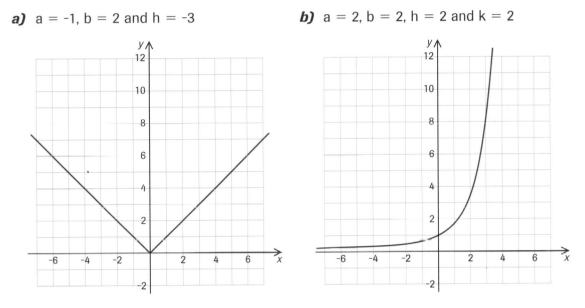

6. An imaginary basic function, nicknamed "toto," is defined by the rule $f(x) = $ toto x. The following ordered pairs belong to this function: (0, 0), (2, 4), (4, 4) and (6, 0). Find the corresponding pairs belonging to function g defined by $g(x) = 2$ toto $0.5(x - 2) + 3$.

7. Modify the function rule for f, defined as $f(x) = -2\left|2x + 4\right| + 4$, to create a function g that has no zeros.

8. A function f is defined by $f(x) = -2\left|2x + 4\right| + 4$. Modify this rule to create a function h, such that the values of the domain that make f positive make h negative.

9. Modify the function rule for f, defined as $f(x) = 4(x - 2)^2 + 3$, to create a function i that has a maximum instead of a minimum.

10. If the four parameters of a given function rule have values that are strictly positive, the curve of this function will be located in the first quadrant. In which quadrant will the function's curve be located if the four parameters of its rule have strictly negative values?

11. Which parameters have been introduced into the rule of the basic function *f* to produce the transformed function *g*?

a)

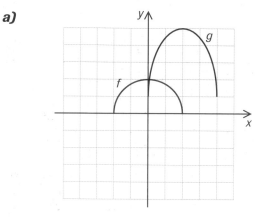

b)

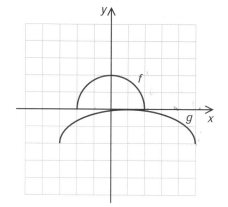

12. The functions defined by the rules below were obtained by transforming the function *f*. Match up each function with the corresponding curve. (Replace ■ with the appropriate letter.)

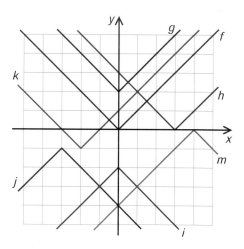

1. ■(x) = -f(x) − 2
2. ■(x) = -f(x + 3) − 1
3. ■(x) = f(x) + 2
4. ■(x) = f(x + 2) − 1
5. ■(x) = -f(x − 4)
6. ■(x) = f(x − 3)

a) Functions *f* and *g* are defined by the following rules:

$$f(x) = (2x + 2)^2 + 1 \qquad g(x) = 4(x + 1)^2 + 1$$

1) What do these functions have in common?
2) Explain why this is so.

b) The following ordered pairs belong to a basic function *f*: (-2, 4), (-1, 1), (0, 0), (1, 1) and (2, 4). Its rule is modified by introducing the parameters **a, b, h** and **k,** with the values 2, -2, 1 and -3 respectively.

1) Are the same ordered pairs obtained for the transformed function *g* if the parameters **h** and **k** are applied before the parameters **a** and **b**?
2) Explain this result.

INVERSE RELATIONS

Will you marry me?

Christmas used to be an ideal time for marriage proposals. The young man would usually "pop" the question to the young lady first, then ask for her father's permission afterwards.

A local paper printed five marriage proposals made during one particular holiday season.

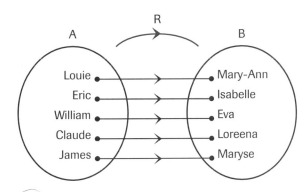

a) State the set of ordered pairs in R.

b) If the roles were reversed to produce the inverse relation R⁻¹, what would be the resulting set?

c) Complete this sentence: If R is a set of ordered pairs (x, y) from set A to set B, then R⁻¹ is ▬▬▬.

Total number of weddings in Québec during the 20th century:

1900: 10 103
1930: 18 543
1960: 36 211
1990: 32 060

Reversing the *x*- and *y*-coordinates of the ordered pairs of a given relation produces its inverse relation.

d) An inverse relation may or may not be a function itself.

   1) Is R⁻¹ in the situation above a function?

   2) Draw the mapping diagram of a relation whose inverse is not a function.

If the inverse of a function is also a function, we represent the inverse of *f* as *f*⁻¹.

e) A function $Y_1 = \sqrt{x}$ is entered into a graphing calculator, resulting in the table of values at right. Graph the curve of this function on paper.

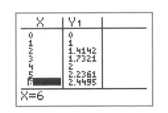

X	Y₁	
0	0	
1	1	
2	1.4142	
3	1.7321	
4	2	
5	2.2361	
6	2.4495	

X=6

f) On the same axes, draw the curve of the inverse by reversing the coordinates of the ordered pairs in *f*, and determine if it is a function.

g) What is the relationship between the curve of *f* and the curve of its inverse?

This is a very important relationship in the study of functions.

h) Below is the rule, the table of values and the graph of the function *f*, which expresses the diameter *D* of a circle as a function of its radius *r*:

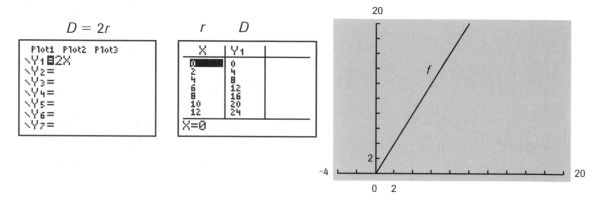

$$D = 2r$$

Give the rule, the table of values and the graph of the inverse function f^{-1}.

We obtain the rule for a function's inverse by switching the independent and dependent variables.

Remember to isolate the dependent variable in the new rule.

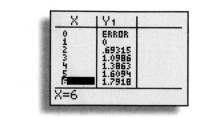

1. Write the inverse and indicate whether it is a function in each case.

a) R = {(1, 3), (2, 4), (3, 5), (4, 8)}   **b)** S = {(-2, 3), (-1, 4), (0, 0), (2, 3), (3, 4)}

2. Graph the inverse and indicate whether it is a function in each case.

a)
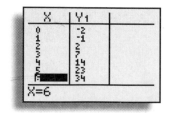

b)

3. Graph the inverse and indicate whether it is a function in each case.

a)

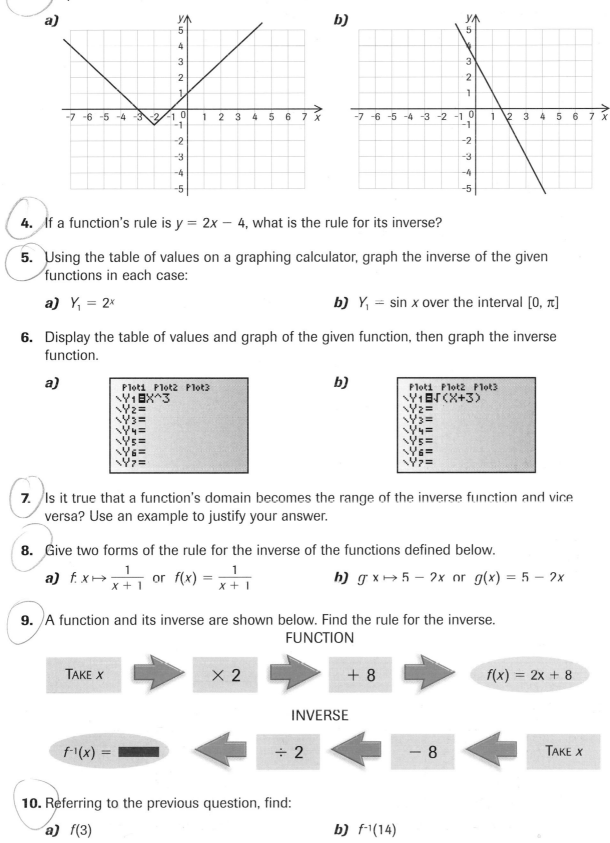

b)

4. If a function's rule is $y = 2x - 4$, what is the rule for its inverse?

5. Using the table of values on a graphing calculator, graph the inverse of the given functions in each case:

a) $Y_1 = 2^x$

b) $Y_1 = \sin x$ over the interval $[0, \pi]$

6. Display the table of values and graph of the given function, then graph the inverse function.

a)

Plot1 Plot2 Plot3
\Y₁⊟X^3
\Y₂=
\Y₃=
\Y₄=
\Y₅=
\Y₆=
\Y₇=

b)

Plot1 Plot2 Plot3
\Y₁⊟√(X+3)
\Y₂=
\Y₃=
\Y₄=
\Y₅=
\Y₆=
\Y₇=

7. Is it true that a function's domain becomes the range of the inverse function and vice versa? Use an example to justify your answer.

8. Give two forms of the rule for the inverse of the functions defined below.

a) $f: x \mapsto \dfrac{1}{x + 1}$ or $f(x) = \dfrac{1}{x + 1}$

b) $g: x \mapsto 5 - 2x$ or $g(x) = 5 - 2x$

9. A function and its inverse are shown below. Find the rule for the inverse.

FUNCTION

| TAKE x | ➡ | × 2 | ➡ | + 8 | ➡ | $f(x) = 2x + 8$ |

INVERSE

| $f^{-1}(x) = $ ▬ | ⬅ | ÷ 2 | ⬅ | − 8 | ⬅ | TAKE x |

10. Referring to the previous question, find:

a) $f(3)$

b) $f^{-1}(14)$

11. Define the inverse of a function in your own words.

12. Determine if the following pairs of functions are the inverse of one another.

a) $f(x) = 5x - 3$ and $g(x) = \dfrac{x - 3}{5}$

b) $h(x) = x + 4$ and $i(x) = x - 4$

13. A function f consists of ordered pairs of integers that satisfy the rule $g(x) = 2x + 3$ over the domain [-3, 3]. Find:

a) ran f

b) dom f^{-1}

c) ran f^{-1}

14. Use a graphing calculator to draw the curve of the inverse of the given functions and determine whether it is a function in each case.

a) $Y_1 = 2x - 3$

b) $Y_2 = x^2 + 3x + 2$

c) $Y_3 = [0.25x]$

a) Are functions f^{-1} and $\dfrac{1}{f}$ the same for a function f? Justify your answer.

b) State the rule for the inverse of the following functions:

1) $f(x) = x$

2) $g(x) = \dfrac{1}{x}$

3) $h(x) = 4$

c) Is it true that all functions whose rule is in the form $f(x) = k - x$ are their own inverses? Justify your answer.

COMPOSITION OF FUNCTIONS

Compositions of isometries and dilatations were investigated previously in the study of geometric transformations. The result of a composition is called a **composite.** Finding the composite of two transformations consists of performing the second transformation on the image from the first one. The order in which they are performed is important. It is also possible to compose functions and find the rule for the composite.

A surtax on goods

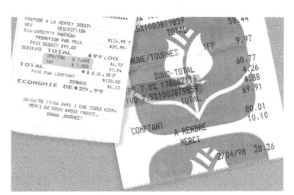

In 1998 the federal government imposed a 7% tax on goods and services (GST). The provincial government then applied its own 7.5% sales tax (QST) to the total after GST.

a) Calculate the price, including taxes, of an item that costs:

1) $100   2) $500   3) $x

This situation actually involves a total of three functions. The first two are easy to identify:

GST function $f: x \mapsto 1.07x$ (map an amount x to $1.07x$)

QST function $g: x \mapsto 1.075x$ (map an amount x to $1.075x$)

Since the QST function is really only applied after the GST has been calculated, there is a third function that is the composite of the first two. It is written $g \circ f$, which reads "f followed by g" or "g of f."

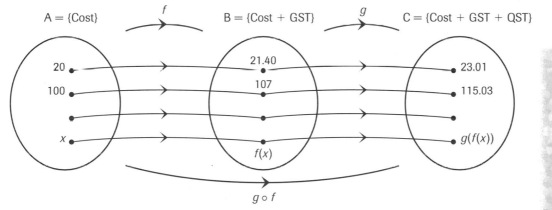

A = {Cost} f B = {Cost + GST} g C = {Cost + GST + QST}

$g \circ f$

The GST (Goods and Services Tax) took effect in Canada on January 1, 1991. It replaced the existing Federal Sales Tax (FST). The QST (Québec Sales Tax) was introduced on January 1, 1992. The GST and QST are "visible" taxes, which means they are not included in the price of goods, but are calculated at the cash register.

b) What is the image of x under the function f?

c) What the image of $f(x)$ under the function g?

d) What is:

1) The source set of the function $g \circ f$?

2) The target set of the function $g \circ f$?

e) What rule is used to calculate the cost of a product, including the two taxes, directly from its original price?

Given two functions $f: A \to B$ and $g: B \to C$, the composite of f and g is the function $g \circ f: A \to C$ that make $g(f(x))$ correspond to x.

$$(g \circ f)(x) = g(f(x))$$

f) In this example, what is the rule for $g \circ f$?

To obtain the rule for the composite $g \circ f$, simply introduce the rule for f into the rule for g.

Therefore, in this example: $f(x) = 1.07x$ and $g(x) = 1.075x$

$$\Downarrow$$
$$g(f(x)) = 1.075f(x)$$
$$\Downarrow$$
$$g(f(x)) = 1.075(1.07x)$$
$$\Downarrow$$
$$g(f(x)) = 1.150\ 25x$$

g) Given a function f where $f(x) = 2x + 1$ and a function g where $g(x) = x^2 - 2x$, find the function rule for:

1) $g \circ f$ 	 2) $f \circ g$

OPERATIONS ON FUNCTIONS

The ice storm

Many industries located in the "triangle of darkness" suffered major losses following the ice storm of January 1998. The federal and provincial governments studied various methods of compensation for the victims. One of the federal proposals included paying the victims a sum of $2000 plus 35% of total losses incurred. The provincial government suggested, among other solutions, that the storm victims be paid a sum of $5000 plus 25% of total losses incurred.

"The ice storm of January (1998) was the worst natural disaster in Canadian history."
La Presse, Feb. 18, 1998, p. A3

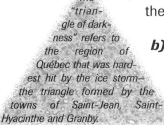

The "triangle of darkness" refers to the region of Québec that was hardest hit by the ice storm—the triangle formed by the towns of Saint-Jean, Saint-Hyacinthe and Granby.

a) What is the function rule for f that associates the amount of federal aid with a loss of x?

b) What is the function rule for g that associates the amount of provincial aid with a loss of x?

The ice storm at a glance

- Up to 100 mm of freezing rain in the hardest hit regions.
- More than a million homes left without power.
- 1000 power transmission towers down.
- 24 000 hydro poles down.
- 10 to 35% of all trees damaged.
- 360 shelters opened for victims.

c) What is the rule for the third function that associates the amount of federal and provincial aid with a loss of x?

d) How can the above rule be obtained using the rules f and g?

e) Is the third function, which associates the financial aid provided by the two levels of government with a loss of x, a composition of the functions f and g?

f) There is a basic difference between the composite of two functions and the sum of two functions. What is the difference?

Euler (1707–1783) emphasized defining a function by an algebraic expression.

In addition to the composition of functions, we can also define the **addition, subtraction, multiplication** and **division** of functions.

> Given two real functions f and g, the new functions are defined as follows:
>
> $$f + g: x \mapsto (f + g)(x) = f(x) + g(x)$$
>
> $$f - g: x \mapsto (f - g)(x) = f(x) - g(x)$$
>
> $$f \cdot g: x \mapsto (f \cdot g)(x) = f(x) \cdot g(x)$$
>
> $$\frac{f}{g}: x \mapsto \left(\frac{f}{g}\right)(x) = f(x) \div g(x) \text{ with } g(x) \neq 0$$

The domain of the sum, difference, product or quotient of two functions is the **intersection** of the domains of the functions on which the operations are performed. However, the domain of the quotient function does not include any value from this intersection that would make the function's denominator equal to zero.

For functions f and g defined by the rules $f(x) = x + 3$ and $g(x) = x - 4$, there are no restrictions on the domain IR. The domain of functions $f + g$, $f - g$ et $f \cdot g$ correspond to IR $\cap$ IR = IR. However, function $\frac{f}{g}$ has as its rule $\frac{f}{g}(x) = \frac{x + 3}{x - 4}$ with $x - 4 \neq 0$, meaning that $x \neq 4$ and that 4 must be excluded from the domain of $\frac{f}{g}$. The domain is therefore IR\{4}.

It is important to point out that the majority of real functions may be written as a sum, difference, product or quotient of other functions.

Function f, whose rule is $f(x) = 2x + 3$, may be considered the sum of two functions:

> If g is the function defined by $g(x) = x + 2$ and h the function defined by $h(x) = x + 1$, then $f = g + h$.

Similarly, function i, whose rule is $i(x) = x^2 - x - 2$, may be considered the product of two functions:

> If j is the function defined by $j(x) = x - 2$ and k the function defined by $k(x) = x + 1$, then $i = j \cdot k$.

1. Imagine two functions *m* and *f* defined as:

$m(x)$ = mother of *x*,

$f(x)$ = father of *x*.

Raoul   Bertha   Joseph   Irene

a) Looking at the parental connections shown on the right, find:

1) $m(f(Celia))$

2) $f(m(Celia))$

Morris   Mary

b) Find an ordered pair belonging to the function:

1) $m \circ f$

2) $f \circ m$

c) Find:

1) $(m \circ f)(Celia)$

2) $(f \circ m)(Celia)$

Celia

2. Consider function *f* defined by $f(x) = 2x$ and function *h* defined by $h(x) = x^2$. Find:

a) $(f \circ h)(-1)$ **b)** $f(h(2))$ **c)** $(h \circ f)(0)$ **d)** $h(f(3))$

e) $f(h(4))$ **f)** $h(f(4))$ **g)** $f(h(-3))$ **h)** $h(f(-3))$

3. Consider functions *f*, *g*, *h* and *i* from IR to IR defined by the following rules:

$f(x) = x - 3$	$g(x) = 2x - 4$	$h(x) = 2$	$i(x) = 4 - 2x$

a) State the function rule that corresponds to:

1) $f + g$ 2) $h \cdot g$ 3) $\dfrac{i}{h}$ 4) $g - i$ 5) $\dfrac{i}{g}$

b) State the domain of each of these functions.

4. Determine the images of each of these functions by referring to the functions defined in the previous exercise:

a) $(f + g)(2)$ **b)** $\dfrac{i}{h}(-2)$ **c)** $(g - i)(0)$ **d)** $(h \cdot g)(-4)$

5. If $f(x) = 3x + 2$ and $g(x) = \dfrac{x - 2}{3}$, then determine the following images:

a) $f(g(1))$ **b)** $g(f(-2))$ **c)** $g(f(0))$ **d)** $f(f(1))$

e) $g(g(-1))$ **f)** $g(f(g(0)))$ **g)** $f(g(a))$ **h)** $g(f(a + 1))$

6. Referring to the previous exercise, determine:

a) The relationship between functions f and g.

b) What is unique about the composite of these two functions.

7. Given the following functions:

$$f: x \mapsto |2x - 1|$$

$$g: x \mapsto 2x + 3$$

$$h: x \mapsto x^2 + x - 1$$

Using a graphing calculator, find the image of:

a) $(f + g)(2)$ **b)** $(f \cdot g)(0)$ **c)** $\dfrac{h}{g}(2)$ **d)** $(h - g)(3)$

8. Functions j and k are defined as follows:

$$j(x) = 2x - 3$$

$$k(x) = \dfrac{x + 1}{2}$$

a) Give the rules for j^{-1} and k^{-1}.

b) Find the images of the following composites:

1) $k^{-1} \circ k(2)$ 2) $k \circ k^{-1}(1)$ 3) $j^{-1} \circ j(0)$ 4) $j \circ j^{-1}(-2)$

c) What do you notice about the results you obtained in the previous question?

9. What can be said of two functions f and g where $g(f(x)) = f(g(x)) = x$?

10. In general, for any given functions f and g, will $f(g(a)) = g(f(a))$?

11. The domain of function f is $\{-3, -2, -1, 0, 1, 2, 3\}$ and that of function g is $\{-6, -3, 0, 3, 6\}$. Find the domain of $f - g$.

12. Show that a linear function in the form $f(x) = ax + b$ may be considered as the sum of two functions.

13. Below is the mapping diagram of two functions f and g. Find the domain and range of the composite $g \circ f$.

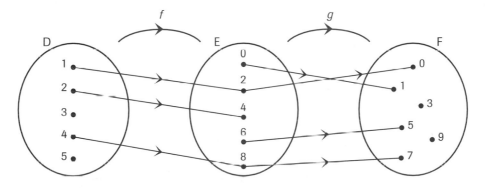

14. In 1998 the federal government taxed the average annual income at a rate of 14%. The Québec government taxed the same salary at 16%. For an average yearly income of $x:

a) What is the function rule for f used to determine the tax paid to the federal government?

b) What is the function rule for g used to determine the tax paid to the Québec government?

c) What is the function rule used to determine the tax paid to both levels of government?

15. The cars produced by an automobile manufacturer sell so poorly that both the manufacturer and the dealerships go bankrupt. To sell off the remaining stock, the manufacturer offers a $1000 rebate and a 10% discount off the original price. The dealers offer a $200 rebate and a 5% discount off the original price.

a) If x represents the original price of the car, find the function rule for f used to determine the price of the car after the manufacturer's rebate only.

b) If x represents the original price of the car, find the function rule for g used to determine the price of the car after the dealer's rebate only.

c) What is the function rule used to determine the car's price after both rebates?

d) What is the function rule used to determine the car's price if the dealer applies his reduction not to the car's original price, but to the price after the manufacturer's rebate?

e) Which of the two functions defined in questions *c)* and *d)* gives the buyer a better deal on the car?

16. Andrea flew to Mexico on a business trip last night. Before leaving, she converted her Canadian currency into American funds. Upon arriving in Mexico, she changed her American dollars into Mexican pesos. If the American dollar was worth CAN$1.40 and the peso US$0.14 on the day she exchanged her funds, find the function rule that associates a sum of Canadian dollars with its equivalent in Mexican pesos.

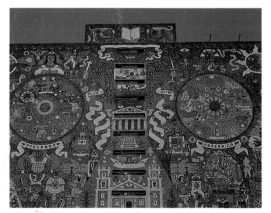

Library of the University of Mexico.

The capital of Mexico, Mexico City, is 2200 m above sea level. With more than 20 000 000 inhabitants, Mexico City is one of the most densely populated cities in the world. It is also one of the world's most polluted cities.

17. Paul can paint an average room in 2 h. It takes Raoul 3 h to do the same job.

a) Complete the two tables of values below:

Paul	Time (h)	0	1	2	3	4	5	...	t
	Rooms	0	$\frac{1}{2}$	1					

Raoul	Time (h)	0	1	2	3	4	5	...	t
	Rooms	0	$\frac{1}{3}$	$\frac{2}{3}$					

b) For each of the previous tables, state the function rule that associates the number y of painted rooms with a given time t.

c) What is the function rule that associates the number of rooms painted by Paul and Raoul working together with a given time t?

d) If they work together, how much time will it take them to paint five rooms?

18. Jenna receives $150 from the school committee to organize a dance. She plans to sell the tickets for $8 each. She estimates her fixed costs at $120, plus $5 per person. Give the function rule that defines the evening's profits based on the number of people in attendance.

19. The length of the congruent sides of the isosceles triangle *ABC* varies according to the altitude x of the triangle. The length of the triangle's base is 10. A function *f* is defined that associates the length of one of the congruent sides with an altitude x. A second function *g* is defined that associates the perimeter of the triangle with the length of one of the congruent sides.

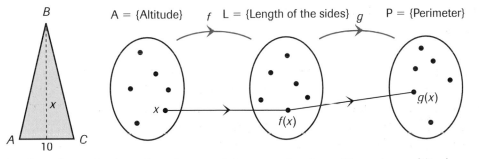

Find the function rule that directly associates a perimeter with a given altitude x.

20. If *f* and *g* are defined as:

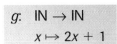

$$f: \ \text{IN} \to \text{IN}$$
$$x \mapsto 2x$$

$$g: \ \text{IN} \to \text{IN}$$
$$x \mapsto 2x + 1$$

a) Find the function rule for $f \cdot g$.

b) Find the function rule for $g \circ f$.

c) Find the range of the function $f \cdot g$.

d) Find the range of the function $g \circ f$.

e) Show that the function rule for $g \circ f$ is also the function rule for $f + g$.

21. Consider the function f defined by the rule $f(x) = 2x^2 + 3x + 1$.

  a) Define two functions g and h such that $f = g + h$.

  b) Define two functions i and j such that $f = i \cdot j$.

  c) Define two functions k and m such that $f = k \circ m$.

22. Functions f, g, h and i are defined as follows:

$$f(x) = |x^2 - 9| \qquad g(x) = \sqrt{x^2 - 4} \qquad h(x) = \sin x \qquad i(x) = 2^x$$

Sketch the graph displayed by a graphing calculator for each of the following functions:

  a) $f \cdot g$ **b)** $\dfrac{f}{g}$ **c)** $\dfrac{f}{h}$

  d) $g \cdot h$ **e)** $g + i$ **f)** $f \circ h$

THINK TANK

a) The rules $Y_1 = x$ and $Y_2 = x^2$ were entered into a graphing calculator. What mathematical model can be associated with the graphs of each of the following rules?

  1) $Y_3 = Y_1 - Y_2$ 2) $Y_4 = Y_1 * Y_2$

  3) $Y_5 = Y_1/Y_2$ 4) $Y_6 = Y_2/Y_1$

b) Given $p(x) = 2x + 3$, $q(x) = kx + 1$ and $r(x) = p(x) + q(x)$.

  1) What value must be assigned to k so that r is a constant function?

  2) What values must be assigned to k so that r is a decreasing function?

  3) What values must be assigned to k so that r is an increasing function?

  4) What happens to q if k = 0?

c) Do the sum, difference, product and quotient of two functions necessarily generate other functions? Justify your answer.

ZERO-DEGREE POLYNOMIAL FUNCTIONS

| THE BASIC CONSTANT |
| FUNCTION |
| TRANSFORMED CONSTANT |
| FUNCTIONS |

THE BASIC CONSTANT FUNCTION

The gift of life

Lara took fertility treatment because she had been unable to conceive. Throughout her pregnancy she underwent a series of ultrasound scans, and the radiologist recorded the number of fetuses detected each time. The results are listed below:

Ultrasound	Fetuses
1	1
2	1
3	1
4	1
5	1

Ultrasound is used to detect a variety of birth defects, such as anencephaly and hydrocephalus, in unborn fetuses.

a) What are the mathematical characteristics of the relation between these two variables?

b) Is this relation a function? If so, provide the corresponding rule.

This relation is the **basic function** of **constant functions**. Introducing parameters into the rule $f(x) = 1$ produces other constant functions.

c) Graph the basic constant function.

d) The **basic constant function** represents a mathematical model. Complete this model's table of **properties**:

An ultrasound is the application of sonar to the human body. Ultrasonic waves emit signals that detect objects and movement. Ultrasound is used primarily in the fields of gynaecology and cardiology.

1. The rule of the basic constant function is ▰▰▰ .
2. The graph of the basic constant function is a ▰▰▰ .
3. The domain of a basic constant function is ▰▰▰ and its range is ▰▰▰ .
4. It has ▰▰▰ zero.
5. Its maximum and minimum have the same value, which is ▰▰▰ .
6. It is both ▰▰▰ and decreasing, or better still, ▰▰▰ over its entire domain.
7. Its sign is always ▰▰▰ .

e) What are this function's properties in this example?

TRANSFORMED CONSTANT FUNCTIONS

The basic constant function generates other constant functions when parameter **a** is introduced into its rule.

The rules of transformed constant functions take the form $g(x) = a \cdot f(x)$ with a $\in$ IR and $f(x) = 1$.

This parameter multiplies the *y*-coordinates of the basic function's points by **a.**

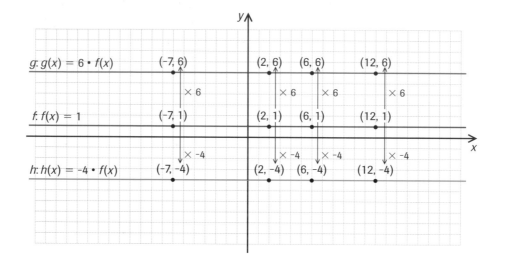

f) List the properties of functions *g* and *h*.

g) Some of the ordered pairs of a constant function *f* are (-3, 2), (-2, 2), (-1, 2), (0, 2), (1, 2), (2, 2) and (3, 2).

1) Find the corresponding ordered pairs belonging to the inverse.

2) Graph the inverse.

3) Is the inverse itself a function?

4) What rule defines the inverse?

h) Explain why it is impossible for the inverse of a constant function to be a function itself.

FIRST-DEGREE POLYNOMIAL FUNCTIONS

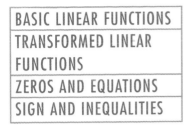
BASIC LINEAR FUNCTIONS

Unicycle acrobat

A unicycle acrobat is preparing for a stage performance and needs to map out his moves as accurately as possible. To this end, he measured the various distances on the stage in metres based on the number of revolutions of the cycle's pedals. Below is the resulting table of values:

Revolutions	Distance (m)
1	1
2	2
3	3
...	...
10	10

a) What distance does the acrobat travel:

1) In 1/2 a revolution?   2) In 3/4 of a revolution?   3) In 6 1/2 revolutions?

b) What possible unicycle movements in this situation would make the number of revolutions and the distance travelled fall within the set of real numbers?

c) How can we be sure that this relation is a function in this case?

d) Find the rate of change in this relation.

e) What rule describes the relation between the *x* variable, which corresponds to the number of revolutions of the pedals, and the *y* variable, which corresponds to the distance in metres?

f) Graph this function.

A function that associates every value with itself is called the **basic function** for the set of **linear functions.** It corresponds to the mathematical model defined by the rule:

$$f(x) = x \quad \text{or} \quad y = x$$

and its graph is represented by a line that bisects the first and third quadrants.

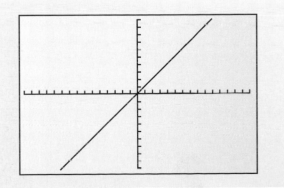

When unrestricted, the **basic linear function** has the following **properties**:

1. Its rule is $f(x) = x$.
2. Its graph is an oblique line.
3. Its domain is IR and its range is IR.
4. It has just one zero: 0.
5. It has no maximum or minimum.
6. It is increasing over its entire domain.
7. It is negative over $]-\infty, 0]$ and positive over $[0, +\infty[$.

This basic function can be transformed by introducing parameters.

TRANSFORMED LINEAR FUNCTIONS

Young entrepreneurs

In order to encourage its students to start up their own businesses, a school takes part in the annual Young Achievers contest. Vicky and Alex have an idea: they plan to manufacture the picture frames for their school's graduation photos. They estimate that their fixed costs will total $100 and that it will cost them $3 to manufacture each frame. They decide to sell the frames for $5 each.

a) Find the function g that relates the company's profits to the number of frames sold.

b) State the function rule for g using the basic function rule, which is $f(x) = x$.

c) Construct a table of values, then graph the basic function f and the transformed function g.

d) What do you notice when comparing the y-coordinates of the functions f and g for the same value of x?

e) Explain why a function in the form $g(x) = ax$ can be called a "direct variation linear function."

f) State the properties of the mathematical model defined by the function g.

g) Find the function h that associates the venture's profits with the number of frames sold.

h) State the function rule for h using the basic linear function and parameters.

i) Construct a table of values, then graph the basic function f and the transformed function h.

The rule of **transformed linear functions** takes the form $f(x) = ax + k$ or $f(x) = ax + b$ with $a \neq 0$.

j) Explain how to obtain the ordered pairs belonging to the function h using those belonging to the basic linear function.

f		(0, 0),	(20, 20)
		↓ × 2	↓ × 2
parameter **a** = 2 ⇒		(0, 0),	(20, 40)
parameter **b** or **k** = -100 ⇒		↓ − 100	↓ − 100
h		(0, -100),	(20, -60)

Notice that the result is the same if we consider the y-intercept and the rate of change.

1. Locate point (0, b), in this case (0, -100).

2. Apply the rate of change **a**, which in this case is 2 to 1, or 20 to 10, or 40 to 20.

ZEROS AND EQUATIONS

Under pressure

Although we may not realize it, we are all under an enormous amount of pressure. Indeed, we carry thousands of cubic metres of air on our shoulders every day! Atmospheric pressure is approximately 100 kPa at sea level. This pressure decreases by 0.012 kPa with every metre of elevation up to a certain altitude. The relation between the altitude and the pressure is expressed by the rule $f(x) = 100 - 0.012x$. The graph of this relation is shown below:

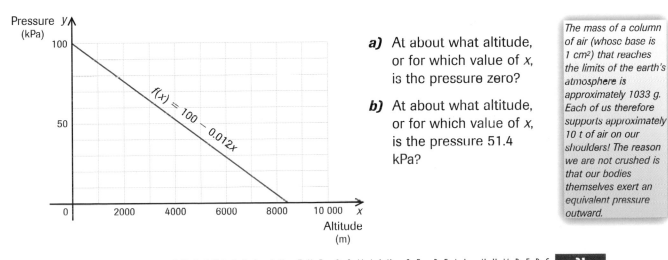

a) At about what altitude, or for which value of x, is the pressure zero?

b) At about what altitude, or for which value of x, is the pressure 51.4 kPa?

The mass of a column of air (whose base is 1 cm²) that reaches the limits of the earth's atmosphere is approximately 1033 g. Each of us therefore supports approximately 10 t of air on our shoulders! The reason we are not crushed is that our bodies themselves exert an equivalent pressure outward.

We can approximate the answers to each of these questions simply by looking at the graph of the function. An approximation is not always adequate, however, and we may want a more precise answer. This answer can be obtained in a variety of ways:

1. Using a graphing calculator:

   – by modifying the scale interval:

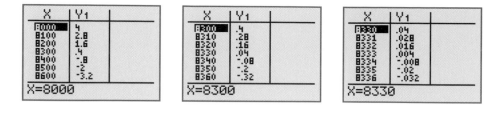

   – using different command sequences:

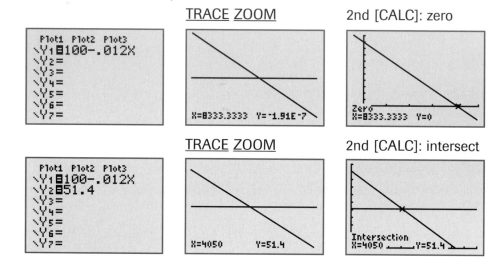

2. Using an algebraic method; that is, stating an equation from the function rule:

$$f(x) = 100 - 0.012x \qquad\qquad\qquad f(x) = 100 - 0.012x$$

$$0 = 100 - 0.012x \qquad\qquad\qquad 51.4 = 100 - 0.012x$$

These equations are **first-degree equations in one variable.** Remember that these equations can be solved by **isolating the variable** after applying the rules for transforming equations.

c) State the rules for transforming equations.

d) Solve the two previous equations algebraically.

e) What is the zero of this function?

f) Using the rule $f(x) = ax + b$ (or $f(x) = ax + k$) find the expression that represents the zero of the transformed linear function.

g) Using the rule $f(x) = ax + b$ (or $f(x) = ax + k$) find the expression that represents the value of x associated with the image c.

SIGN AND INEQUALITIES

The boiling point

Water boils at 100°C at sea level. Less heat is required to boil water at higher altitudes, however, because of the drop in atmospheric pressure. The relationship between altitude and the boiling point of water is represented by function f, whose rule is $f(x) = -0.0033x + 100$. The graph of this function is shown below.

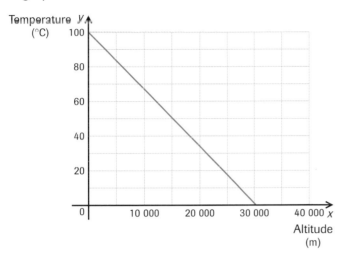

Water can be boiled anywhere on earth, but not at the same temperature. Water boils when the pressure of the steam is equal to that of the atmosphere. In Montréal (15m above sea level), the atmospheric pressure is 101.1 kPa and water boils at 100°C. In Mexico City (2277 m), the atmospheric pressure is 76.8 kPa and water boils at 93°C. On Mount Everest (8846 m), where the atmospheric pressure is only 31.3 kPa, water boils at 70°C!

a) Given that the domain of the function is [0, 30 303.030 3] and that the range is [0, 100], determine the approximate altitude above which water boils at less than 50°C.

b) Determine the approximate altitude below which water boils at more than 60°C.

c) What inequalities correspond to questions a) and b)?

These inequalities are **first-degree inequalities in one variable.** As was the case with equations, we may need either a simple approximation or a more precise answer. A good estimate can be made simply by looking at the graph. For a more precise answer, try one of the following approaches:

1. Use a graphing calculator:

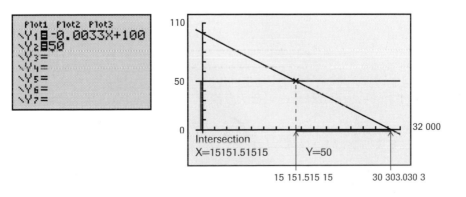

2. Use an algebraic method; that is, state an inequality using the function rule:

$f(x) = -0.0033x + 100$ $f(x) = -0.0033x + 100$

$f(x) = -0.0033x + 100 < 50$ $f(x) = -0.0033x + 100 > 60$

These inequalities may be solved by **isolating the variable** after applying the rules for transforming inequalities.

How are inequalities manipulated? What are the rules for transforming them? These are important questions. To answer them, study the inequalities on the number line below.

d) Complete the following inequalities:

1) $-6 < 4$
     $-6 + 2$ ■ $4 + 2$

2) $-6 < 4$
     $-6 - 2$ ■ $4 - 2$

3) $-6 < 4$
     -6×2 ■ 4×2

4) $-6 < 4$
     $-6 \div 2$ ■ $4 \div 2$

5) $-6 < 4$
     -6×-2 ■ 4×-2

6) $-6 < 4$
     $-6 \div -2$ ■ $4 \div -2$

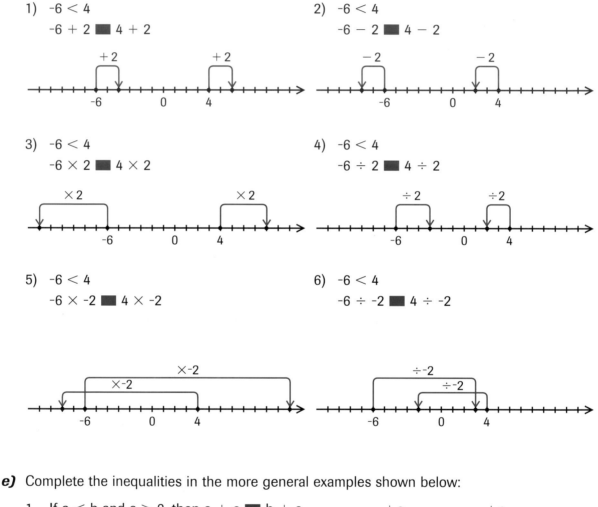

e) Complete the inequalities in the more general examples shown below:

1. If $a < b$ and $c > 0$, then $a + c$ ■ $b + c$.

If $a < b$ and $c > 0$, then $a - c$ ■ $b - c$.

2. If a < b and c > 0, then a • c ■ b • c.

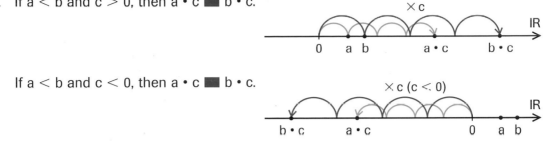

If a < b and c < 0, then a • c ■ b • c.

The rules for transforming inequalities without variables are used to formulate the rules that apply to inequalities with variables (inequations).

RULES FOR TRANSFORMING INEQUALITIES

For a, b ∈ IR and c ∈ IR*:

1. Rule for addition or subtraction

Adding or subtracting the same amount from both sides of an inequality does not change the direction of the inequality.

INEQUALITIES WITHOUT VARIABLES	INEQUALITIES WITH VARIABLES
If a < b, then a + c < b + c and a − c < b − c.	If ax < b, then ax + c < b + c and ax − c < b − c.
If a > b, then a + c > b + c and a − c > b − c.	If ax > b, then ax + c > b + c and ax − c > b − c.

2. Rule for multiplication or division

Multiplying or dividing both sides of an inequality by a number that is strictly positive does not change the direction of the inequality.

If a < b and c > 0, then ca < cb and $\frac{a}{c} < \frac{b}{c}$.	If ax < b and c > 0, then cax < cb and $\frac{ax}{c} < \frac{b}{c}$.
If a > b and c > 0, then ca > cb and $\frac{a}{c} > \frac{b}{c}$.	If ax > b and c > 0, then cax > cb and $\frac{ax}{c} > \frac{b}{c}$.

Multiplying or dividing both sides of an inequality by a number that is strictly negative reverses the direction of the inequality.

If a < b and c < 0, then ca > cb and $\frac{a}{c} > \frac{b}{c}$.	If ax < b and c < 0, then cax > cb and $\frac{ax}{c} > \frac{b}{c}$.
If a > b and c < 0, then ca < cb and $\frac{a}{c} < \frac{b}{c}$.	If ax > b and c < 0, then cax < cb and $\frac{ax}{c} < \frac{b}{c}$.

These rules are used to manipulate inequalities and, more specifically, to isolate the variable in first-degree inequalities in one variable to find their solution set.

EXAMPLE 1

To solve the inequality $18 - 4x \geqslant x + 33$ in IR.

$$18 - 4x \geqslant x + 33$$
$$18 - 18 - 4x \geqslant x + 33 - 18 \quad \text{(Subtraction rule)}$$
$$-4x \geqslant x + 15$$
$$-4x - x \geqslant x - x + 15 \quad \text{(Subtraction rule)}$$
$$-5x \geqslant 15$$
$$\frac{-5x}{-5} \leqslant \frac{15}{-5} \quad \text{(Division rule)}$$
$$x \leqslant -3$$

The solution set is thus the set of real numbers less than or equal to -3, which is written $]-\infty, -3]$. A number line illustrates this solution set.

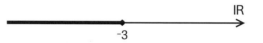

EXAMPLE 2

We solve $\left\{ x \in \text{IN} \mid \dfrac{2x - 9}{-4} < \dfrac{x}{2} \right\}$ in the following manner:

$$\frac{2x - 9}{-4} < \frac{x}{2}$$
$$-4\left(\frac{2x - 9}{-4}\right) > -4\left(\frac{x}{2}\right) \quad \text{(Multiplication rule)}$$
$$2x - 9 > -2x$$
$$2x + 2x - 9 + 9 > -2x + 2x + 9 \quad \text{(Addition rule)}$$
$$4x > 9$$
$$\frac{4x}{4} > \frac{9}{4} \quad \text{(Division rule)}$$
$$x > \frac{9}{4}$$

The solution set is {3, 4, 5, . . .}, appearing on the number line as follows:

f) Solve the following inequalities in IR:

1) $2x + 3 < -9$

2) $-2x + 8 \leqslant x + 4$

3) $2(2x + 3) < 4(x - 1)$

4) $\dfrac{x + 2}{4} + 1 > x$

5) $2x \geqslant x$

6) $x - 1 > x + 1$

g) Given the linear functions f, g and h defined as follows:

$$f(x) = 3(x - 1) + 2 \qquad g(x) = 4 - 2x \qquad h(x) = \frac{2x - 1}{4}$$

Find, both algebraically and graphically, the interval of the domain over which:

1) $f(x) > 0$

2) $g(x) < 2$

3) $h(x) \geqslant x$

4) $f(x) > g(x)$

5) $g(x) \leqslant h(x)$

6) $f(x) + g(x) < h(x)$

Solving first-degree inequalities is closely related to studying the sign of linear functions.

h) If a function is represented by an oblique line on the plane, can it have a maximum or minimum? Explain your answer.

i) Describe the line depicting a function that is:

1) Increasing.

2) Decreasing.

j) If the rule of the linear function is $f(x) = ax + b$, what is the rule for its inverse?

k) Is the inverse of a linear function always a function itself? Justify your answer.

When unrestricted, the **properties** of a **transformed linear function** are the following:

1. Its rule is in the form $f(x) = ax + b$ (or $f(x) = ax + k$).

2. Its graph is an oblique line.

3. Its domain is IR and its range is IR.

4. It has one zero: -b/a (ou -k/a).

5. It has no maximum or minimum.

6. If a > 0, it is increasing over its entire domain; if a < 0, it is decreasing over its entire domain.

7. If a > 0, it is negative over]-∞, -b/a] and positive over [-b/a, +∞[.
   If a < 0, it is positive over]-∞, -b/a] and negative over [-b/a, +∞[.

8. Its inverse is a transformed linear function.

Various operations can be performed on linear functions, including compositions.

l) Given the linear functions $f(x) = a_1x + b_1$ and $g(x) = a_2x + b_2$, give the rules for the following functions:

1) $f \circ g$

2) $g \circ f$

3) $f + g$

4) $f - g$

5) $f \cdot g$

6) $\dfrac{f}{g}$

m) To which mathematical model do each of the six functions above correspond?

INVESTMENT 4

1. Find all the properties of the following functions:

   a) $f(x) = -3x$

   b) $g(x) = 2x - 3$

   c) $h(x) = -6x + 2$

2. Given the functions f, g and h defined in the previous exercise, state the rules for the following functions:

   a) $g \circ f$ **b)** $h \circ g$ **c)** $f \cdot g$ **d)** $g - h$ **e)** $\dfrac{h}{f}$

3. What are the rules for the inverses of the functions f, g, and h defined in exercise 1?

4. In each case, find the function rule whose table of values is shown below.

   a)

X	Y₁	
-2	-7	
-1	-5	
0	-3	
1	-1	
2	1	
3	3	
4	5	

   X=4

   b)

X	Y₁	
-2	14	
-1	9	
0	4	
1	-1	
2	-6	
3	-11	
4	-16	

   X=4

Of the 17 794 703 motor vehicles registered in Canada in 1994, 3 669 792 were trucks and tow-trucks.

Source: Statistics Canada

5. A truck transports 10 kg boxes. The truck has a mass of 5000 kg when empty. Find:

   a) The mass of the truck when loaded with 90 boxes.

   b) The number of boxes the truck is transporting if its total mass is 6540 kg.

   c) The function rule used to express the total mass of the truck based on the number of boxes it is transporting.

6. Cellular telephone companies offer customers a variety of subscription plans. If customers do not understand how the plans work, they may end up paying more than they should. The monthly plans of four different companies are shown on the right.

Cellular Telephone Rates

Company	Monthly rate	Free minutes included	Cost of each additional minute
TELCEL	$15	–	$0.30
INTER	$20	20	$0.25
LORI	$30	60	$0.20
FONO	$50	150	$0.10

   a) What is the function rule for each company's rate plan?

   b) Find which company offers the best rate for the following amounts of usage:

   1) 50 min of calls per month.

   2) 120 min of calls per month.

   3) Between 150 and 170 min of calls per month.

   4) Over 170 min of calls per month.

7. A trucker notices that the price of diesel fuel has gone up by 5¢ a litre per year over the past few years.

 a) If the current price of diesel fuel is 54¢ a litre:

 1) What is the rule for calculating the price *p* of diesel fuel from the number *y* of elapsed years?

 2) What is the rule for calculating the number of elapsed years from the current price of diesel fuel.

 b) What is the relationship between the two functions?

8. The formula $C = \frac{5}{9}(F - 32)$ is used to transform degrees Fahrenheit into degrees Celsius. Give the rule for the inverse function.

9. By assigning a value to one of the variables in the rule for a linear function, we get a first-degree equation in one variable. Solve these equations in IR:

 a) $2 = 4x - 2$

 b) $y = 2(5 - 3) + 8$

 c) $0 = 2(x + 3) - 8$

 d) $10 = 4x - \frac{x}{2} + 6$

10. At a glance, determine which of the following inequalities are equivalent to $x > -6$. State the property that justifies your answer.

 a) $x + 4 > -6 + 4$

 b) $x - 10 < -6 - 10$

 c) $-x > 6$

 d) $6 > -x$

 e) $-4x < 24$

 f) $\frac{x - 6}{-3} > \frac{-6 - 6}{-3}$

11. The screen at right shows one method of solving an inequality.

 a) Justify each of the steps shown using the rules for solving inequalities.

 b) What symbol should replace the cursor to complete the solution to the inequality.

```
88-4X>X+3
                    1
-4X>X-85
                    1
-5X>-85
                    1
X■17
```

12. Solve each of the following inequalities algebraically:

 a) $5(x - 2) > 3x + 1$

 b) $-2.5(8 + x) < -x + 3(1.5x - 4)$

 c) $-(6x + 2) > 16 - 3x$

 d) $(x + 3)(x - 2) > (x + 8)(x + 1)$

 e) $\frac{-\sqrt{2}(x + 1)}{\sqrt{3}} > \sqrt{6}(x - 1)$

 f) $\sqrt{2}x + \sqrt{3}x \geqslant \sqrt{5}$

13. Find the following sets and justify each of the steps in the solution. Draw each set on a number line.

 a) $\{x \in \text{IN} \mid 3x - 4 > 6 - x\}$

 b) $\{x \in \text{IN} \mid 12 - 11x \leqslant 8 - (6 + x)\}$

 c) $\{x \in \mathbb{Z} \mid 14 + 2x < 6\}$

 d) $\{x \in \mathbb{Z} \mid 2.5x + 14 \geqslant 6.5x\}$

 e) $\{x \in \text{IR} \mid \frac{6 - x}{3} > 14\}$

 f) $\left\{x \in \text{IR} \mid \frac{2x - 6}{-2} \leqslant \frac{1 - x}{3}\right\}$

14. Find the interval of the independent variable for which each of the functions below is negative.

a)

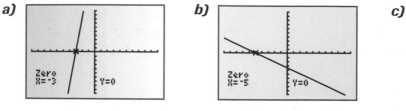

Zero
X=-3   Y=0

b)

Zero
X=-5   Y=0

c)

15. Solve the inequality $-2 < 1 - 4x$ using the procedure outlined below.

a) The first term of the inequality is equal to Y_1 and the second, to Y_2. Enter these rules into the graphing calculator.

b) Display the graph of these functions.

c) Find the coordinates of the point of intersection.

d) Over what interval:

1) Is the curve of the first function located below the curve of the second?

2) Are the images in the first function less than those in the second?

3) Is $Y_1 < Y_2$ or $-2 < 1 - 4x$?

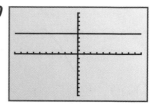

Plot1 Plot2 Plot3
\Y1◻-2
\Y2◻1-4X
\Y3=
\Y4=
\Y5=
\Y6=
\Y7=

Intersection
X=.75   Y=-2

16. Given functions *f*, *g* and *h* defined as follows:

$$f(x) = 2x - 1 \qquad g(x) = 2(4 - 2x) \qquad h(x) = \frac{2x - 1}{3}$$

Graphically determine the values of the domain for which:

a) $f(x) > 0$ **b)** $g(x) \leq 0$ **c)** $h(x) \geq 0$ **d)** $f(x) > g(x)$ **e)** $g(x) \leq h(x)$

17. The rules of two functions are provided. What do you notice about the graphs of these functions? Justify your answer using rates of change.

a) $f(x) = \frac{3}{2}x + 4$ and $g(x) = -\frac{2}{3}x - 2$ **b)** $h(x) = \frac{x}{5} + \frac{2}{3}$ and $i(x) = 0.2x - \frac{3}{2}$

18. Use a graphing calculator to find the coordinates of the point of intersection for each pair of functions in question 17. Show algebraically that the resulting coordinates are precise.

19. The graph of a linear function is represented by a line that passes through the point (3, -5) and has a rate of change of -2/3. What is the function rule?

20. The graph of a linear function is represented by a line that passes through points (-2, 3) and (3, -4). What is the function rule?

21. The graph of a linear function is represented by a line that passes through the point (-2, 3). The function's value when $x = 0$ is 5/4. What is the function rule?

22. A linear function is defined as $f(x) = -2x + 3$. What is the distance between the two points whose x-coordinates are -2 and 2?

23. A linear function is defined as $g(x) = 4x - 2$. What are the coordinates of the point located halfway between the points where the graph intersects the axes?

24. The table at right shows how the value of a car is related to the number of years since its purchase.

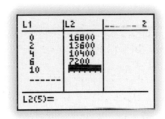

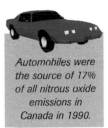

Automobiles were the source of 17% of all nitrous oxide emissions in Canada in 1990.

   a) What is the function rule for calculating the value v of the car based on the time since its purchase?

   b) What is the value of the car after 10 years?

25. A disk with a radius of 3 cm has an arc of any length x removed. Two radii are used to close the figure. The problem concerns the relation between the length x of the missing arc and the perimeter of the resulting shape.

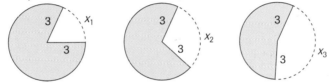

   a) What is the rule for this relation?

   b) Find all the properties of this relation.

26. Dennis is responsible for renting the photocopiers used by the various departments in a school. The French Department averages 5000 photocopies a week, while the Mathematics Department averages 3000. Two photocopy companies offer the following rates: Photoco charges $40 a week for rental plus 2.5¢ per copy; Copyco charges $105 a week for rental plus 0.8¢ per copy.

The photocopy was invented in 1903 by the American, G. C. Beidler. Although the first photocopier arrived on the market in 1907, photocopying did not become popular until the 1960s.

   a) What are the function rules that relate the total cost to the number of photocopies made per week?

   b) Which company should Dennis choose for each department?

   c) For what number of copies would the cost be the same with both companies?

   d) Photoco is offering a promotion for the upcoming semester: it will waive its $40 rental fee. Copyco responds by reducing its rental fee by $40. Which company should Dennis choose now?

   e) Because Photoco's profits decreased last semester, the company raises its price to 3¢ a copy, without any fees. Copyco decides to continue the promotion in *d)* for another three months. Which company should Dennis choose in this case?

27. It costs $500 plus $20 per person to rent a reception hall for a wedding banquet. The wine costs an additional $50, plus $3 per person, per round. Provide the function rule for calculating:

a) The cost of the wedding banquet.　　　**b)** The cost of one round of wine.

c) The cost of the banquet and two rounds of wine.

28. Gabriella serves refreshments at 12 bingo nights organized by a community centre. According to the bingo experts, the number (N) of people attending each night depends on the admission charge c, and generally follows the rule $N(c) = -60c + 400$. According to these same experts, Gabriella can expect a net profit of approximately $1.50 per person. Each night she must pay equipment rental fees of $50.

a) What is the function rule for P that allows Gabriella to calculate her profits for the entire 12 nights based on the admission charge c?

b) Calculate the profits she can make in 12 nights if the admission charge is $5 per person.

c) What admission charge would allow Gabriella to make a profit of $55?

a) On the right is a series of patterns made of small squares.

1) Consider the relation between the pattern's position in the series and the number of small squares it contains. Complete the table of values for this relation.

Position of pattern	1	2	3	4	5	6	...	x
Number of squares	2	5	8					

2) Why is this a linear relationship?

3) Find all the properties of this relation.

b) A trapezoid can always be broken down into a parallelogram and a triangle with the same altitude. For a given altitude a, find:

1) The linear function that associates the area of the parallelogram with its base b.

2) The linear function that associates the area of the triangle with its base t.

3) The function that associates the area of the trapezoid with a base b of the parallelogram and a base t of the triangle.

c) Show that the image of the function in part 3 of *b)* corresponds to the formula for calculating a trapezoid's area; that is, one half the product of the sum of the bases multiplied by the altitude.

QUADRATIC FUNCTIONS

THE BASIC QUADRATIC FUNCTION

A series of podiums

Series of patterns can produce relationships. To identify these relations, simply consider the pattern's position and the number of basic elements required to build it. Below is a very basic series of patterns made of small squares.

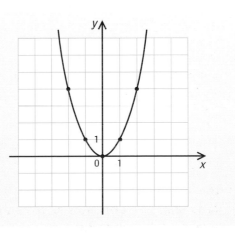

Canadian speed skaters Éric Bédard, Marc Gagnon, Derrick Campbell and François Drolet won the gold medal in the Men's 5000 m relay at the Winter Games in Nagano.

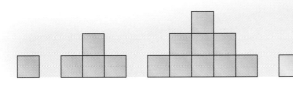

Position of pattern	1	2	3	4	5	...	x
Number of squares							

a) Is this relation a function?

b) Is this relation's rate of change constant?

c) What is the rule for this relation?

d) Graph this relation. Graph the mathematical model that corresponds to this relation.

e) Graph the inverse and indicate if it is a function.

This function is the basic function for second-degree polynomial functions, also known as **quadratic functions.**

The **properties** of the **basic quadratic function** are:

1. Rule: $f(x) = x^2$
2. Graph: parabola
3. Domain: IR   Range: IR_+
4. Zero: 0
5. Extreme: 0 (minimum)
6. Variation: decreasing over $]-\infty, 0]$ and increasing over $[0, +\infty[$
7. Sign: positive over IR (and negative at {0})

TRANSFORMED QUADRATIC FUNCTIONS

Migraines

Several medications are being tested in a laboratory. One of these is a pill that relieves migraine headaches. On a scale of 5, the degree of relief felt over a period of hours follows the shape of the curve shown below.

a) To which mathematical model does this function correspond?

b) How long will the effects of the medication last?

c) Express the maximum degree of relief as a percent.

d) Relative to the parabola of the basic quadratic function, identify the transformations used to obtain the parabola shown on the right.

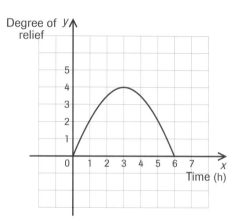

"Migraine" is the popular expression for the medical term hemicrania, which means "pain on one side of the head."

It is possible to transform the basic quadratic function by introducing parameters that modify the coordinates of its points. This can be achieved by introducing into its rule:

1. A parameter **a,** which produces the rule $f(x) = ax^2$:

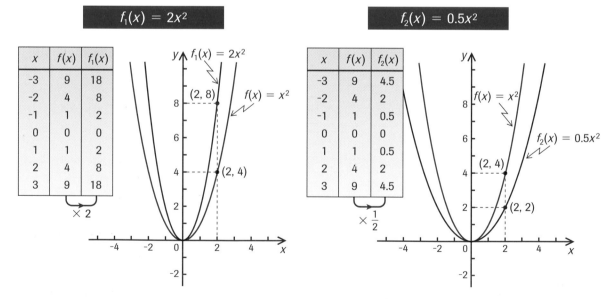

x	f(x)	$f_1(x)$
-3	9	18
-2	4	8
-1	1	2
0	0	0
1	1	2
2	4	8
3	9	18

× 2

x	f(x)	$f_2(x)$
-3	9	4.5
-2	4	2
-1	1	0.5
0	0	0
1	1	0.5
2	4	2
3	9	4.5

× $\frac{1}{2}$

For the corresponding x-coordinates, the y-coordinates were multiplied by 2.

For the corresponding x-coordinates, the y-coordinates were multiplied by $\frac{1}{2}$.

Multiplying the y-coordinates causes a vertical scale change that corresponds to a stretch if a > 1 and a shrink if 0 < a < 1.

A negative value for parameter **a** results in a reflection across the x-axis.

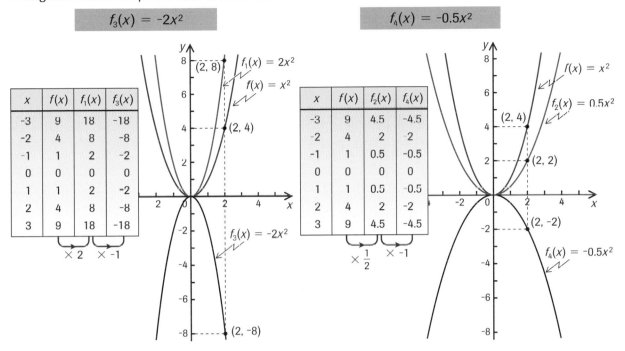

$$f_3(x) = -2x^2$$

$$f_4(x) = -0.5x^2$$

x	f(x)	$f_1(x)$	$f_3(x)$
-3	9	18	-18
-2	4	8	-8
-1	1	2	-2
0	0	0	0
1	1	2	-2
2	4	8	-8
3	9	18	-18

× 2   × -1

x	f(x)	$f_2(x)$	$f_4(x)$
-3	9	4.5	-4.5
-2	4	2	-2
-1	1	0.5	-0.5
0	0	0	0
1	1	0.5	-0.5
2	4	2	-2
3	9	4.5	-4.5

× $\frac{1}{2}$ × -1

2. A parameter **b,** which produces the rule $f(x) = (bx)^2$:

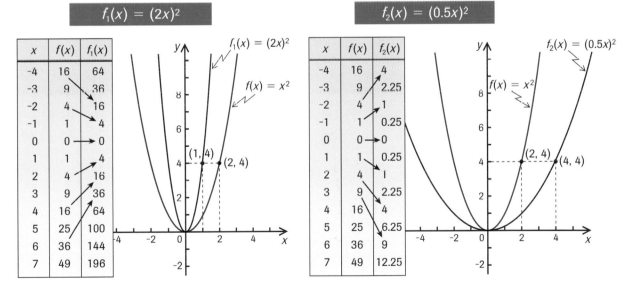

$$f_1(x) = (2x)^2$$

$$f_2(x) = (0.5x)^2$$

x	f(x)	$f_1(x)$
-4	16	64
-3	9	36
-2	4	16
-1	1	4
0	0	0
1	1	4
2	4	16
3	9	36
4	16	64
5	25	100
6	36	144
7	49	196

x	f(x)	$f_2(x)$
-4	16	4
-3	9	2.25
-2	4	1
-1	1	0.25
0	0	0
1	1	0.25
2	4	1
3	9	2.25
4	16	4
5	25	6.25
6	36	9
7	49	12.25

For the corresponding y-coordinates, the x-coordinates were divided by 2.

For the corresponding y-coordinates, the x-coordinates were divided by $\frac{1}{2}$.

Dividing the x-coordinates causes a horizontal scale change that corresponds to a shrink if b > 1 and a stretch if 0 < b < 1.

A negative value for parameter **b** results in a reflection across the y-axis. This does not in any way affect the shape of the basic parabola because of its symmetry across the y-axis.

3. A parameter **h,** which produces the rule $f(x) = (x - h)^2$:

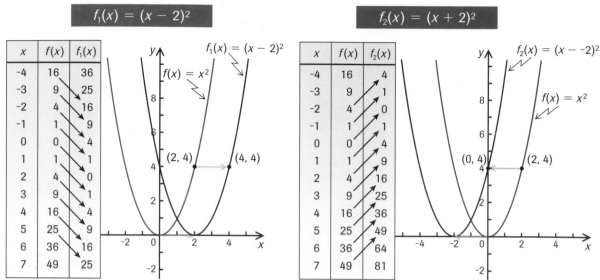

x	f(x)	$f_1(x)$
-4	16	36
-3	9	25
-2	4	16
-1	1	9
0	0	4
1	1	1
2	4	0
3	9	1
4	16	4
5	25	9
6	36	16
7	49	25

x	f(x)	$f_2(x)$
-4	16	4
-3	9	1
-2	4	0
-1	1	1
0	0	4
1	1	9
2	4	16
3	9	25
4	16	36
5	25	49
6	36	64
7	49	81

For the corresponding y-coordinates, the x-coordinates were increased by 2.

For the corresponding y-coordinates, the x-coordinates were increased by -2.

Parameter **h** results in a translation of h units to the right if its value is positive, or h units to the left if its value is negative.

4. A parameter **k,** which produces the rule $f(x) = x^2 + k$:

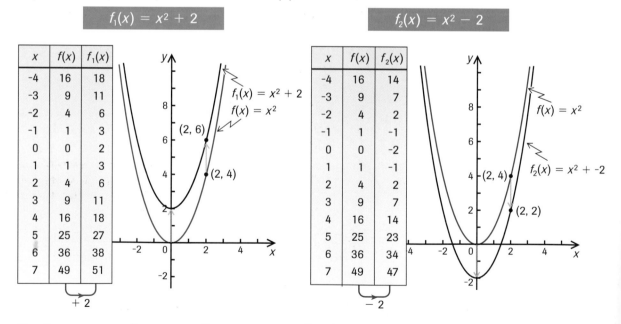

x	f(x)	$f_1(x)$
-4	16	18
-3	9	11
-2	4	6
-1	1	3
0	0	2
1	1	3
2	4	6
3	9	11
4	16	18
5	25	27
6	36	38
7	49	51

+ 2

x	f(x)	$f_2(x)$
-4	16	14
-3	9	7
-2	4	2
-1	1	-1
0	0	-2
1	1	-1
2	4	2
3	9	7
4	16	14
5	25	23
6	36	34
7	49	47

- 2

For the corresponding x-coordinates, the y-coordinates were increased by 2.

For the corresponding x-coordinates, the y-coordinates were increased by -2.

Parameter **k** results in a translation of k units up if its value is positive, or k units down if its value is negative.

As we have seen, the basic quadratic function can be modified using four parameters. However, these same changes can actually be produced using only three parameters. Parameter **b** can be integrated into parameter **a** by applying a property of exponents.

$f(x) = a(b(x - h))^2 + k$

$\Downarrow$

$f(x) = a(b^2(x - h)^2) + k$　　　(By the property $(ab)^m = a^m b^m$.)

$\Downarrow$

$f(x) = ab^2(x - h)^2 + k$　　　(By the associative property of multiplication.)

$\Downarrow$

$f(x) = a(x - h)^2 + k$　　　(New value represented by a.)

Note that **ab²** forms a new value that acts as parameter **a**. That is why the notation shown below is considered the **standard form** for the quadratic function rule:

$$f(x) = a(x - h)^2 + k \text{ with } a \neq 0$$

e) Show that these three rules denote the same function:

$f(x) = 0.5(2(x - 1))^2 + 3$　　　$g(x) = 0.5(4(x - 1)^2) + 3$　　　$h(x) = 2(x - 1)^2 + 3$

f) By transforming the standard form algebraically, we obtain another notation for the quadratic function rule, called the **general form**. Complete the following steps:

$$f(x) = a(x - h)^2 + k$$
$$f(x) = a(x^2 - \blacksquare x + \blacksquare) + k$$
$$f(x) = ax^2 - \blacksquare x + \blacksquare + k$$
$$f(x) = ax^2 + \blacksquare x + \blacksquare$$

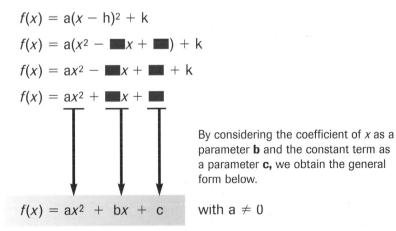

By considering the coefficient of x as a parameter **b** and the constant term as a parameter **c,** we obtain the general form below.

$$f(x) = ax^2 + bx + c \quad \text{with } a \neq 0$$

The rule of a transformed quadratic function can be expressed in two ways:

1. **Standard form**: $f(x) = a(x - h)^2 + k$ with $a \neq 0$;

2. **General form** $f(x) = ax^2 + bx + c$ with $a \neq 0$.

g) Notice that parameter **a** is the same in both notations. With respect to **h** and **k,** the relationships are shown below. Justify each step.

1) We get: $\mathbf{b} = -2ah$

$\Downarrow$

$$\mathbf{h} = -\frac{\mathbf{b}}{\mathbf{2a}}$$

2) We get: $\mathbf{c} = ah^2 + k$

$\Downarrow$

$$k = c - ah^2$$

$\Downarrow$

$$k = c - a\left(-\frac{b}{2a}\right)^2$$

$\Downarrow$

$$k = c - a\left(\frac{b^2}{4a^2}\right)$$

$\Downarrow$

$$k = c - \frac{ab^2}{4a^2}$$

$\Downarrow$

$$k = c - \frac{b^2}{4a}$$

$\Downarrow$

$$\mathbf{k} = \frac{\mathbf{4ac - b^2}}{\mathbf{4a}}$$

These two relationships are used to alternate quickly between the two forms of the equation, as well as to give the coordinates of the parabola's vertex.

$$\mathbf{h} = -\frac{\mathbf{b}}{\mathbf{2a}} \text{ and } \mathbf{k} = \frac{\mathbf{4ac - b^2}}{\mathbf{4a}}$$

h) Express the function rules below in their other form, and provide the coordinates of the parabola's vertex in each case.

1) $f(x) = 2x^2 - 2x - 4$

2) $g(x) = 2(x + 2)^2 - 4$

3) $h(x) = 6x^2 - 9x + 3$

4) $i(x) = 3(x - 2)^2 + 4$

To locate the parabola of a quadratic function, simply apply the transformations using the critical ordered pairs from the basic function:

Basic function: (-2, 4), (-1, 1), (0, 0), (1, 1), (2, 4)

Transformed function: (■, ■), (■, ■), (■, ■), (■, ■), (■, ■)

The critical ordered pairs of the function $f(x) = 2(x - 3)^2 - 2$ are determined thus:

(-2, 4), (-1, 1), (0, 0), (1, 1), (2, 4)

(1, 6), (2, 0), (3, -2), (4, 0), (5, 6)

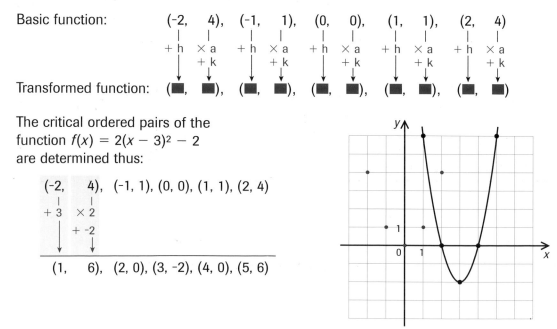

i) Graph the functions defined by the following rules:

1) $f(x) = 3(x - 1)^2 + 1$ 2) $g(x) = -2(x - 2)^2 - 1$ 3) $h(x) = 0.5(x + 1)^2 + 2$

4) $i(x) = 2x^2 + 3x + 1$ 5) $j(x) = -x^2 + 4x - 5$

ZEROS AND EQUATIONS

Stocks plummet!

Miriam and Phil purchased some stock at $7.20 a share as part of an assignment for their economics course. The two students have followed the performance of their stock closely ever since. Unfortunately, the current economic forecast is not good: the value of their shares is plummeting! Below are the data they compiled during the first four months:

Floor of the Montréal Exchange.

x	$f(x)$
0	7.20
1	5.00
2	3.20
3	1.80
4	0.80

After doing a mathematical analysis of the data and plotting them, Miriam and Phil notice that the value of their shares corresponds to the graph of a quadratic function. They ask themselves the following question: "Judging by this model, at what point will our shares be worthless?"

The stock index indicates whether the daily prices of shares have gone up or down. Stock prices are calculated by averaging the prices of securities listed on the Stock Exchange from different sectors of the economy— crude oil, pulp and paper, banks, etc. In New York, Dow Jones sets the average price of shares using 30 securities drawn from different sectors. The Montréal Exchange uses 60 securities to set its average price; the Toronto Stock Exchange uses 300.

They decide to use "regression" to find the quadratic function rule that best represents their data.

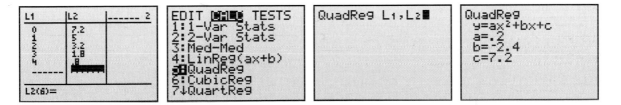

a) What is the function rule in its:

1) General form?   2) Standard form?

b) Using a calculator, determine at what point their shares will be worthless ($0).

c) Show that the same answer can be obtained algebraically by taking the function rule and completing steps similar to the ones shown below.

$$f(x) = a(x - h)^2 + k$$
$$\downarrow$$
$$0 = a(x - h)^2 + k \text{ or } a(x - h)^2 + k = 0$$
$$a(x - h)^2 = -k$$
$$(x - h)^2 = -\frac{k}{a} \implies x - h = \sqrt{-\frac{k}{a}} \text{ or } x - h = -\sqrt{-\frac{k}{a}}$$
$$\implies x_1 = \sqrt{-\frac{k}{a}} + h \text{ or } x_2 = -\sqrt{-\frac{k}{a}} + h$$

Depending on the rule's form, the zeros of the quadratic function are as follows:

Standard form	General form
$f(x) = a(x - h)^2 + k$	$f(x) = ax^2 + bx + c$

$$x_1 = \sqrt{-\frac{k}{a}} + h \text{ and } x_2 = -\sqrt{-\frac{k}{a}} + h \qquad\qquad x_1 = \frac{-b + \sqrt{b^2 - 4ac}}{2a} \text{ and } x_2 = \frac{-b - \sqrt{b^2 - 4ac}}{2a}$$

We get:

1. Two real zeros if $-\frac{k}{a} > 0$.

2. One real zero if $-\frac{k}{a} = 0$.

3. No real zero if $-\frac{k}{a} < 0$.

We get:

1. Two real zeros if $b^2 - 4ac > 0$.

2. One real zero if $b^2 - 4ac = 0$.

3. No real zero if $b^2 - 4ac < 0$.

Expressions $-\frac{k}{a}$ and $(b^2 - 4ac)$ are the discriminants.

d) Find the zeros of the quadratic functions defined as follows:

1) $f(x) = -2(x + 3)^2 + 8$ 2) $g(x) = 2x^2 + 3x - 2$

Finding the zeros of a quadratic function involves solving a **second-degree equation in one variable.**

e) In some cases, it is easy to factor the first term and apply the zero-product law. Use this method to solve the following quadratic equations:

1) $x^2 - 7x + 12 = 0$ 2) $2x^2 - x - 6 = 0$

Solving quadratic equations by finding the zeros is also useful for determining the elements of the domain whose images are not 0. This is how to find the elements in the domain of the function $f(x) = 2(x - 2)^2 - 5$ whose image is 3. This amounts to solving the following quadratic equation:

$$2(x - 2)^2 - 5 = 3 \text{ or } 2(x - 2)^2 - 8 = 0$$

The coordinates of the parabola's vertex and the zeros are the only elements needed to find all the properties of quadratic functions.

SIGN AND INEQUALITIES

Profits are rolling in!

A new company starts manufacturing in-line skates. According to financial forecasts, a certain number of skates must be produced to turn a profit. The company must be careful not to overproduce, however, as this will lead to a surplus in its inventory. The rule $P(x) = -50x^2 + 700x - 2000$ describes the relation between the number of pairs of skates sold, in thousands, and the resulting profit in thousands of dollars.

The company wants to know the number of skates it must manufacture to turn a profit. Here is what the function looks like on a graph:

Lachine Canal bike path.

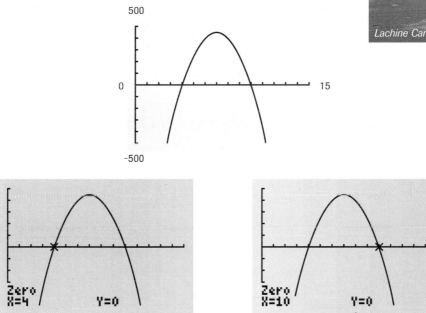

a) For which values of the domain, defined by the values in the window below, is this function:

1) Zero?   2) Positive?   3) Negative?

b) Which second-degree inequality corresponds to each of the following statements?

1) The function is positive.

2) The function is negative.

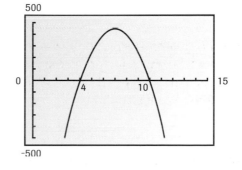

c) If the domain is expanded to include IR, what is the solution set of the following inequalities?

1) $-50x^2 + 700x - 2000 < 0$ 2) $-50x^2 + 700x - 2000 > 0$

We want to find the number of pairs of skates the company must produce to generate profits of over \$337.5 K. This involves solving the inequality $-50x^2 + 700x - 2000 > 337.5$, or finding the interval of the domain over which $P(x) > 337.5$.

d) To find this interval:

1) We can define a second function Q, based on the second term of the inequality, and then locate the interval over which $P(x)$ is greater than $Q(x)$. Identify this interval.

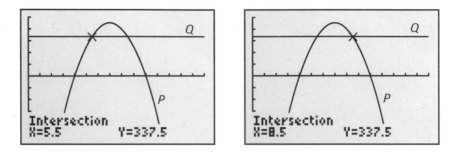

2) We can also locate the interval over which $P - Q$ is positive, or $P(x) - Q(x) > 0$. Identify this interval.

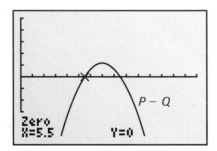 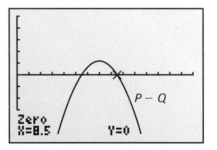

e) Solve the given inequalities in IR using the graphs displayed below.

1) $x^2 - 5 < -3x + 5$ 2) $-4x^2 > (x - 2)^2 - 5$

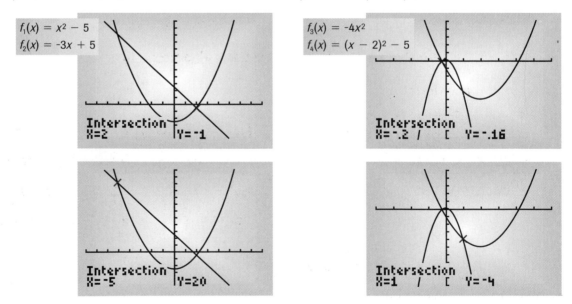

f) Solve the same inequalities as those in *e)* using a single quadratic function:

1) $x^2 - 5 < -3x + 5$

2) $-4x^2 > (x \quad 2)^2 \quad 5$

Note that the sign of a given quadratic function *f* follows a pattern. This pattern is related to the sign of parameter **a** and the zeros of the function.

g) Every possible scenario is displayed below. In each case, express the sign of the function in relation to the sign of parameter **a**, as in 1).

1) $a > 0$ and 2 zeros 2) $a > 0$ and 1 zero 3) $a > 0$ and no zero

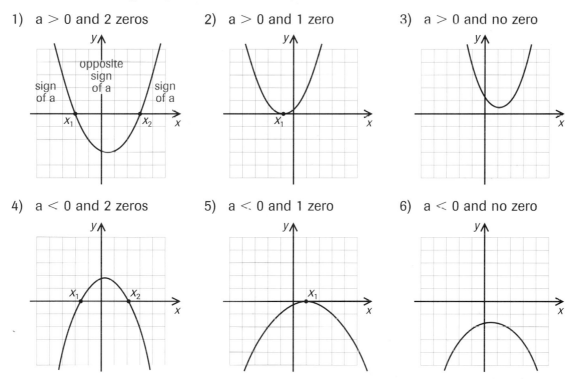

4) $a < 0$ and 2 zeros 5) $a < 0$ and 1 zero 6) $a < 0$ and no zero

h) What can be said about the sign of a quadratic function whose domain values are:

1) Outside the zeros? 2) Inside the zeros?

This pattern is used to solve a second-degree inequality **algebraically.**

The method is as follows:

1. Make one of the sides equal to zero.

    1. $ax^2 + bx + c \geq 0$ or $a(x - h)^2 + k \geq 0$

2. Find the zeros, if any.

    2. If $b^2 - 4ac < 0$ or $-\dfrac{k}{a} < 0 \Rightarrow$ no zero.

    If $b^2 \quad 4ac = 0$ or $-\dfrac{k}{a} = 0 \Rightarrow$ one zero.

    If $b^2 - 4ac > 0$ or $-\dfrac{k}{a} > 0 \Rightarrow$ two zeros.

3. Study the sign of the quadratic expression in relation to the sign of **a.**

    3.

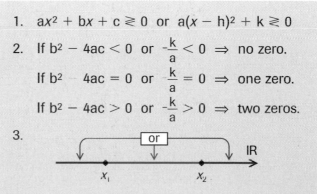

4. Find and check the solution set.

To solve the inequality $3x^2 + 5x + 1 \geqslant x^2 - 2x + 5$ in IR.

1. Make one of the inequality's sides equal to zero.

$$3x^2 + 5x + 1 \geqslant x^2 - 2x + 5$$

$$2x^2 + 7x - 4 \geqslant 0$$

2. Find the values of x that make the expression $2x^2 + 7x - 4$ equal to 0. Using parameters $a = 2$, $b = 7$ and $c = -4$, we obtain:

$$x_1 = \frac{-b + \sqrt{b^2 - 4ac}}{2a} \Rightarrow \frac{-7 + \sqrt{7^2 - 4(2 \times -4)}}{2 \times 2} = -4$$

$$x_2 = \frac{-b - \sqrt{b^2 - 4ac}}{2a} \Rightarrow \frac{-7 - \sqrt{7^2 - 4(2 \times -4)}}{2 \times 2} = 0.5$$

3. Because the value of parameter **a** is +2, the result is:

4. The solution set is $]-\infty, -4] \cup [0.5, +\infty[$.

    The result can be checked using a few numeric values.

i) Solve the following inequalities in IR.

1) $x^2 - 11x + 24 > 0$ 2) $x^2 - 8x < 20$

3) $-x^2 > 2x + 1$ 4) $x^2 > 1$

Solving second-degree inequalities in one variable involves examining the sign of a function.

The curve of a quadratic function is a parabola whose axis of symmetry is always parallel to the y-axis. It is easy to find the intervals over which the function is increasing or decreasing:

1. If a > 0, the function decreases to h, then increases.

2. If a < 0, the function increases to h, then decreases.

j) Prove that the inverse of a quadratic function is not itself a function.

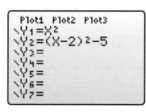

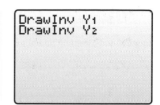

k) Complete the steps below and define the inverse algebraically.

Function	Inverse

$$y = a(x - h)^2 + k \implies \qquad x = a(y - h)^2 + k$$

$$a(y - h)^2 = \rule{2cm}{0.3cm}$$

$$(y - h)^2 = \rule{2cm}{0.3cm}$$

$$y - h = \rule{2cm}{0.3cm} \text{ or } y - h = \rule{2cm}{0.3cm}$$

$$y = \rule{2cm}{0.3cm} \text{ or } y = \rule{2cm}{0.3cm}$$

Note that the rules for two functions are used to define the inverse.

Thus, **transformed quadratic functions** (which are unrestricted) have the following **properties.** The sign of parameter **a** plays a key role.

1. Rule: $f(x) = a(x - h)^2 + k$ or $f(x) = ax^2 + bx + c$.

a > 0

2. Graph: parabola opening upward.

3. dom: IR; ran: $[k, +\infty[$.

4. Zeros: 0, 1 or 2 zeros depending on the value of $-\dfrac{k}{a}$ or of $b^2 - 4ac$.

5. Extreme: minimum k at h.

6. Variation: decreasing over $]-\infty, h]$ and increasing over $[h, +\infty[$.

7. Sign: negative between its zeros; otherwise positive.

a < 0

2. Graph: parabola opening downward.

3. dom: IR; ran: $]-\infty, k]$.

4. Zeros: 0, 1 or 2 zeros depending on the value of $-\dfrac{k}{a}$ or of $b^2 - 4ac$.

5. Extreme: maximum k at h.

6. Variation: increasing over $]-\infty, h]$ and decreasing over $[h, +\infty[$.

7. Sign: positive between its zeros; otherwise negative.

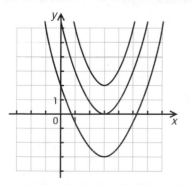

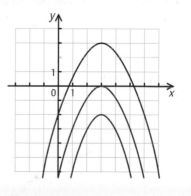

INVESTMENT 5

1. Write each rule in standard or general form.

   a) $f(x) = 2x^2 - 6x + 1.5$

   b) $g(x) = -2(x + 3)^2 - 5$

   c) $h(x) = (x + 2)(2x - 1)$

   d) $y = 3x^2 - 6x$

   e) $y = x^2 - 4$

   f) $i(x) = (2 - 2x)^2 + 1$

2. Find the values of parameters **a, h** and **k** in each of the following functions:

   a) $f(x) = 2(x + 4)^2 - 2$

   b) $g(x) = 2(3x + 6)^2 + 4$

   c) $h(x) = -2x^2 + 3x - 1$

   d) $l(x) = (2x + 1)(x - 3)$

   e) $m(x) = -2(x - 4)(2x - 1) + 3$

   f) $n(x) = 2x^2 - 4x + 4$

3. Write the following rules in standard form using only three parameters.

   a) $f(x) = 2(3x - 3)^2 + 4$ **b)** $g(x) = -1(-2x + 4)^2 - 2$ **c)** $h(x) = 0.5(-x + 3)^2 - 1$

4. A square's area is a function of the length s of its side. Find all properties of this function's mathematical model.

5. A circle's area is a function of the length r of its radius. Find all the properties of this function's mathematical model.

   The Babylonians usually calculated the circumference of a circle by multiplying its diameter by 3, which amounts to stating that $\pi = 3$. They also calculated the area of circles using $\pi = 3$.

6. Given the function $f(x) = x^2$:

   a) Graph the inverse of f, using the ordered pairs in the table of values.

   b) Is the inverse also a function?

   c) Define the inverse algebraically.

7. Take the critical ordered pairs that form the basic quadratic function—that is, (-2, 4), (-1, 1), (0, 0), (1, 1), (2, 4)—and by performing various operations on these coordinates, graph the following quadratic functions:

   a) $f(x) = 2(x - 3)^2 - 1$

   b) $g(x) = -0.5(x + 2)^2 + 3$

   c) $h(x) = 2x^2 + 3x - 2$

   d) $i(x) = -x^2 + 5x - 6$

8. What is the function rule f for a parabola that has a vertex (-2, 1) and a vertical scale change of -2?

9. Find the rules for the functions graphed below using the coordinates of the vertex and the other given point.

a)

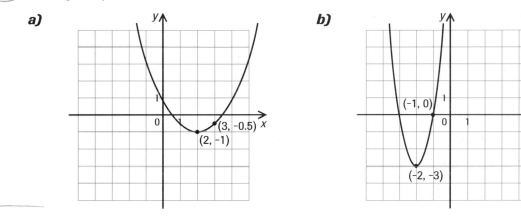

b)

10. Given function f whose rule is $f(x) = x^2 + 3x - 4$.

a) State:

1) The domain of f.

2) The range of f.

b) For which value of x is:

1) $f(x) = -6$?   2) $f(x) = 0$?

c) For what values of x is $x^2 + 3x - 4 > 0$?

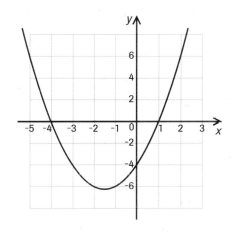

11. Find all the properties of the following functions:

a) $m(x) = -2(x - 1)^2 + 2$

b) $n(t) = -0.25t^2 - 2t + 1$

12. Solve the quadratic equations below using a graphing calculator.

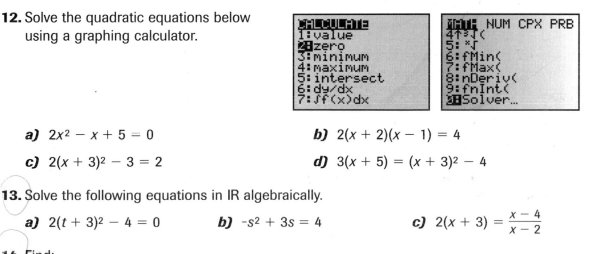

a) $2x^2 - x + 5 = 0$

b) $2(x + 2)(x - 1) = 4$

c) $2(x + 3)^2 - 3 = 2$

d) $3(x + 5) = (x + 3)^2 - 4$

13. Solve the following equations in IR algebraically.

a) $2(t + 3)^2 - 4 = 0$

b) $-s^2 + 3s = 4$

c) $2(x + 3) = \dfrac{x - 4}{x - 2}$

14. Find:

a) $\{x \in \mathbb{IR} \mid 2x^2 - x = 3(x + 2)\}$

b) $\{a \in \mathbb{IR} \mid a(a + 3) = 2a - 5\}$

15. Using the function rule, find and solve the quadratic equation associated with the y-coordinate of the point shown.

a) $f(x) = x^2 + x - 6$

b) $g(x) = -(x - 2)^2 + 4$

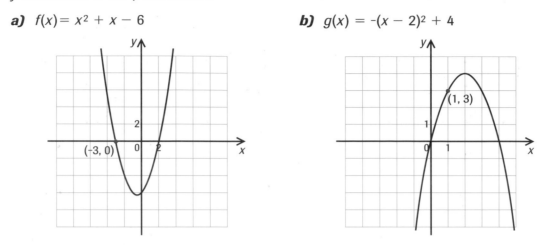

16. Below is the graph of a function and its table of values in increments of 0.5. Find and solve the quadratic equation associated with the y-coordinate of the given point.

a)

b)

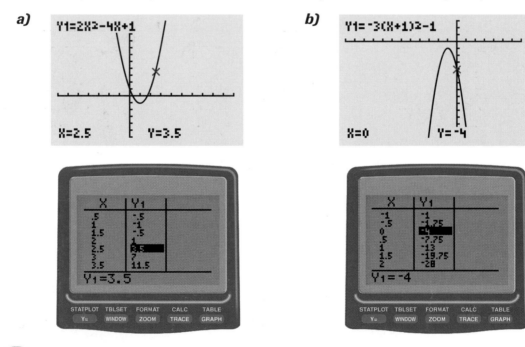

17. A farmer uses 100 m of wire-mesh to build a rectangular enclosure. If x represents the length of the enclosure, find the function that associates the enclosure's area with a given length.

a) Explain why $A(x) = x(50 - x)$ corresponds to this function's rule.

b) Graph this function.

c) Show that point (10, 400) belongs to this function.

d) What are the dimensions of the rectangle with the largest area?

18. Using the information provided by the graphs below, find the solution set of the corresponding inequalities in the form $Y_1 > 0$.

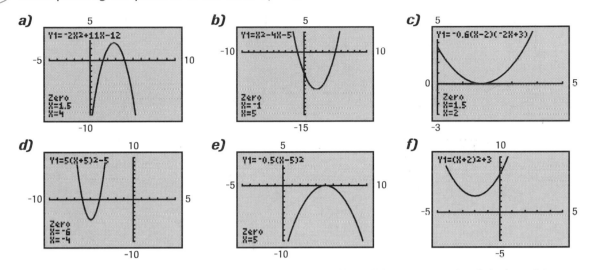

a)

b)

c)

d)

e)

f)

19. Find the intervals of the independent variable over which $Y_1 < 0$ in each of these tables of values.

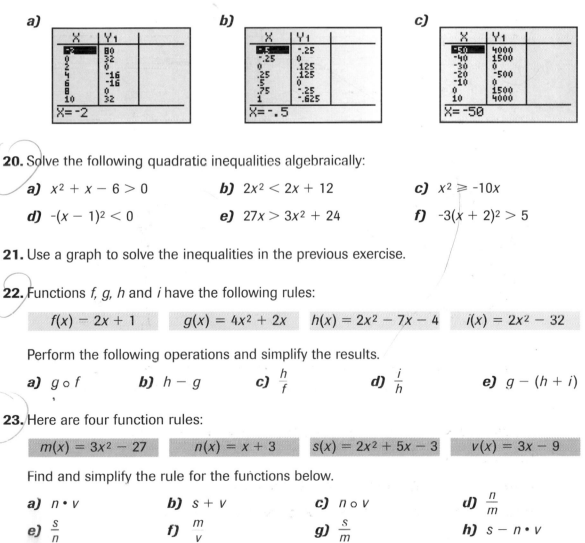

a)

b)

c)

20. Solve the following quadratic inequalities algebraically:

a) $x^2 + x - 6 > 0$

b) $2x^2 < 2x + 12$

c) $x^2 \geq -10x$

d) $-(x - 1)^2 < 0$

e) $27x > 3x^2 + 24$

f) $-3(x + 2)^2 > 5$

21. Use a graph to solve the inequalities in the previous exercise.

22. Functions f, g, h and i have the following rules:

| $f(x) = 2x + 1$ | $g(x) = 4x^2 + 2x$ | $h(x) = 2x^2 - 7x - 4$ | $i(x) = 2x^2 - 32$ |

Perform the following operations and simplify the results.

a) $g \circ f$

b) $h - g$

c) $\dfrac{h}{f}$

d) $\dfrac{i}{h}$

e) $g - (h + i)$

23. Here are four function rules:

| $m(x) = 3x^2 - 27$ | $n(x) = x + 3$ | $s(x) = 2x^2 + 5x - 3$ | $v(x) = 3x - 9$ |

Find and simplify the rule for the functions below.

a) $n \cdot v$

b) $s + v$

c) $n \circ v$

d) $\dfrac{n}{m}$

e) $\dfrac{s}{n}$

f) $\dfrac{m}{v}$

g) $\dfrac{s}{m}$

h) $s - n \cdot v$

24. Function g is defined by $g(x) = x^2 - 2x$. Use algebra to decide if the following expressions are true.

a) $g(a + b) = g(a) + g(b)$ **b)** $g(ac) = g(a) \cdot g(c)$ **c)** $g(a^c) = (g(a))^c$

25. Function f is defined by $f(x) = ax^2$.

If $n \neq 0$, use algebra to show that:

a) $f(n + 1) \neq f(n - 1)$ 　　　　　　　　**b)** $f(n) + f(n) = 2f(n)$

c) $f(2n) - f(n) \neq f(n)$ 　　　　　　　　**d)** $f(n + 1) \neq f(n) + f(1)$

26. In the 16th century Isaac Newton discovered that the height h attained by a thrown object depends on its initial speed s_0, the elapsed time t, since its release, and the initial height h_0 from which it was thrown. The formula below illustrates the relationship between these variables.

$$h = -4.9t^2 + s_0 t + h_0$$

a) Find the height of an object, relative to the ground, 5 s after it was thrown upwards at a speed of 10 m/s from the top of the Statue of Liberty.

b) How long will it be before the object hits the ground?

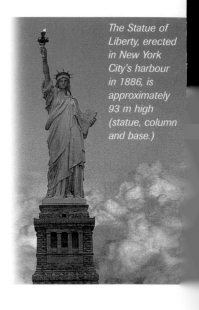

27. A pig farmer compiles the data below regarding the age, in months, and the average mass, in kilograms, of his pigs.

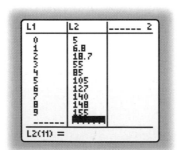

a) Find the rule for this function if a pig reaches its maximum mass of 215 kg at approximately 18 months of age.

b) An analysis of this table of values suggests why pigs are butchered when they are 5, 6 or 7 months old. What is this reason?

28. Below are two rectangles whose dimensions are given in centimetres. The area of each is indicated by the variables A_1 and A_2.

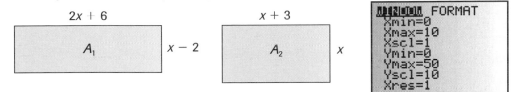

2x + 6

A_1

x − 2

x + 3

A_2

x

```
WINDOW FORMAT
 Xmin=0
 Xmax=10
 Xscl=1
 Ymin=0
 Ymax=50
 Yscl=10
 Xres=1
```

Use a graph to find the values of x where:

a) $A_1 > A_2$

b) $A_1 < A_2$

29. A restaurant posts the prices of its all-dressed pizzas. The prices are based on the pizza's radius.

Pizzas

Radius (cm)	7	10	12	15	20	25	30
Price ($)	6.84	12	15.04	19	24	27	...

a) Using a graphing calculator, find the rule that expresses the pizza's price as a function of its radius.

b) What is the diameter of an all-dressed pizza that costs $15.75?

30. A small company offers travellers a helicopter shuttle service from the airport to the downtown core. The service costs $10 per person and 300 people use it every day. The company's owner estimates she will lose 15 customers a day for every $1 increase in the price of the service.

a) Complete the following table of values:

Helicopter Shuttle

Increase ($)	Price ($)	Passengers	Revenue ($)
0	10	300	3000
1	▪	▪	▪
2	▪	▪	▪
3	▪	▪	▪
...	▪	▪	▪
x	▪	▪	▪

b) What is the function rule for f used to express the price as a function of the price increase?

c) What is the function rule for g used to express the number of passengers as a function of the price increase?

d) Function h is used to express revenue as a function of the price increase. Define function h in terms of functions f and g.

e) What price increase will result in the highest revenue for the company?

31. A small company bases its contribution C to a union fund on its profit levels p, which in turn depend on the number n of products it sells throughout the year. This can be expressed by the following rules: $C = 0.10(p - 10\ 000)$ et $p = 1000n - n^2$.

In 1992, 73.8% of public sector employees in Québec were unionized, along with 36.9% of private sector workers. Approximately 60% of these belonged to the Confederation of National Trade Unions (CNTU) and the Québec Federation of Labour (QFL).

a) What is the company's contribution if it sells 500 products?

b) Write a formula to calculate company contributions directly from n.

32. Complete the algebraic steps below and show that the rule for a quadratic function expressed using its zeros is $f(x) = a(x - x_1)(x - x_2)$.

$$f(x) = a(x - h)^2 + k = a\left((x - \blacksquare)^2 + \frac{k}{a}\right)$$ (By removing the common factor a.)

$$= a\left((x - h)^2 - (\blacksquare)\right)$$ (By equivalence of the sign.)

$$= a\left((x - h)^2 - (\blacksquare)^2\right) \text{ for } \frac{-k}{a} \geqslant 0$$ (Any positive number is equivalent to the square of its square root.)

$$= a\left((x - h + \blacksquare)(x - h - \blacksquare)\right)$$ (Difference of squares.)

$$= a\left((x - (h - \blacksquare))(x - (h + \blacksquare))\right)$$ (By grouping the two last terms in each factor.)

$$= a(x - x_1)(x - x_2)$$ (The expressions representing the zeros.)

33. Complete the following algebraic steps showing that the rule for a quadratic function may also be written as $f(x) = a(x^2 - Sx + P)$, where S and P stand for the sum and product of the zeros.

$$f(x) = a(x - x_1)(x - x_2)$$ (Using the rule shown in the previous exercise.)

$$= a(x^2 - xx_2 - \blacksquare + x_1x_2)$$ (By multiplying the two factors inside the parentheses.)

$$= a(x^2 - x(x_2 + \blacksquare) + x_1x_2)$$ (By removing the common factor x from the two middle terms.)

$$= a(x^2 - Sx + \blacksquare)$$ (By replacing the sum and product of the zeros by S and P.)

34. Find the quadratic function rule for f whose zeros are -2 and 3. The corresponding parabola passes through point (-1, -6).

35. Find the quadratic function rule for g whose corresponding parabola has its vertex at (2, -4). The parabola passes through point (0, 0).

36. The equation $d = 0.0056v^2 + 0.14v$ defines a function used to calculate a vehicle's stopping distance, in metres, relative to its speed in kilometres per hour.

a) This function is the product of two linear functions. Identify these functions.

b) At what speed was the car going if it needed 20 m to stop?

37. The product of two linear functions is a quadratic function.

a) Reproduce the two lines in this graph and draw the parabola corresponding to the product of these two linear functions.

b) Find the quadratic function rule for the product of these functions.

c) What is the relationship between the zero of each linear function and the zeros of the quadratic function?

d) What are the coordinates of the parabola's vertex?

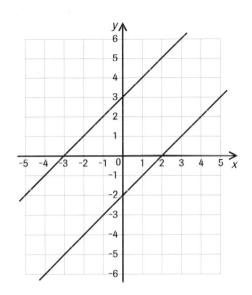

38. What are the characteristics of a parabola obtained by multiplying two linear functions having the same zero?

39. Find the rules for the three functions whose graphs appear below, given that the quadratic function is the product of the two other functions.

a)

b)

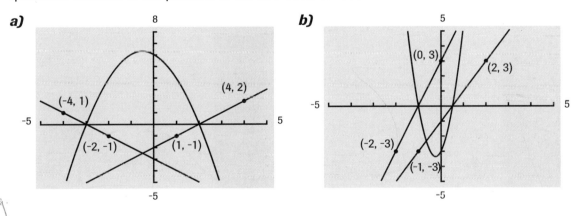

40. Test out a few examples using a graphing calculator and identify the type of function that is the product of:

a) A constant function and a linear function.

b) A constant function and a quadratic function.

c) A linear function and a quadratic function.

41. The product of any two linear functions is a quadratic function. Perform the multiplication below and express the result in the general form by finding the expressions that correspond to a, b and c.

If $f(x) = a_1x + b_1$ and $g(x) = a_2x + b_2$, then $(f \cdot g)(x) = f(x) \cdot g(x) =$ ▬▬▬ .

42. Test out a few examples using a graphing calculator and identify the type of function that is the quotient of:

a) A linear function and a constant function.

b) A linear function and a linear function.

c) A quadratic function and a linear function.

d) A quadratic function and a quadratic function.

a) On the right is a series of patterns made of small squares. Consider the relation between the pattern's position in the series and the number of squares it contains.

1) Complete the table of values for this relation.

Position of pattern	1	2	3	4	5	6	7	...	x
Number of squares	3	6	10	15					

2) Find the function rule for this relation, knowing that it is quadratic.

3) Find all the properties of the function in this example.

b) Consider the relation between the number of sides and the number of diagonals in this series of regular polygons.

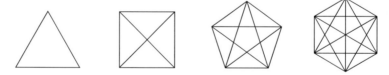

1) Complete the table of values below.

Sides	3	4	5	6	7	8	...	x
Diagonals	0	2	5					

2) Find the function rule for this relation, knowing that it is quadratic.

3) Find all the properties of the function in this example.

c) A parabola passes through points (-1, -8), (1, 0) and (2, 10). Find the function rule it represents by identifying the values of the parameters in the general form.

 ABSOLUTE VALUE FUNCTIONS

| THE CONCEPT OF ABSOLUTE VALUE |
| THE BASIC ABSOLUTE VALUE FUNCTION |
| TRANSFORMED ABSOLUTE VALUE FUNCTIONS |
| ZEROS AND EQUATIONS |
| SIGN AND INEQUALITIES |
| FINDING THE RULE |

THE CONCEPT OF ABSOLUTE VALUE

An estimation error

The rules governing lotteries require that the winner answer a skill-testing question before claiming the prize. Usually this question consists of calculating the value of a numeric expression.

The prize for a summer sports contest is an all-terrain vehicle. There are two finalists in the contest. Since there is only one prize, the winner must be chosen by eliminating one of the two. Both are given 10 s to calculate the value of the expression below. If no one provides the correct answer, the person who guesses closest wins the prize.

$$-2(8 + -3) + 12(25 - -10)$$

I say 400.

I say 420.

a) How far is each guess from the correct answer?

b) Who wins the all-terrain vehicle?

Essentially, both contestants have made an equivalent mistake.

This situation shows that sometimes a number and its sign must be considered separately.

Thus, a person carrying out the movements indicated by the following integers travels a greater distance than the sum of the integers themselves: (-2) + (9) + (-6) + (4).

c) What distance did this person actually travel?

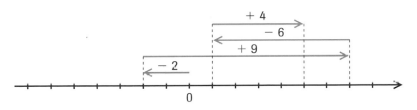

The need to deal with numbers independently of their sign led to the concept of **absolute value.**

> The **absolute value** of a real number is its value with its sign removed. The number is placed between vertical lines to signify that we are to ignore its sign.

Therefore, $|+5| = 5$ and $|-5| = 5$. The same is true for any real number.

The absolute value of x usually appears as **abs(x)** on calculators and computers.

d) Find the hidden values on the screens below:

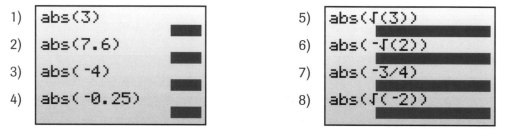

1) abs(3)
2) abs(7.6)
3) abs(-4)
4) abs(-0.25)

5) abs(√(3))
6) abs(-√(2))
7) abs(-3/4)
8) abs(√(-2))

e) Find the value of:

1) $|6 - 4|$ 2) $|6 - 10|$ 3) $|-6 \times 4|$ 4) $\left|\dfrac{-12}{-3}\right|$

Absolute value can also apply to a variable or to an algebraic expression. In these cases, however, the sign of the value the variable or expression represents is unknown. To solve this problem, we use the following definitions:

> $\forall\, x \in$ IR, we have : $|x| = x$ if the value of x is positive.
> and $|x| = -x$ if the value of x is negative.

According to this definition, when a value is negative, we take its opposite value. Thus, to eliminate the vertical lines indicating absolute value from an algebraic expression, we keep the expression the same if its value is positive, and use its opposite if its value is negative.

f) Eliminate the absolute values from the following expressions. The sign of each expression's value is indicated.

1) $|x + 3|$ if $x + 3 > 0$ or $x > -3$ 2) $|5 - 3x|$ if $5 - 3x < 0$ or $x > \dfrac{5}{3}$

3) $|-2(x - 1)|$ if $-2(x - 1) < 0$ 4) $|x^2 - 4|$ if $x^2 - 4 > 0$

Such a definition gives absolute value a number of properties:

1. $\forall x \in \mathbb{R}: |x| \geqslant 0$

2. $\forall x \in \mathbb{R}: |x| = |-x|$

3. $\forall x, y \in \mathbb{R}: |x \cdot y| = |x| \cdot |y|$

4. $\forall x, y \in \mathbb{R}^*: \left|\dfrac{x}{y}\right| = \dfrac{|x|}{|y|}$

g) Confirm each property using three different examples.

The concept of absolute value can be used to define a function from the set of real numbers to the set of real numbers.

THE BASIC ABSOLUTE VALUE FUNCTION

Level of the lock

A technician records the water level over a 10 min period to see if a lock is working properly. To study the changes in the water level, he builds a table of values in which the time $t = 0$ corresponds to when the water is at level 0. (The platework of the lock's gate contains markings that indicate the water level.)

St. Lambert Locks

Time (min)	Level (m)
-5	5
-4	4
-3	3
-2	2
-1	1
0	0
1	1
2	2
3	3

Côte Sainte-Catherine Locks

Locks are confined sections of canals constructed where the water level changes significantly. Locks are used to raise or lower ships from one level of the canal to another. They are usually shaped like rectangular basins with gates at both ends.

a) Does this situation correspond to a function? Justify your answer.

b) Calculate a few rates of change using the table. Are these rates constant?

c) Are there any relationships between the rates of change and known functions? If so, what are they?

d) Describe the relationship between time and water level in your own words.

This situation corresponds to the **basic absolute value function.** The rule for this function's mathematical model is $f(x) = |x|$. Its graph is shown below.

e) Describe the function's graph in your own words.

f) The curve of the function's mathematical model is composed of two rays. What is the equation for each of these rays?

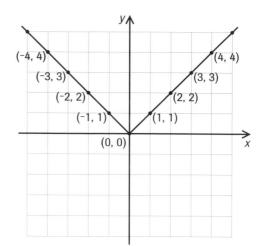

In this function:

– If x is positive, the image of x is x.

– If x is negative, the image of x is the opposite of x, or $-x$.

Whatever the value of x, its image is always positive.

g) Explain how an expression like $-x$ can correspond to a positive value.

The basic absolute value function is defined as:

$$f: \mathbb{R} \rightarrow \mathbb{R}$$
$$: x \longmapsto f(x) = |x| = \begin{array}{l} x \text{ if } x \geqslant 0 \\ -x \text{ if } x < 0 \end{array}$$

It is thus a function defined in two parts.

h) Complete this table of the **properties** of the **basic absolute value function.**

1. Rule: ▮▮▮▮
2. Graph: ▮▮▮▮ with a vertical axis of symmetry.
3. Domain: ▮▮▮▮   Range: ▮▮▮▮
4. Zero: ▮▮▮▮
5. Extreme: ▮▮▮▮ in ▮▮▮▮.
6. Variation: Decreasing over ▮▮▮▮ and increasing over ▮▮▮▮.
7. Sign: ▮▮▮▮ over ▮▮▮▮.
   ▮▮▮▮ over ▮▮▮▮.

i) How many ordered pairs are needed to determine the curve of the basic absolute value function?

j) Identify these ordered pairs.

TRANSFORMED ABSOLUTE VALUE FUNCTIONS

Distance on a number line

Every house or building on a street has a number that could be considered an *x*-coordinate. Longer streets are usually divided into two sections: east and west, or north and south. The division occurs at a street running perpendicular to the one being divided. The dividing street then acts as the reference point (or 0) for the numbering scheme of the buildings.

Sherbrooke Street was named in honour of Sir John Coape Sherbrooke (1764–1830) who served as governor of British North America between 1816 and 1818.

a) How many numbers are there between 36 Sherbrooke Street West and 20 Sherbrooke Street East?

This situation can be depicted mathematically on a number line: the zero on the *x*-axis corresponds to Saint-Laurent Blvd., the street running perpendicular to Sherbrooke Street. Negative *x*-coordinates correspond to Sherbrooke Street West, and positive *x*-coordinates, to Sherbrooke Street East. It is therefore possible to find the **distance** between any point whose *x*-coordinate is *x* and a given point whose *x*-coordinate is h.

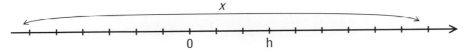

b) If *x* is a variable, to what might the distance between h and *x* correspond?

c) What can be done to make this distance a positive number?

d) What is the function rule that associates any point *x* on the *x*-axis with its distance from a point whose *x*-coordinate is h?

It is possible to transform the basic absolute value function by introducing the parameters **a, b, h** and **k** into its rule.

> The rule for a transformed absolute value function takes the form
> $$f(x) = a\,|b(x - h)| + k$$

Parameters play the same role here as they do in the other functions.

e) Examine the role of each parameter in the following rules, tables of values, graphs and ordered pairs. Then fill in the blanks for each conclusion.

1) **Role of a:**

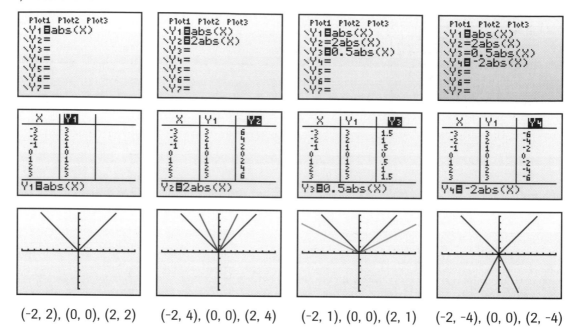

(-2, 2), (0, 0), (2, 2)   (-2, 4), (0, 0), (2, 4)   (-2, 1), (0, 0), (2, 1)   (-2, -4), (0, 0), (2, -4)

Introducing parameter **a** into the rule results in a ▬▬▬ of factor a in the corresponding graph and a ▬▬▬ of a in the *y*-coordinates of the ordered pairs.

2) **Role of b:**

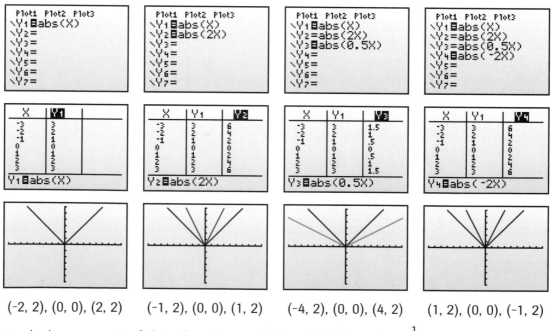

(-2, 2), (0, 0), (2, 2)   (-1, 2), (0, 0), (1, 2)   (-4, 2), (0, 0), (4, 2)   (1, 2), (0, 0), (-1, 2)

Introducing parameter **b** into the rule results in a ▬▬▬ of factor $\frac{1}{b}$ in the corresponding graph and a ▬▬▬ of b in the *x*-coordinates of the ordered pairs.

3) Role of h:

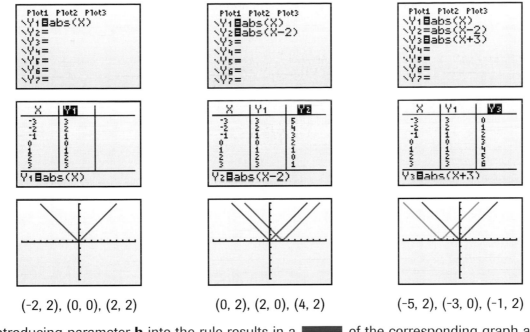

(-2, 2), (0, 0), (2, 2)   (0, 2), (2, 0), (4, 2)   (-5, 2), (-3, 0), (-1, 2)

Introducing parameter **h** into the rule results in a ▬▬▬ of the corresponding graph and the addition of h to the ▬▬▬ of the ordered pairs.

4) Role of k:

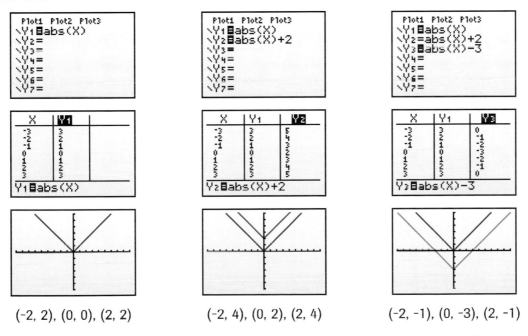

(-2, 2), (0, 0), (2, 2)   (-2, 4), (0, 2), (2, 4)   (-2, -1), (0, -3), (2, -1)

Introducing parameter **k** into the rule results in a ▬▬▬ of the corresponding graph and the addition of k to the ▬▬▬ of the ordered pairs.

The rule for the transformed absolute value function can actually be expressed using only three parameters because of a property of absolute values.

f) Identify this property, which was applied below.

$$f(x) = a\,|b(x - h)| + k \iff f(x) = a\,|b| \cdot |x - h| + k$$

Since the product **a** | **b** | forms a new value that acts as parameter **a,** the standard form of the rule for the transformed absolute value function is:

$$f(x) = a|x - h| + k$$

The ordered pairs of any transformed absolute function may be found by performing a few operations on the basic function's critical ordered pairs.

For any function whose rule is in the form $f(x) = a|x - h| + k$, if the ordered pair (x, y) belongs to the basic function, then the ordered pair $(x + h, ay + k)$ belongs to the transformed function.

The graph of the function $g(x) = 2|x - 1| - 3$ may be obtained from the basic function's critical ordered pairs by multiplying the y-coordinates by 2, adding 1 to the x-coordinates and subtracting 3 from the y-coordinates.

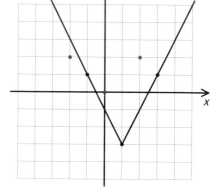

Basic function: (-2,   2),   (0, 0),   (2, 2)

× 2

+ 1   − 3

Transformed function: (-1,   1),   (1, -3),   (3, 1)

g) Compare the slope of each branch of the curve with the value of parameter **a.** What do you notice?

h) Using tables of values, confirm this observation in the transformed functions below.

  1) $f(x) = 3|x - 2| + 3$ 2) $g(x) = -1.5|x - 4| + 2$ 3) $h(x) = |4(x - 1)| - 2$

i) Prove that the coordinates of the curve's vertex are always (h, k).

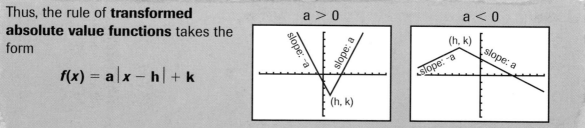

Thus, the rule of **transformed absolute value functions** takes the form

$$f(x) = a|x - h| + k$$

The curve is in the shape of a V opening upwards if a > 0 and downwards if a < 0. The vertex is (h, k) and the branches have a slope of a and -a.

j) Is the inverse of an absolute value function itself a function? Justify your answer.

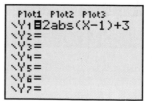

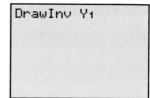

1. Find the value of each expression:

a) $|-12|$

b) $|8 - 10|$

c) $|-8 \times -5|$

d) $\left|\dfrac{-18}{-12}\right|$

e) $|-15 + -12|$

f) $|-15| \times |3|$

g) $|-25| - |-13|$

h) abs(-3) − abs(5)

i) 2abs(-3 + -5)

j) abs(12 × -3) ÷ -4

k) -2abs(-12) + abs(-24) ÷ -2

2. True or false?

a) $|-5 + 3| = |-5| + |3|$

b) $\left|\dfrac{-15}{3}\right| = \dfrac{|-15|}{|3|}$

c) $|n - 1| = |-n + 1|$

d) -x represents a negative value.

e) The absolute value of a number can be strictly negative.

3. Find an equivalent expression, without an absolute value, that satisfies the given condition.

a) $|-x + 3|$ if (-x +3) has a positive value.

b) $|2x - 3|$ if $x > \dfrac{3}{2}$

c) $|15 - 3a|$ if $a > 5$

d) $-|-x - 9| + 3$ if $x > -9$

e) $2b + |-8 + 2b| - 3$ if $b < 4$

4. Write the rules below in standard form.

a) $f_1(x) = |3x - 12| + 5$

b) $f_2(x) = 2|4x - 8| - 3$

c) $f_3(x) = -\dfrac{1}{3}|6x - 4| - 4$

d) $f_4(x) = -2|4 - 2x| + 1$

e) $f_5(x) = -|-2x| + 3$

f) $f_6(x) = \dfrac{1}{2}|4 - 6x| + 3$

5. Here are the rules of several transformed absolute value functions. Indicate the transformation(s) that associate the curves of the transformed functions with the curve of the basic function. Use a graphing calculator to check your answers.

a) $f(x) = 5|x|$

b) $g(x) = |x + 3|$

c) $h(x) = |2x|$

d) $i(x) = |x| - 4$

e) $j(x) = 3|2x|$

f) $k(x) = |x + 2| - 4$

g) $n(x) = -|x - 2| + 2.5$

h) $m(x) = -3|-2x|$

i) $p(x) = |2x - 4|$

j) $q(x) = -|2(x + 3)| + 4$

k) $r(x) = 3|2(x - 1)| - 3$

l) $s(x) = -|-x + 1| - 3$

René Descartes was probably the first, in 1637, to use the term "function."

6. Match the rules on the right with the graphs below.

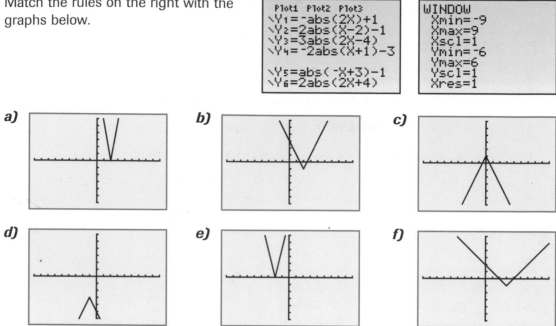

a)

b)

c)

d)

e)

f)

7. For each of the functions defined in exercise 6, find:

a) The coordinates of the curve's vertex.

b) The equation of the axis of symmetry.

c) The y-intercept.

d) The number of zeros.

8. Sketch each of the following functions.

a) $f(x) = |2x - 6|$

b) $g(x) = |-4 - 4x|$

c) $h(x) = \frac{1}{3}|3x| - 5$

d) $i(x) = \frac{1}{2}|x - 4| + 3$

e) $j(x) = -|3x + 9| - 2$

f) $k(x) = \frac{2}{3}|-3x + 12| + 5$

9. State the domain and range of each function in exercise 8.

10. Draw the curves of the following functions on the same axes:

$$Y_1 = \text{abs}(x) + 3$$

$$Y_2 = \text{abs}(x + 3)$$

Over what interval do the curves coincide?

11. Functions c and e are defined by $c(x) = |x| - 10$ and $e(x) = -|x| + 10$. What is the area of the square defined by the graph of these functions?

12. Sides AB and AC of triangle ABC are associated with the graph of the function defined by $y = -\frac{5}{3}|x + 6| + 10$. Side BC is the line $y = -5$. If the axes are scaled in centimetres, what is the area of triangle ABC?

13. Pete bought some shares on the stock market. During the first 60 days, the value of the shares, in dollars, varied according to the rule $V(n) = -\frac{1}{3}|n - 24| + 15$, where n is the number of days since the shares' purchase.

a) Graph the function V for this period.

b) What was the value of the shares when they were purchased?

c) What is the value of the shares after 60 days?

d) State the function's domain and range for the given period.

e) If the same rule continues to apply, could Pete's shares eventually become worthless? If so, how many days after their acquisition?

14. Three identical mirrors are hanging on the wall of a hairdressing salon as shown in the graph on the right. The axes are scaled in metres. Each mirror is 2 m wide and is symmetrical about the axis passing through its vertex. The sides of the angle at the top of the centre mirror correspond to a function whose rule is $y = -\frac{1}{2}|x - 5| + 3.5$.

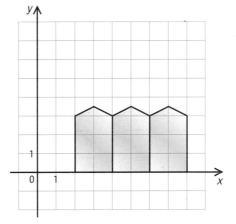

a) What is the rule of the function associated with the sides of the angle at the top of:

1) The first mirror?

2) The third mirror?

b) What is the total area of the three mirrors?

15. Ten days ago a group of wildlife preservation officers brought an injured raccoon to a veterinary clinic. Since then, the animal's mass has changed according to the rule $M(d) = \frac{1}{3}|d - 4| + 6$, where M is its mass in kilograms and d, the number of days since it was hospitalized.

a) What is the raccoon's mass upon arriving at the clinic?

b) What is its present mass?

c) What was its minimum mass?

d) How long did the raccoon lose weight after arriving at the clinic?

e) The veterinarian will not release the raccoon into the forest until its mass is at least 12 kg. If the animal's mass continues to increase following the same rule, use a graph to determine how long it will be before the raccoon is released.

The raccoon is a small, furry creature that hunts small prey in shallow water. Very skillful with its front paws, the raccoon catches crustaceans, mollusks, frogs and fish. When hunting, the raccoon appears to actually wash its food before eating.

a) Determine if each statement is true or false.

$\forall\ x, y \in \mathbb{IR}$:

1) $|x + y| = |x| + |y|$

2) $|x - y| = |x| - |y|$

3) $|x + y| \leq |x| + |y|$

4) $|x - y| \geq |x| - |y|$

b) If $x, y \in \mathbb{IR}$, where $x > 0$ and $y < 0$, simplify the following expressions:

1) $x|xy| - 2|xy^2| - |x^2y|$

2) $|x^2y^2| + 2\dfrac{|x^2y^3|}{|y|} + |xy| \cdot |xy|$

c) Given the function $f: \mathbb{IR} \rightarrow \mathbb{IR}$

$$x \longmapsto f(x) = a|x - h| + k.$$

What are the parameters affecting:

1) the domain of f?

2) the range of f?

ZEROS AND EQUATIONS

Harvest time

Many fruits are harvested in the fall, and the quality of the harvest often depends on the climate throughout the season. During a given night, a fruit farmer notices that the temperature varies according to the rule $T(x) = |x - 8| - 3$, where x is the number of hours since sundown. This relation is shown on the graph below.

The apple harvest in Québec is measured in bushels:

1 bushel = 42 pounds or about 19 kg.

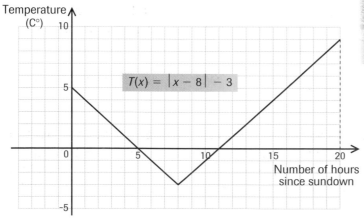

$T(x) = |x - 8| - 3$

Temperature (C°) / Number of hours since sundown

Louis Hébert brought the first apple trees to New France in 1617. It was not until 1650, however, that the Sulpicians planted the first orchard on the slopes of Mount Royal. Fruit farming has grown steadily in Québec ever since.

a) Referring to the graph, estimate how long after sundown it took for the temperature to reach:

1) 4°C 　　　 2) 0°C 　　　 3) -3°C 　　　 4) -5°C

b) You may want to calculate the exact value of the domain corresponding to the previous images. A good method of doing this is shown below for 4°C and 0°C. Find the values of the domain associated with the images -3°C and -5°C.

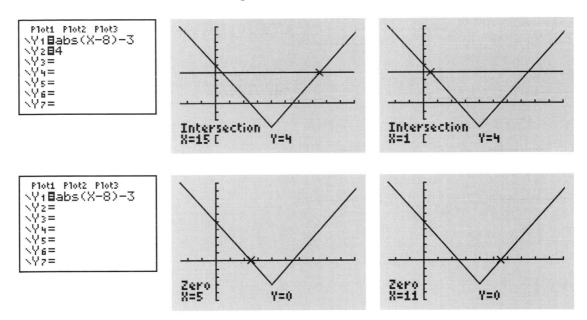

The values of the domain associated with the image 0 are called the **zeros** of the function.

c) Can an absolute value function have a single zero or no zero? If so, use a graph to illustrate your answer.

d) Find the zeros of the following functions using a graphing calculator:

1) $f(x) = 2|2x + 3| - 2$ 2) $g(x) = |4 - x| - 8$ 3) $h(x) = 2|x - 3| - 2$

Finding the **zeros** of a transformed absolute value function involves finding those values where $f(x) = 0$ or $a|x - h| + k = 0$; that is, solving an **absolute value equation.**

Although graphical methods are quite useful, it is important to develop the ability to solve absolute value equations algebraically.

The **algebraic method** is based on the definition of absolute value, and depends on whether the values of the domain make the argument (the expression between the vertical lines) positive or negative. The absolute value must be isolated and the **critical value,** which affects the sign of the argument, must be identified. The critical value is the value of x that reduces the argument to zero.

EXAMPLE 1

To find the zeros of the function $f(x) = |x| - 6$, the equation $|x| - 6 = 0$ must be solved. Below is the method for solving the equation:

1. **Isolate the absolute value** to get a simpler equation:

$$|x| - 6 + 6 = 0 + 6$$
$$|x| = 6$$

2. Apply the **definition of the absolute value** of an algebraic expression after finding the critical value.

1) For $x < 0$, we have:

$$|x| = 6$$
$$^-x = 6$$
$$x = ^-6$$

2) For $x \geqslant 0$, we have:

$$|x| = 6$$
$$x = 6$$
$$x = 6$$

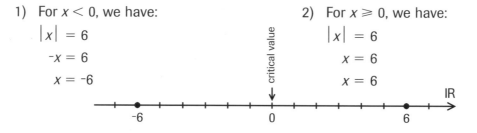

3. The solution set of the equation is {-6, 6} and the zeros of function f are -6 and 6.

EXAMPLE 2

To find the zeros of the function $g(x) = 2|x - 3| - 10$, the equation $2|x - 3| - 10 = 0$ must be solved in IR.

1. **Isolate the absolute value function** to obtain a simpler equation:

$$2|x - 3| - 10 + 10 = 10$$
$$2|x - 3| = 10$$
$$|x - 3| = 5$$

2. Apply the **definition of the absolute value** of an algebraic expression after finding the critical value.

1) For $x - 3 < 0$, or $x < 3$, we have:

$$|x - 3| = 5$$
$$^-(x - 3) = 5$$
$$^-x + 3 = 5$$
$$^-x = 2$$
$$x = ^-2$$

2) For $x - 3 \geqslant 0$, or $x \geqslant 3$, we have:

$$|x - 3| = 5$$
$$x - 3 = 5$$
$$x = 8$$

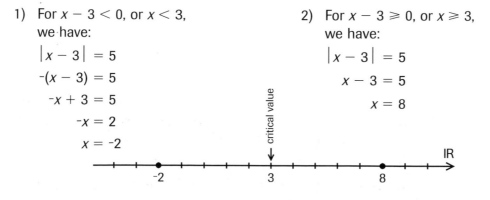

3. The solution set of the equation is {-2, 8} and the zeros of function g are -2 and 8.

EXAMPLE 3

We want to find the values of the domain associated with the image 2 in the function h, whose rule is $h(x) = 2|x - 5| + 6$. This involves solving the equation $2|x - 5| + 6 = 2$ in IR.

1. **Isolate the absolute value:**

$$2|x - 5| + 6 = 2$$
$$\Downarrow$$
$$2|x - 5| + 6 - 6 = 2 - 6$$
$$\Downarrow$$
$$2|x - 5| = -4$$
$$\Downarrow$$
$$|x - 5| = -2$$

2. Since an absolute value cannot be negative, there is no solution in this case. There is no value of the domain that corresponds to 2 in this function.

EXAMPLE 4

We want to solve the equation $|x - 2| + 2x = 1$.

1. **Isolate the absolute value:**

$$|x - 2| + 2x = 1 \Rightarrow |x - 2| = 1 - 2x$$

2. Apply the **definition of absolute value:**

1) For $x - 2 < 0$, or $x < 2$, we have:

$$|x - 2| = 1 - 2x$$
$$-(x - 2) = 1 - 2x$$
$$-x + 2 = 1 - 2x$$
$$x + 2 = 1$$
$$x = -1$$

2) For $x - 2 \geqslant 0$, or $x \geqslant 2$, we have:

$$|x - 2| = 1 - 2x$$
$$x - 2 = 1 - 2x$$
$$3x - 2 = 1$$
$$3x = 3$$
$$x = 1$$

The value 1 does not belong to the domain of the variable and must therefore be rejected.

3. The solution set of the equation is {-1}.

To summarize:

Finding the zeros of a function with absolute values consists of solving an absolute value equation. Below is the algebraic procedure that can be used:

1. **Isolate** the absolute value and check if the equation has solutions.

2. Eliminate the vertical lines around the absolute value after finding the critical value by applying the **definition of absolute value.**

3. Solve the resulting two equations with respect to the critical value.

4. Deduce the solution set from the equation or the zeros of the function.

1. Give the number of zeros in each of the functions illustrated below.

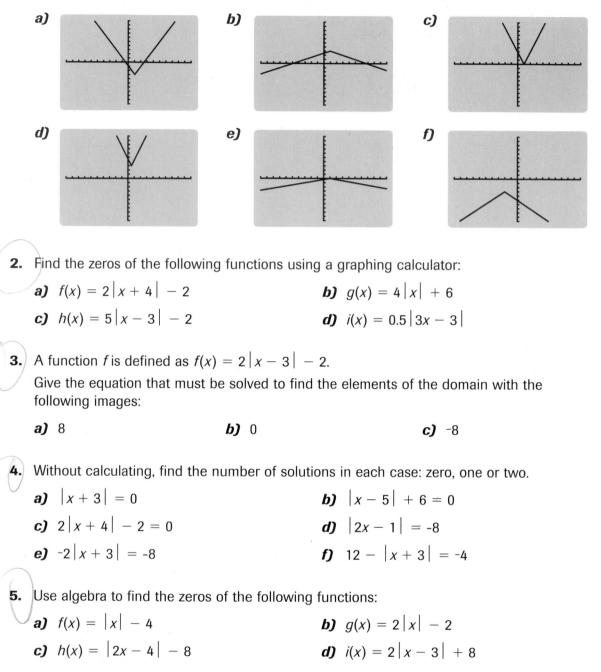

a)

b)

c)

d)

e)

f)

2. Find the zeros of the following functions using a graphing calculator:

a) $f(x) = 2|x + 4| - 2$

b) $g(x) = 4|x| + 6$

c) $h(x) = 5|x - 3| - 2$

d) $i(x) = 0.5|3x - 3|$

3. A function f is defined as $f(x) = 2|x - 3| - 2$.

Give the equation that must be solved to find the elements of the domain with the following images:

a) 8

b) 0

c) -8

4. Without calculating, find the number of solutions in each case: zero, one or two.

a) $|x + 3| = 0$

b) $|x - 5| + 6 = 0$

c) $2|x + 4| - 2 = 0$

d) $|2x - 1| = -8$

e) $-2|x + 3| = -8$

f) $12 - |x + 3| = -4$

5. Use algebra to find the zeros of the following functions:

a) $f(x) = |x| - 4$

b) $g(x) = 2|x| - 2$

c) $h(x) = |2x - 4| - 8$

d) $i(x) = 2|x - 3| + 8$

6. State the equation and solution set suggested by the screens below.

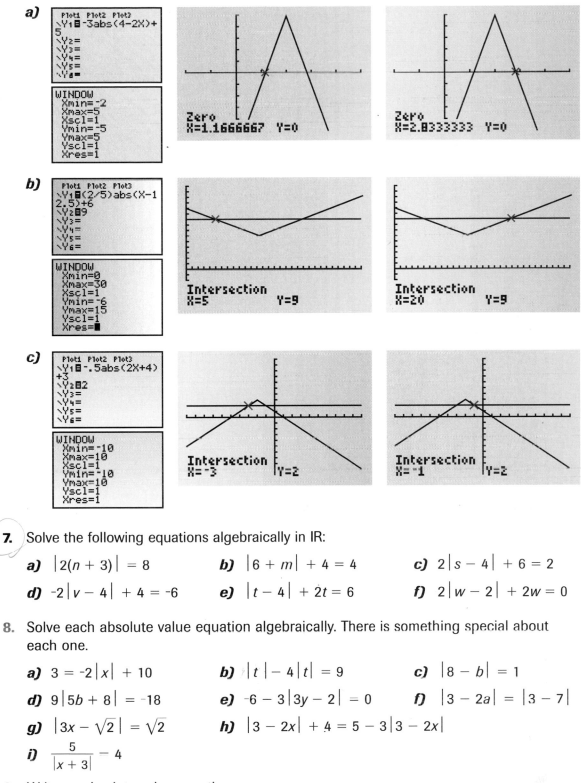

a)

```
Plot1 Plot2 Plot3
\Y1■-3abs(4-2X)+
5
\Y2=
\Y3=
\Y4=
\Y5=
\Y6=
```
```
WINDOW
 Xmin=-2
 Xmax=5
 Xscl=1
 Ymin=-5
 Ymax=5
 Yscl=1
 Xres=1
```
Zero
X=1.1666667 Y=0

Zero
X=2.8333333 Y=0

b)

```
Plot1 Plot2 Plot3
\Y1■(2/5)abs(X-1
2.5)+6
\Y2■9
\Y3=
\Y4=
\Y5=
\Y6=
```
```
WINDOW
 Xmin=0
 Xmax=30
 Xscl=1
 Ymin=-6
 Ymax=15
 Yscl=1
 Xres=■
```
Intersection
X=5   Y=9

Intersection
X=20   Y=9

c)

```
Plot1 Plot2 Plot3
\Y1■-.5abs(2X+4)
+3
\Y2■2
\Y3=
\Y4=
\Y5=
\Y6=
```
```
WINDOW
 Xmin=-10
 Xmax=10
 Xscl=1
 Ymin=-10
 Ymax=10
 Yscl=1
 Xres=1
```
Intersection
X=-3   Y=2

Intersection
X=-1   Y=2

7. Solve the following equations algebraically in IR:

a) $|2(n + 3)| = 8$

b) $|6 + m| + 4 = 4$

c) $2|s - 4| + 6 = 2$

d) $-2|v - 4| + 4 = -6$

e) $|t - 4| + 2t = 6$

f) $2|w - 2| + 2w = 0$

8. Solve each absolute value equation algebraically. There is something special about each one.

a) $3 = -2|x| + 10$

b) $|t| - 4|t| = 9$

c) $|8 - b| = 1$

d) $9|5b + 8| = -18$

e) $-6 - 3|3y - 2| = 0$

f) $|3 - 2a| = |3 - 7|$

g) $|3x - \sqrt{2}| = \sqrt{2}$

h) $|3 - 2x| + 4 = 5 - 3|3 - 2x|$

i) $\dfrac{5}{|x + 3|} - 4$

9. Write an absolute value equation:

a) that has no solution;   **b)** that has a single solution;   **c)** that has two solutions.

10. State the conditions that must be applied to the parameters so that the function defined by:

$$f(x) = a|x - h| + k$$

a) has one zero; **b)** has two zeros; **c)** has no zero.

11. State the equation represented on the screens and find its solution set.

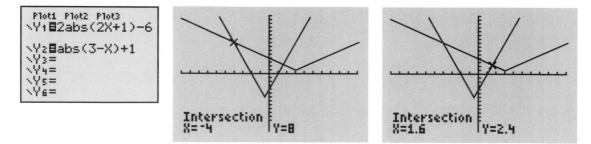

12. Solve the following equations in IR using a calculator.

a) $2|4 - 2x| = 8$

b) $2|x - 6| = 2(x + 3)$

c) $6 - |2x + 4| = |x - 8|$

d) $|x^2 + 5x + 4| = |x + 2.5|$

e) $|x - 2| + 2|x + 3| = 5$

f) $|x - 2| \cdot 2|x + 3| = 5$

g) $\dfrac{2|x + 3|}{|2x - 4|} = 1$

h) $|x - |2x - 4| + 2| = 3$

13. Given the functions f and g defined by the following rules:

$$f(x) = 2x - 3 \qquad\qquad g(x) = |x + 2|$$

a) What is the function rule for $f \circ g$.

b) For what value of x is $(f \circ g)(x) = 5$?

14. A geometry teacher asks his students to draw a 120 mm line segment without using geometry tools. He uses the following rule to determine the measurement error:

$$E(x) = |x - 120| \text{ where } x \text{ is the length of the line segment drawn by each student.}$$

a) What length could Kim's line segment have if the measurement error is 6 mm?

b) What line segment lengths are possible if the maximum relative error permitted is 4%?

15. A boat is placed on a steel support frame so that its hull can be repaired. This situation is depicted in the graph on the right, with the axes scaled in metres. Beams BC and CD correspond to the function whose equation is $y = \frac{3}{5}|x - 8| + 1.55$. Beams AB and DE each measure 3 m. What is the total width of the steel support frame AE ?

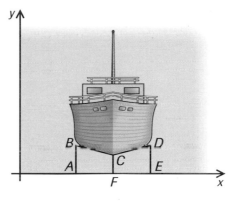

16. The side of a garage is shown in the graph on the right, with the axes scaled in metres. Each sloping side of the roof corresponds to the curve associated with the rule $y = -\frac{1}{2}|x - 4| + 6$. The height of the wall DE equals 2.5 m. A circular light fixture is installed on each sloping side of the roof such that the centre of each light is 4.5 m from the ground.

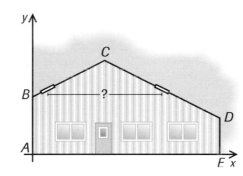

a) What is the height of the wall AB?

b) What is the width of the garage AE?

c) What is the distance between the centres of the two lights?

17. In mid-March a group of meteorologists records the total accumulation of snowfall over a 36 h period, using an observation deck designed specifically for that purpose. An analysis of the data establishes that the depth of the snow, in centimetres, varies according to the rule $A(t) = \frac{2}{3}|t - 15| + 6$ where t is the time in hours.

a) On the deck, what was:

  1) The minimum depth of the snow?

  2) The maximum depth of the snow?

b) At what time was the total depth of the snow:

  1) 14 cm? 2) 12 cm? 3) 10 cm?

c) For how many hours did the snow's depth increase?

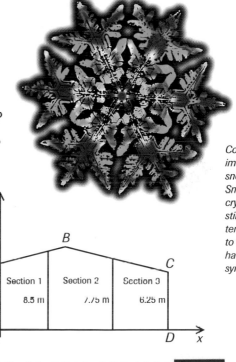

Computer-coloured image of a snowflake. Snowflakes that crystallize slowly in still air and at temperatures close to the freezing point have a hexagonal symmetry.

18. A theatre troupe requires stages of various dimensions for its performances. The largest of these stages is composed of three sections. The graph on the right, scaled in metres, shows an overhead view of this stage. Sides AB and BC belong to the function whose rule is $y = -\frac{1}{4}|x - 7| + 9$. Find the area of each section.

19. If seen from a boat, the profile of a mountain close to the shore resembles an isosceles triangle. The congruent sides are represented by the function whose rule is $h(x) = -0.6|x - 1550| + 750$ where $h(x)$ is the height of the mountain and x is the distance from the port. The scale of the graph is in metres.

a) What is the height of the mountain?

b) How far are points A and B from the port?

c) Tourists can visit the observation post located on the west side of the mountain, at an altitude of 300 m. What distance must they travel to get to the observation post from the foot of the mountain at A?

a) Certain properties of absolute values are often used to solve equations involving two distinct absolute values:

$$\forall\ x, y \in \mathbb{R},\ |xy| = |x| \cdot |y| \qquad\qquad \forall\ x, y \in \mathbb{R},\ \left|\frac{x}{y}\right| = \frac{|x|}{|y|}$$

$$\forall\ x, y \in \mathbb{R},\ |x| = |y| \Rightarrow x = y \vee x = -y$$

Solve the following equations algebraically in $\mathbb{R}$ using these properties.

1) $|x - 2| = |x + 3|$

2) $|x + 3| \cdot |x - 2| = 6$

3) $\dfrac{|x + 4|}{|x - 5|} = 2$

4) $2|x - 3| = 6|x + 2|$

b) Some equations contain the same absolute value expression more than once. They are solved using familiar models. This is true for the equation $|2x + 1|^2 + 2|2x + 1| - 8 = 0$.

1) What kind of equation is this?

2) This equation can be solved by introducing a new variable. Solve it using $u = |2x + 1|$.

SIGN AND INEQUALITIES

Spray it on!

To protect his crop from frost, a farmer installs a sprinkler system that starts up automatically whenever the temperature dips to 0°C. The temperature over the past 20 h has varied according to the rule $T(x) = |x - 8| - 3$, where x is the number of hours since sundown.

Pipes equipped with high pressure sprinklers are used to irrigate crops evenly.

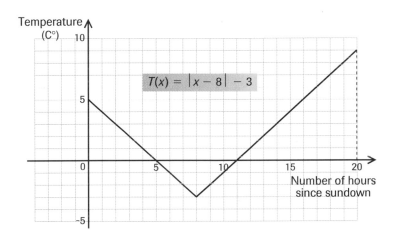

a) According to the graph, during what period was the sprinkler system on that night?

b) Examine the sign of this function over its domain.

c) Write two inequalities that can be stated with respect to the image 0 of this function, then describe the solution set of each.

Examining the sign of a function involves identifying the interval over which the function is either positive or negative over its domain. In other words, finding the interval of the domain over which $T(x) \geqslant 0$ and the interval over which $T(x) \leqslant 0$.

An inequality may be stated not only with respect to the image 0, but also with respect to any other of the function's images.

d) What inequalities may be stated with respect to the image -2?

e) Solve the given inequalities using the information displayed below.

1) $|x - 8| - 3 \leqslant 3$

2) $|x - 8| - 3 \leqslant -3$

3) $|x - 8| - 3 \leqslant -5$

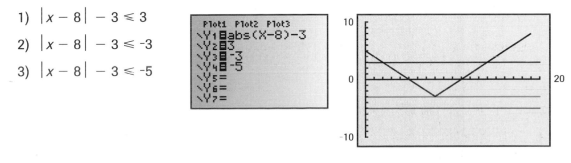

The solution set of an inequality with an absolute value:

• May be an interval or the union of intervals.

• May be a single value (one solution).

• May be empty (no solution).

f) Here are the rules and graphs of two absolute value functions. Solve the inequalities below using these graphs.

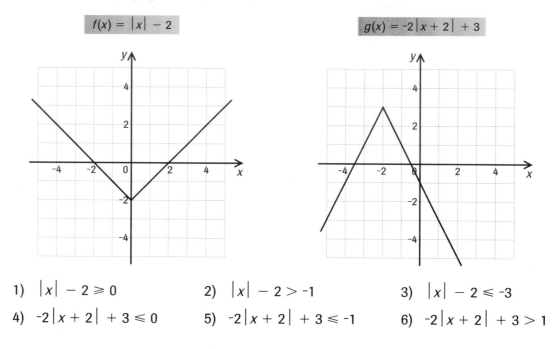

$$f(x) = |x| - 2$$

$$g(x) = -2|x + 2| + 3$$

1) $|x| - 2 \geqslant 0$

2) $|x| - 2 > -1$

3) $|x| - 2 \leqslant -3$

4) $-2|x + 2| + 3 \leqslant 0$

5) $-2|x + 2| + 3 \leqslant -1$

6) $-2|x + 2| + 3 > 1$

Inequalities involving an absolute value may be solved **graphically** or **algebraically.**

Simple absolute value inequalities may take either of the following forms:

$$|x| \leqslant n \qquad\qquad |x| \geqslant n \qquad \text{for } n \geqslant 0$$

Each of these inequalities is associated with a subset of the number line.

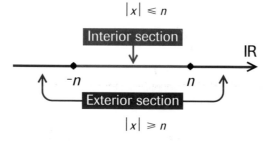

$$|x| \leqslant n$$

Interior section

IR

$-n$ n

Exterior section

$$|x| \geqslant n$$

EXAMPLE 1

We want to solve inequality $|x| > 3$ in IR.

If the exterior sections correspond to the symbol $>$, then the solution set is:

This result can also be obtained by applying the definition of absolute value:

1) For $x < 0$,

$|x| > 3 \Rightarrow$ $-x > 3$
  $x < -3$

2) For $x \geqslant 0$

$|x| > 3 \Rightarrow$ $x > 3$

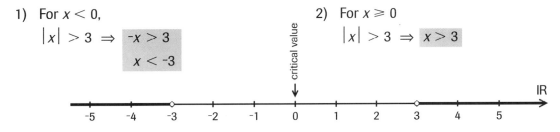

The solution set is therefore: $]-\infty, -3[\cup]3, +\infty[$.

EXAMPLE 2

We want to solve the inequality $|x - 7| - 4 < -2$ in IR.

1. The absolute value is isolated by performing a few manipulations:

$$|x - 7| - 4 < -2$$
$$|x - 7| - 4 + 4 < 2 + 4$$
$$|x - 7| < 2$$

> Once the absolute value is isolated:
>
> $< \Rightarrow$ interior section
> $> \Rightarrow$ exterior section

2. The absolute value is eliminated by applying its definition:

1) For $x - 7 < 0$ or $x < 7$,

$|x - 7| < 2 \Rightarrow$ $-(x - 7) < 2$
  $-x + 7 < 2$
  $-x < -5$
  $x > 5$
  $5 < x < 7$

2) for $x - 7 \geqslant 0$ or $x \geqslant 7$,

$|x - 7| < 2 \Rightarrow$ $(x - 7) < 2$
  $x - 7 < 2$
  $x < 9$
  $7 \leqslant x < 9$

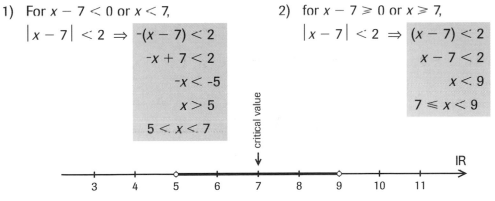

3. Next, simply deduce the solution set: $]5, 7[\cup [7, 9[=]5, 9[$.

These two examples illustrate one method of solving inequalities that involve absolute values:

1. Isolate the absolute value.

2. Determine the region (interior or exterior) based on the form of the resulting inequality.

3. Eliminate the absolute value by applying the definition of absolute value.

4. Solve the two resulting inequalities.

5. Describe the solution set.

1. $|\text{Argument}| \geq ...$

2.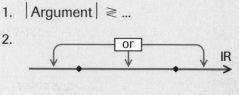

3. 1) argument < 0

   2) argument ≥ 0

4. 1) $-(\text{argument}) \geq ...$

   2) argument $\geq ...$

Check results? Smart idea!

Thus, examining the sign of an absolute value function is part of solving absolute value inequalities.

INVESTMENT 8

1. The graph of different functions is shown below. If the increment is 1 and the zeros are integers, examine each function's sign.

a)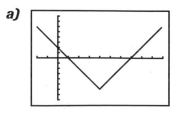

b)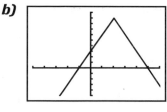

c)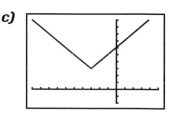

2. Use a graphing calculator to examine the sign of the following functions:

a) $f(x) = 2|x - 5|$

b) $g(x) = -|x + 2| + 3$

c) $h(x) = 2|4 - 2x| - 4$

3. Use a graph to solve the inequality $|2x + 2| < 6$.

    a) Give the equivalent inequality where one of the sides equals zero.

    b) Define a function using the non-zero side and display its graph.

    c) State the zeros of the function.

    d) Deduce the solution set of the inequality.

4. Solve the inequality in the previous exercise, but this time using two functions and the coordinates where the curves intersect.

5. Here are the rules and graphs of two absolute value functions. Use them to find the solution set of the inequalities below.

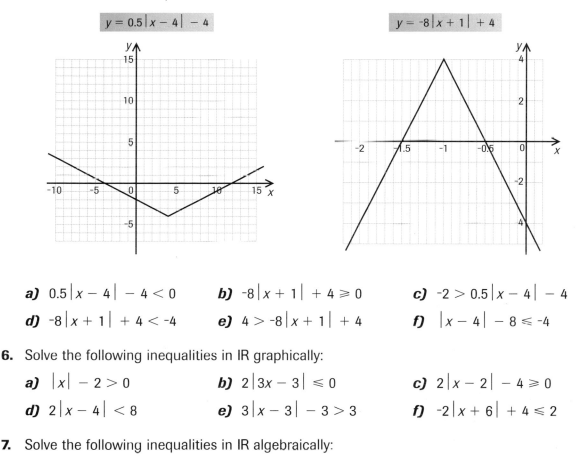

$y = 0.5|x - 4| - 4$

$y = -8|x + 1| + 4$

    a) $0.5|x - 4| - 4 < 0$ **b)** $-8|x + 1| + 4 \geqslant 0$ **c)** $-2 > 0.5|x - 4| - 4$

    d) $-8|x + 1| + 4 < -4$ **e)** $4 > -8|x + 1| + 4$ **f)** $|x - 4| - 8 \leqslant -4$

6. Solve the following inequalities in IR graphically:

    a) $|x| - 2 > 0$ **b)** $2|3x - 3| \leqslant 0$ **c)** $2|x - 2| - 4 \geqslant 0$

    d) $2|x - 4| < 8$ **e)** $3|x - 3| - 3 > 3$ **f)** $-2|x + 6| + 4 \leqslant 2$

7. Solve the following inequalities in IR algebraically:

    a) $2|x - 3| - 4 \leqslant 0$ **b)** $0.5|x + 3| - 6 < 2$

    c) $-2|2x - 4| + 2 \leqslant -4$ **d)** $|x + 5| - 4 \geqslant 1 - 2x$

8. Hugh and Mary own a shop that sells jeans. Between January 1, 1996 and January 1, 1998, their inventory, in thousands of dollars, varied according to the rule $f(x) = -6.25|x - 8| + 120$ where x is the time in months since January 1, 1996. Their inventory is insured against fire and theft for $95\ 000. During what period was the value of their inventory greater than the value of the insurance?

9. Over a period of 90 days, the dollar value of a share in Prolick Industries follows the rule $v(x) = 0.25|x - 24| + 32$ where x is the number of elapsed days during this period.

a) What was the minimum value of the share during this period?

b) For what number of days was the value of the share:

1) Less than or equal to $35?

2) Greater than its initial value?

10. During road tests on a new automobile, the car's speed, in kilometres per hour, varies according to the rule $s = -4|t - 30| + 120$ where t is the elapsed time in seconds since the start of the test. Over what time period was the car's speed greater than or equal to 90 km/h?

11. Boats must sail beneath a bridge to reach the marina from a cove. The bridge's vertical clearance is constantly changing because of the tide. The clearance varies according to the rule $c(t) = \frac{2}{5}|t - 12.5| + 6$ where t is the elapsed time, in hours, since the tide began to rise. A sailboat requires 8 m clearance to pass under the bridge.

a) What inequality corresponds to the time when the sailboat cannot sail under the bridge?

b) How much time does a sailboat have to sail under the bridge during a tidal cycle?

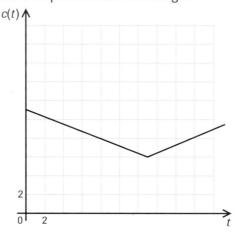

Waves are caused by the combined gravitational pull of the Sun and the Moon on ocean waters. Although considerably smaller than the Sun, the Moon's gravitational pull is greater due to its proximity to Earth. The Moon completes its orbit of the Earth in 24 h 50 min, and during this cycle, generates the phenomenon of high and low tides. This revolution time of slightly more than 24 h accounts for the daily shift in tide times.

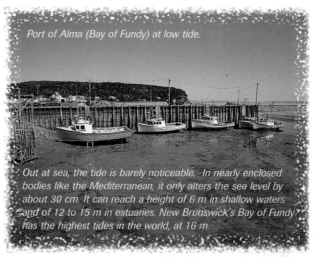

Port of Alma (Bay of Fundy) at low tide.

Out at sea, the tide is barely noticeable. In nearly enclosed bodies like the Mediterranean, it only alters the sea level by about 30 cm. It can reach a height of 6 m in shallow waters and of 12 to 15 m in estuaries. New Brunswick's Bay of Fundy has the highest tides in the world, at 16 m.

a) Given the inequality $|3 - 4x| \leq$ ■■, replace the missing side by:

1) A real number, so that the solution set is empty.

2) A first-degree algebraic expression, so that the inequality's solution set consists of a single value.

3) A second-degree algebraic expression, so that the inequality's solution set is empty.

b) Find the solution set of the following inequalities. Justify your answer algebraically or graphically.

1) $|x + 2| > -|x + 3|$

2) $|x + 2| < x - 3$

c) With the help of a graphing calculator, find the solution set of the inequality $|x - 3| > |x + 5|$ using at least two different strategies.

FINDING THE RULE

Fresh water reservoir

In order to repair its reservoir, a city needed to reduce the water volume from 40 000 m³ to 16 000 m³. It takes a pump, operating at a steady rate, 8 h to remove the required amount of water. The same pump is then used to refill the reservoir to its maximum capacity of 40 000 m³.

The data show that the amount of water in the reservoir changed over time according to the absolute value function shown below. State the function rule.

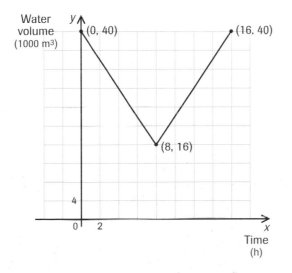

Charles-J. Des Baillets Water Filtration Plant, Montréal

Water is drawn from the St. Lawrence River upstream at the Lachine Rapids. It is then directed to either the Des Baillets or Atwater filtration plants for purification. Excess water is then stored in seven underground reservoirs, six of which are located beneath Mount Royal. The total capacity of the seven reservoirs is 830 000 m³.

a) Write the rule of a transformed absolute value function in standard form, introducing the coordinates of the vertex of this curve.

We therefore obtain a rule for which the value of two out of three parameters is known. Only the value of parameter **a** needs to be found.

b) Find the value of **a** using the coordinates (0, 40).

1) What is this value?   2) What is the function rule?

c) What does parameter **a** stand for in this case?

d) How long after the repairs began was the reservoir completely full?

e) If another pump is used, whose capacity is 4000 m³/h, how much time would it take to reduce the water volume to 16 000 m³?

f) If a third pump is used, whose capacity is 2500 m³/h, and the drainage process lasts 9 h, what would be the minimum volume of water left in the reservoir?

g) Not counting the vertex, how many points on the curve of an absolute value function must be known to determine its rule?

h) Below is the most common situation where the coordinates of three points on the curve of an absolute value function are known.

1) The value of parameter **a** is easy to calculate. What is its value?

2) It is possible to state the equation for each branch of the curve. What are these equations?

3) Explain how to find the coordinates of the point of intersection that marks the vertex of the curve. What are these coordinates?

4) State the rule for the absolute value function whose curve is shown on the right.

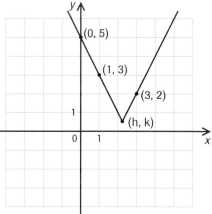

The rule for an absolute value function can be found by identifying the values of its parameters.

The last step is to find the rule for the inverse of absolute value functions.

i) Sketch the inverse of the function shown below.

```
Plot1 Plot2 Plot3
\Y1=2abs(X+2)-3
\Y2=
\Y3=
\Y4=
\Y5=
\Y6=
\Y7=
```

```
DrawInv Y1
```

j) Show, by completing the steps below, that the inverse of an absolute value function is not itself a function, since it is defined by two rules over the same domain.

Rule for the function:
$$y = a|x - h| + k$$
$$\Downarrow$$

Rule for the inverse:
$$x = a|y - h| + k$$
$$\Downarrow$$
$$x - k = a|y - h|$$
$$\Downarrow$$
$$|y - h| = \frac{x - k}{a}$$

1. If $y - h \geq 0$ or $y \geq h$, then $y - h = \frac{x - k}{a} \Rightarrow y = \frac{x - k}{a} + h$

2. If $y - h < 0$ or $y < h$, then ▬▬▬▬ $\Rightarrow$ ▬▬▬▬

k) Complete the table of **properties** of **transformed absolute value functions.**

	$a > 0$	$a < 0$
Rule	▬▬▬	▬▬▬
Graph	▬▬▬	▬▬▬
Domain	▬▬▬	▬▬▬
Range	▬▬▬	▬▬▬
Zero	▬▬▬	▬▬▬
Extremes	▬▬▬	▬▬▬
Variation	▬▬▬	▬▬▬
Sign	▬▬▬	▬▬▬
Inverse	▬▬▬	▬▬▬

INVESTMENT 9

1. Find the rule for an absolute value function whose graph has the following characteristics:

   a) Its vertex is (3, 5) and the curve passes through the point (5, 8).

   b) Its curve passes through (-2, 1) and has its vertex at (-4, 4).

   c) Its curve passes through (-1.5, -5) and has its vertex at (-4, 0).

   d) Its maximum is 6 and its zeros are -2 and 6.

   e) Its curve passes through (4, 2), (-2, 2) and (1, -10).

   f) Its curve passes through (0, 5), the y-coordinate of the vertex is 2, and the slope of one of the rays is 2.

   g) Its curve intersects the axes at (-3, 0), (1, 0) and $\left(0, \frac{3}{2}\right)$.

2. What is the function rule for the curves shown below?

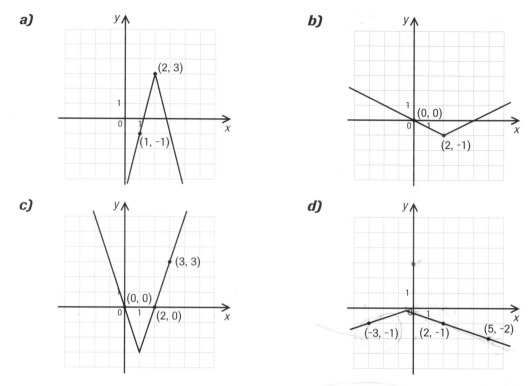

a) (2, 3) (1, -1)

b) (0, 0) (2, -1)

c) (3, 3) (0, 0) (2, 0)

d) (-3, -1) (2, -1) (5, -2)

3. Below are the tables of values for two absolute value functions. State the function rule in each case.

a)

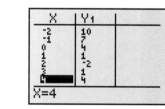

X	Y₁
-3	2
-2	0
-1	2
0	4
1	6
2	8
3	10

X=3

b)

X	Y₁
-2	10
-1	7
0	4
1	1
2	-2
3	1
4	4

X=4

4. The curve of an absolute value function has a branch passing through the points (2, 0) and (4, 3). The x-coordinate of the vertex is 1. What is the function rule?

5. The half rays of the curve of an absolute value function belong to the lines whose equations are $y = 2x + 3$ and $y = -2x - 1$. What is the function rule?

6. What is the rule for the inverse of the function defined by $h(x) = 2|4 - 2x| - 6$?

7. The curves of two absolute value functions form a rhombus.
Points $A(-1, 3)$, $B(3, 15)$ and $C(7, 3)$ are three vertices of this rhombus.

a) What are the coordinates of the fourth vertex?

b) What are the rules of these two functions?

c) What are the points of intersection of the sides of the rhombus and the x-axis?

d) What is the area of the rhombus?

8. A function defined by $f(x) = |x - 2| + 1$ is graphed on the right. Find the function rule for the graph generated by each of the following transformations:

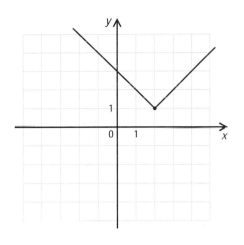

a) $t_{(0, -3)}$

b) $t_{(-5, -7)}$

c) s_x

d) s_y

e) $gr_{(x, -4, 0)}$

f) A reflection across the line whose equation is $y = 2$.

g) A reflection across the axis whose equation is $x = 6$.

h) A 180° rotation about the centre (4, 0).

9. The front of a house is drawn on a Cartesian plane whose axes are scaled in metres. The sloping sides of the house's roof belong to the rays represented by the function $y = -\frac{2}{3}|x| + 8$. Slopes *AB*, *DE* and *GH* are parallel, as are slopes *BC*, *EF* and *HK*.

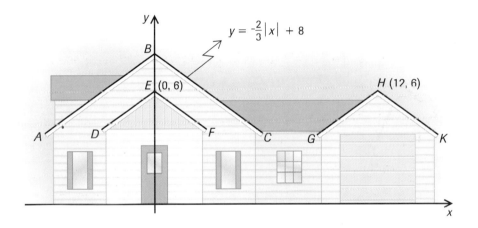

What is the function rule for:

a) The roof *GHK* of the garage?

b) The roof *DEF* of the entrance?

10. Below are the number of vacant apartments in a city over the past 10 years:

Years	1	2	3	4	5	6	7	8	9	10
Vacancies	40	58	75	92	110	93	76	56	39	22

a) What is the function rule for this scenario?

b) Based on this function, how many vacancies will there be in the coming year?

11. The MAYA company had a billboard produced and posted it on the side of a building. Each letter is constructed using horizontal, vertical or oblique segments. The oblique segments are associated with the curves of absolute value functions. The situation is illustrated on the Cartesian plane below, whose axes are scaled in metres. State the function rule for the oblique sides of each letter and indicate the domain of each.

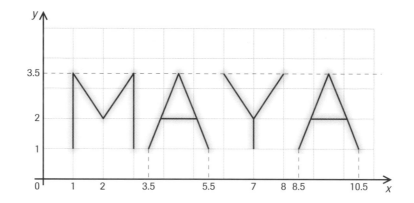

12. The sides of a kite are represented by two absolute value functions whose vertices are (0, 30) and (0, -150). One of the zeros is 30. The axes are scaled in centimetres on the plane at right.

a) What is the equation of the function associated with the longer sides?

b) What is the kite's area?

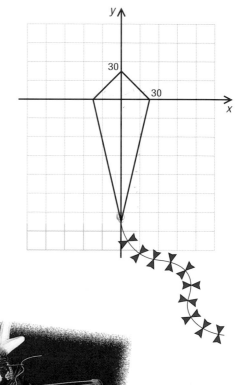

Kites have served many purposes over the centuries. In 200 BC, the Chinese general, Han Sin, had the idea of using a kite to measure the distance between his army and the battlements he was attacking. His men were then able to dig accurate underground tunnels and enter by surprise.

Invented in China around 400 BC, the kite gradually arrived in different parts of the world through trade.

13. Some agriculture students conduct experiments on the sowing of wheat. At the end of the summer, they notice that the yield of the harvest varied according to the density of the planting. The data they compiled are shown on the right.

Density (grains/m²)	150	300	400	450	700
Yield (in %)	40	75	100	85	25

a) Graph these ordered pairs.

b) Find the function rule that best represents this relation.

14. Two lines have the equations $y = \frac{3}{5}x - 2$ and $y = -\frac{3}{5}x + 4$. Find the rules for two absolute value functions whose curves make up the graph of the two given lines.

15. Given $f(x) = |x|$ and $g(x) = 2|x|$.

a) Define the following functions:

   1) $f + g$ 2) $f - g$ 3) $f \cdot g$ 4) $\frac{f}{g}$

b) State the type of each function in a).

16. Given the functions $f(x) = |x - 2| + 4$ and $g(x) = |x - 2| - 2$:

a) Define $f + g$ and $f - g$.

b) Graph the functions f, g, $f + g$ and $f - g$ on the same axes.

c) Find the domain and range of $f + g$ and $f - g$.

d) What type of function is $f \cdot g$?

17. Over the past 24 months, the net income and expenses of a company, in thousands of dollars, vary according to the rules $y = 5.5|x - 14| + 43$ and $y = -2.5|x - 14| + 75$ respectively, where x is the number of elapsed months.

a) What is the function rule that represents the company's profits over the past 24 months?

b) For how many months was this company in the red?

c) What were the company's profits during the last month?

a) Draw the lines whose equations are $y = -\frac{4}{3}x + 10$ and $y = \frac{1}{4}x + 4$. Can the same graph be generated by the equations of two absolute value functions? Justify your answer.

b) Points (-2, 9), (-1, 7) and (0, 5) belong to the graph of an absolute value function. Is it possible to find the function rule? Justify your answer.

c) Solve the following system of equations using a graph:
$$|x| + x + |y| + y = 10 \qquad |x| - x + |y| - y = 4$$

SQUARE ROOT FUNCTIONS

THE CONCEPT OF A SQUARE ROOT
THE BASIC SQUARE ROOT FUNCTION
TRANSFORMED SQUARE ROOT FUNCTIONS
ZEROS AND EQUATIONS
SIGN AND INEQUALITIES
FINDING THE RULE

THE CONCEPT OF A SQUARE ROOT

The side of the square

The concept of a square root goes back a long way. It was used to designate the length of the side of a square with a known area. It is therefore a relationship between two measurements.

Finding the length of the side is easy for certain areas, not so easy for others. That is why these numbers came to be designated by the first letter of the term "latus," which means "side." Thus, the length of the side of a square whose area is 2 units was written as $\ell 2$, which later became $\sqrt{2}$.

Area of square	Length of side
1	1
2	$\sqrt{2}$
3	$\sqrt{3}$
4	2
5	$\sqrt{5}$
6	$\sqrt{6}$
7	$\sqrt{7}$
8	$\sqrt{8}$
9	3
...	...

Claudius Ptolemy (c. AD 90–168) was the first to develop the ingenious method of using the chords of a circle to calculate square roots.

The $\sqrt{}$ symbol to indicate a number's square root first appeared in 1525 in a work by Christoff Rudolff.

Since a square's area is obtained by multiplying the length of its side by itself, $\sqrt{2}$ indicates the number that, when multiplied by itself, results in 2.

a) What does $\sqrt{a}$ mean?

Over the centuries mathematicians have searched for different ways of finding the decimal form of these numbers. It was shown that in the majority of cases, the desired decimal was non-terminating and non-periodic. Such numbers were called **irrational** numbers, and their values could only be approximated.

b) The early Babylonians suggested the following approximation: $\sqrt{a^2 + b} \approx a + \dfrac{b}{2a}$.
Use this method to calculate the length of the sides of the squares whose areas are:

1) 19   2) 70   3) 150

c) Today, with the arrival of calculators, these methods have lost their significance. Explain why a calculator cannot process irrational numbers.

The square root concept led to irrational numbers which are more numerous than rational ones, even though it is impossible to find a real number that corresponds to the square root of a negative number.

d) Explain why it is impossible to find a real number that corresponds to the square root of a negative number.

e) Explain why there are always two numbers that, when multiplied by each other, result in a positive real number.

> There are two square roots for any positive real number a:
>
> • the positive square root is written $\sqrt{a}$ or $a^{\frac{1}{2}}$;
>
> • the negative square root is written $-\sqrt{a}$ or $-\left(a^{\frac{1}{2}}\right)$.
>
> Thus, $\forall a \in IR_+$, $x^2 = a \Rightarrow (x = \sqrt{a}) \lor (x = -\sqrt{a})$.

Since square roots can be written in exponential form, they are governed by the laws of exponents. These laws can be used to deduce certain rules for manipulating square roots or radicals.

Law of square roots (or radicals)

1. $(\sqrt{a})^2 = \sqrt{a} \cdot \sqrt{a} = a$ because $a^{\frac{1}{2}} \cdot a^{\frac{1}{2}} = a^1 = a$

2. $\sqrt{a} \cdot \sqrt{b} = \sqrt{ab}$ because $a^{\frac{1}{2}} \cdot b^{\frac{1}{2}} = (ab)^{\frac{1}{2}}$

3. $\dfrac{\sqrt{a}}{\sqrt{b}} = \sqrt{\dfrac{a}{b}}$ because $\dfrac{a^{\frac{1}{2}}}{b^{\frac{1}{2}}} = \left(\dfrac{a}{b}\right)^{\frac{1}{2}}$

We can also can show that:

4. $a\sqrt{x} + b\sqrt{x} = (a + b)\sqrt{x}$ as well as $a\sqrt{x} - b\sqrt{x} = (a - b)\sqrt{x}$

5. $\dfrac{\sqrt{a}}{\sqrt{b}} \cdot \dfrac{\sqrt{b}}{\sqrt{b}} = \dfrac{\sqrt{ab}}{b}$ as well as $\dfrac{1}{\sqrt{a} + \sqrt{b}} \cdot \dfrac{\sqrt{a} - \sqrt{b}}{\sqrt{a} - \sqrt{b}} = \dfrac{\sqrt{a} - \sqrt{b}}{a} \quad \dfrac{\sqrt{a} - \sqrt{b}}{b}$

f) Perform the following operations:

1) $\dfrac{\sqrt{12}}{\sqrt{3}}$ 2) $\sqrt{5}(2 - \sqrt{5})$ 3) $(\sqrt{7})^2$ 4) $(\sqrt{3} + 1)^2$

g) Use the product property to simplify the radicand, if possible.

1) $\sqrt{72}$ 2) $\sqrt{300}$ 3) $-4\sqrt{50}$ 4) $2a\sqrt{125a^3}$

h) Perform the following operations after simplifying the radicands, if possible.

1) $2\sqrt{12} + 3\sqrt{75}$ 2) $4\sqrt{45} - 2\sqrt{90}$ 3) $\dfrac{12\sqrt{8} - \sqrt{50}}{4}$ 4) $\dfrac{3\sqrt{48} - \sqrt{75}}{2\sqrt{3}}$

i) Rationalize the denominator of the following fractions by applying the 5th property above.

1) $\dfrac{3}{\sqrt{3}}$ 2) $\dfrac{4\sqrt{5}}{\sqrt{20}}$ 3) $\dfrac{\sqrt{3}}{\sqrt{3} + 1}$ 4) $\dfrac{4 + 2\sqrt{2}}{\sqrt{2}}$

THE BASIC SQUARE ROOT FUNCTION

In the beginning . . .

While investigating the relationship between the length of a square's sides and its area, the geometers of old prepared the groundwork for a function called the **square root function.**

Thus, any square having an area of x units squared, has a side measuring $\sqrt{x}$ units.

Area of square	Length of side
1	1
2	$\sqrt{2}$
3	$\sqrt{3}$
4	2
5	$\sqrt{5}$
6	$\sqrt{6}$
7	$\sqrt{7}$
8	$\sqrt{8}$
9	3
...	...

a) What is the rule defining such a function?

Hero of Alexandria (c. AD 75-150) built his reputation and part of his fame on his work with square roots.

b) Use a graphing calculator to determine if the elements in the domain of the square root function could be of the type indicated. If not, justify your answer.

1) Negative numbers.

2) Fractions or positive decimals.

3) Periodic and non-terminating decimals.

4) Non-periodic and non-terminating decimals.

c) Can this function's images be:

1) Positive integers?

2) Negative integers?

3) Fractions or positive decimals?

4) Non-terminating, repeating rational numbers?

5) Irrational numbers?

d) Any positive real number x has two numbers that correspond to its square root: $\sqrt{x}$ and $-\sqrt{x}$. Why do we only choose the positive square root to define the basic square root function?

$\forall\, x \in \mathrm{I\!R}_+,\ \exists\, x_1,\, x_2 \in \mathrm{I\!R}: \ldots$

e) The graph of the basic square root function $f(x) = \sqrt{x}$ is drawn using the initial table of values. Which ordered pairs are best used to do a quick sketch of the graph?

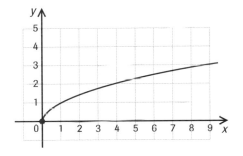

f) The curve of the graph at right seems to be increasing very slowly and approaching a certain value. It also never appears to attain large values. Is this true? Justify your answer.

g) Why are the negative numbers in IR not part of the function's domain?

h) Is there any similarity between the shape of this curve and the shape of other curves you know? If so, which curve(s)?

i) Study the graph obtained using the sequence «Drawlnv Y₁» if $Y_1 = \sqrt{x}$.

Study the graph of the inverse of the basic square root function more closely. Below is the curve of the basic square root function and its reflection across the bisector of the first quadrant. The rule for this reflection is: $\mathbf{s}_\boxtimes: (x, y) \mapsto (y, x)$.

j) Find the image under $\mathbf{s}_\boxtimes$ of each of the following ordered pairs:

$(0, 0) \mapsto (\blacksquare, \blacksquare)$

$(1, 1) \mapsto (\blacksquare, \blacksquare)$

$(4, 2) \mapsto (\blacksquare, \blacksquare)$

$(9, 3) \mapsto (\blacksquare, \blacksquare)$

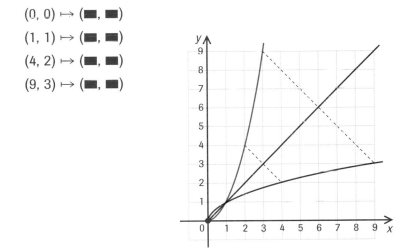

k) What is the function rule for the image curve?

l) Show how to find the rule for the basic quadratic function by reversing the variables in the rule for the basic square root function:

$$f: \quad y = \sqrt{x}$$
$$f^{-1}: \quad x = \sqrt{y} \implies \sqrt{y} = x \implies \blacksquare\blacksquare \quad \text{(By squaring the two sides.)}$$

m) What is the range and domain of this inverse?

This explains why we only get the branch of the parabola located in the first quadrant.

n) Complete the table of **properties** for the **basic square root function.**

Rule	▬▬
Graph	▬▬
Domain	▬▬
Range	▬▬
Zero	▬▬
Extreme	▬▬
Sign	▬▬
Variation	▬▬
Inverse	▬▬

```
Y1B√X
Y2B(X²)(X≥0)
Y3=
Y4=
Y5=
Y6=
Y7=
Y8=
```

X	Y1	Y2
0	0	0
1	1	1
2	1.4142	4
3	1.7321	9
4	2	16
5	2.2361	25
6	2.4495	36

X=0

X=9   Y=3

TRANSFORMED SQUARE ROOT FUNCTIONS

The speed of sound

Does sound travel faster in warmer or colder weather? This question was posted to an Internet news group and a prominent physicist sent the following reply: "Based on the temperature in degrees Celsius, the speed of sound in air, in metres per second, can be calculated using the following rule:

$$V(T) = 331\sqrt{\frac{T}{450} + 1} \text{ with } T \geqslant -273$$

a) Does sound travel faster in warmer or colder weather?

b) Find the change in speed if the temperature rises from 20°C to 30°C. Express this change in kilometres per hour.

This is a square root function transformed by the introduction of parameters. As with any other function, the basic square root function can be transformed by introducing the parameters **a, b, h** and **k** into its rule. This results in a rule of the form $f(x) = a\sqrt{b(x - h)} + k$, where the role of each parameter is already known.

In aviation, the unit of speed equal to the speed of sound is called the "Mach." It was named in honour of Ernst Mach (1838–1916), an Austrian physicist and philosopher who established the role of the speed of sound in aerodynamics.

Supersonic aircraft reach speeds greater than the speed of sound. A plane that reaches Mach 2 is travelling at twice the speed of sound in air.

Once again, note that relative to the basic function:

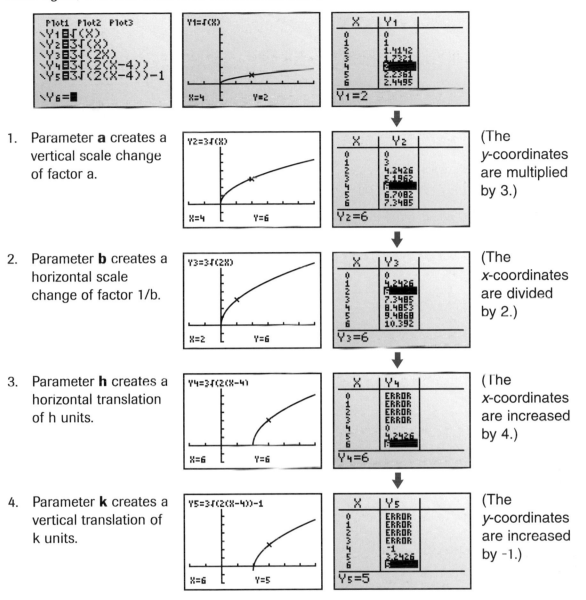

1. Parameter **a** creates a vertical scale change of factor a.

(The y-coordinates are multiplied by 3.)

2. Parameter **b** creates a horizontal scale change of factor 1/b.

(The x-coordinates are divided by 2.)

3. Parameter **h** creates a horizontal translation of h units.

(The x-coordinates are increased by 4.)

4. Parameter **k** creates a vertical translation of k units.

(The y-coordinates are increased by -1.)

The graph of any transformed function can be drawn by performing simple calculations on the coordinates of the critical points of the basic function (0, 0), (1, 1), (4, 2) and (9, 3).

c) Find the critical pairs of the function $g(x) = 3\sqrt{2(x - 4)} - 1$ using those belonging to the basic function:

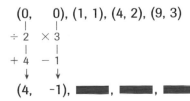

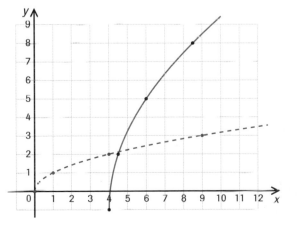

In general, if (x, y) is an ordered pair of the basic square root function, then $\left(\dfrac{x}{b} + h,\ ay + k\right)$ is an ordered pair belonging to the transformed function $f(x) = a\sqrt{b(x - h)} + k$.

The rule of a transformed square root function can always be reduced to three parameters. Thus, in the rule $f(x) = a\sqrt{b(x - h)} + k$, the parameter **b** can have a positive or negative value. In each case, it is possible to reduce the value of **b.**

1. If $b \geqslant 0$, we can say:

$$f(x) = a\sqrt{b \cdot 1(x - h)} + k$$

⇓ (Because $\sqrt{ab} = \sqrt{a} \cdot \sqrt{b}$)

$$f(x) = a\sqrt{b}\sqrt{1(x - h)} + k$$

2. If $b < 0$, we can say:

$$f(x) = a\sqrt{|b| \cdot \text{-}1(x - h)} + k$$

⇓

$$f(x) = a\sqrt{|b|}\sqrt{\text{-}1(x - h)} + k$$

Considering $a\sqrt{b}$ and $a\sqrt{|b|}$ as the new value of parameter **a,** we get:

⇓

$$f(x) = a\sqrt{1(x - h)} + k$$

⇓

$$f(x) = a\sqrt{\text{-}1(x - h)} + k$$

Thus, the standard form of the equation may be written as:

$$f(x) = a\sqrt{1(x - h)} + k \text{ or } f(x) = a\sqrt{\text{-}1(x - h)} + k$$

or:

$$f(x) = a\sqrt{b(x - h)} + k \text{ where } b = 1 \text{ or } b = \text{-}1.$$

d) Simplify the rules below to three parameters. Use a calculator to check that the simplified rules and the given rules are equivalent.

1) $f(x) = 3\sqrt{\text{-}4x + 8} - 3$

2) $g(x) = 5\sqrt{12 - 4x} + 1$

e) What is the basic difference between the graphs obtained when the value of **b** is positive and when the value of **b** is negative?

f) Explain why the image of $(0, 0)$ in the basic function is always (h, k) in the transformed function.

g) The radicand must be positive for there to be a square root. This condition is used to find the domain of the function. Using the radicand, find the domain of the function $h(x) = 3\sqrt{\text{-}2(x - 4)} - 5.$

h) What role do **h** and **k** play in determining the domain and the range?

 **INVESTMENT 10**

1. Simplify the radicand, if possible.

a) $\sqrt{32}$

b) $\sqrt{243}$

c) $8\sqrt{28}$

d) $-6\sqrt{108}$

e) $3\sqrt{a^3 - 2a^2b + ab^2}$

f) $2\sqrt{a^2 - 4}$

2. Find the product and simplify the radicand, if possible.

a) $\sqrt{3} \times \sqrt{8}$

b) $\sqrt{24} \times \sqrt{72}$

c) $-\sqrt{27} \times 2\sqrt{18}$

d) $(\sqrt{2} + 3)(\sqrt{2} - 3)$

e) $(1 - \sqrt{2})^2$

f) $\sqrt{3}(2 - \sqrt{6})$

g) $3\sqrt{2}(2\sqrt{3} - 4\sqrt{2})$

h) $(5\sqrt{5} + 2)(2 - \sqrt{5})$

3. Simplify the following expressions, if possible:

a) $\dfrac{\sqrt{20}}{2\sqrt{10}}$

b) $\dfrac{3\sqrt{27}}{\sqrt{18}}$

c) $\dfrac{\sqrt{8} + \sqrt{2}}{\sqrt{2}}$

d) $\dfrac{\sqrt{6} - \sqrt{3}}{2\sqrt{5}}$

e) $\dfrac{\sqrt{b} - \sqrt{ab}}{\sqrt{b}}$

4. Find the value of parameters **a, b, h** and **k** in the following rules:

a) $f(x) = \sqrt{9x - 27} + 2$

b) $f(x) = 2\sqrt{2 - 4x} - 3$

5. Find the vertex coordinates of the semi-parabola for each of the following functions.

a) $f(x) = 4\sqrt{2x + 6} - 3$

b) $g(x) = \sqrt{5}\sqrt{0.25x + 1} - 2$

6. Find the *y*-intercept of the following functions:

a) $f(x) = 2\sqrt{x + 3} + 4$

b) $g(x) = 3\sqrt{2x - 10} + 2$

c) $h(x) = -2\sqrt{2x + 3} + 2$

7. Compare the graphs of the pairs of functions below.

a) $f(x) = \sqrt{x}$ and $g(x) = -\sqrt{x}$

b) $f(x) = \sqrt{x}$ and $g(x) = \sqrt{-x}$

8. If $f(x) = a\sqrt{b(x - h)} + k$, indicate whether the statements below are always true.

a) Parameters **h** and **k** do not modify the shape of the semi-parabola.

b) Function *f* has a zero if k < 0.

c) If the curve of the function *f* is located entirely in the third quadrant, then a < 0 and b < 0.

9. Below are the graphs of square root functions. Find the sign of parameters **a** and **b**.

a)

b)

c)

d)

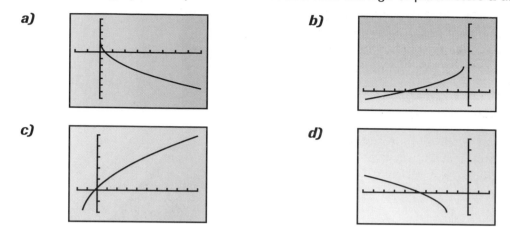

10. Describe the transformations that must be applied to the graph of the basic square root function to produce the graph of the function whose rule is:

a) $y = 3\sqrt{x - 5} - 4$

b) $y = -\sqrt{x + 1} + 3$

c) $y = 2\sqrt{-x} - 2$

d) $y = -1.5\sqrt{75 - 25x} + 3$

11. Graph the following functions:

a) $f(x) = -3\sqrt{x} + 7$

b) $g(x) = 2\sqrt{1 - x}$

c) $h(x) = -\sqrt{2x + 10} + 2$

d) $i(x) = -3\sqrt{0.5(x + 2)} - 1$

e) $j(x) = -\sqrt{-(x + 2)} - 3$

f) $k(x) = 3\sqrt{-2(x - 4)} - 5$

12. Given the function f defined as $f(x) = 2\sqrt{5 - 2x} - 6$:

a) State the rule for f in the form that uses the four parameters.

b) What is the value of each of the parameters **a, b, h** and **k**?

c) Find the domain and range of f.

13. State the rules below in standard form, where $b = 1$ or $b = -1$.

a) $f(x) = 3\sqrt{4x + 4} - 3$

b) $g(x) = -2\sqrt{-2x + 4} - 2$

c) $i(x) = -3\sqrt{10 - 25x} + 4$

d) $j(x) = -\sqrt{8x + 6}$

e) $k(x) = 4\sqrt{0.01x + 240} - 6$

f) $n(x) = -0.5\sqrt{8 - \frac{1}{4}x} + 1$

14. The approximate distance D, in kilometres, we can see when looking at the horizon is represented by the formula $D = 3.56\sqrt{a}$, where a is the altitude, in metres, from the observation point.

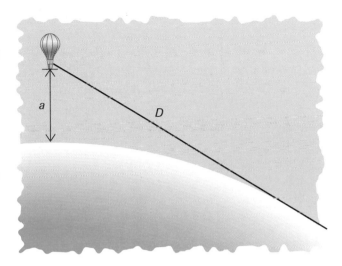

a) Graph the function in this particular situation.

b) What is the maximum distance a person in a hot air balloon can see, if the balloon is floating at an altitude of 580 m?

15. Find the domain and range of the following functions:

a) $f(x) = -0.85\sqrt{2x + 7} - 9$

b) $g(x) = (\sqrt{3} + 1)\sqrt{5 - 3x} + 6$

16. A rocket's speed increases by 128 m/s every second. The time t, in seconds, it takes the rocket to travel a distance d, in metres, can be calculated using the rule

$$t = 0.125\sqrt{d}.$$

a) How long will it take the rocket to travel:

1) 1 km?   2) 100 km?

b) Find all the properties of the function defined by this rule if the rocket's operating distance is 230.4 km.

Kennedy Space Center, Florida

A rocket escaped the earth's gravitational pull for the first time in 1957, when Russia's famous Sputnik satellite was sent into orbit.

17. Write the equations of two square root functions whose graphs are a parabola with a vertex at (-3, -2).

18. Given functions f and g whose equations are:

$f(x) = 2\sqrt{2x - 6} + 2$ $g(x) = 2\sqrt{-2x - 6} + 2$

Are the curves of these functions congruent? Justify your answer.

19. A hotel's dining room was moved into a large solarium whose roof is in the shape of a semi-parabola having the equation $y = \sqrt{4x - 20} + 6$. The solarium is 9 m wide. This scenario is represented on the Cartesian plane at right, whose axes are scaled in metres.

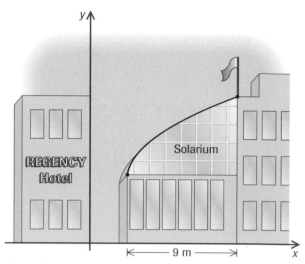

a) What is the distance between the hotel and the solarium?

b) How high is the solarium wall that faces the hotel?

c) How far above the ground is the base of the flagpole?

---

a) The graph of function $g(x) = a\sqrt{x}$ where $a > 0$ is the image of the graph of function $f(x) = \sqrt{x}$ following a vertical scale change of factor a.

1) Describe the equivalent horizontal scale change.

2) What happens if $a < 0$?

b) Graph the function $f(x) = \sqrt{x^2 - 5x + 6}$ using a graphing calculator.

1) How do you explain the discontinuity in the graph?

2) Determine the interval over which the function is undefined.

ZEROS AND EQUATIONS

Raining cats and dogs

Nadia and Frank needed to complete an assignment on rainfall for their ecology course. Since the weather forecast called for 24 consecutive hours of rain, Nadia and Frank began recording the amount of rainfall, in millimetres, at midnight. The data enabled them to determine, by regression, that the quantity q of rainfall followed the rule $q = 5\sqrt{5(x - 2)}$ where x is the number of hours since midnight.

a) What time did it start to rain?

b) How long did it take for the first 25 mm of rain to fall?

These questions lead to the search for a zero and the solution of radical equations.

c) Is the following property true for the set of real numbers?
$$\text{If } a = b \Rightarrow a^2 = b^2$$

d) Explain how to eliminate the radical in the following radical equations:

1) $\sqrt{x} = 2$ 2) $\sqrt{2x - 6} = 0$ 3) $\sqrt{x + 2} = x$

e) Solve the equations in *d)* after eliminating the radical, then check to see if the solutions found are also solutions for the given radical equations.

This leads to the question: Does "squaring each side of the equation" constitute a rule for transforming equations? Essentially, the squares of equal expressions are equal. However, the process of squaring increases the degree of the equation, and the more this occurs, the more solutions the equation can have.

f) Complete the solution for each of the given equations. Equation 2) was obtained by squaring each side of equation 1).

1) $ax = b$
   $x = \blacksquare$

2) $a^2x^2 = b^2$
   $x^2 = \blacksquare$
   $x = \blacksquare$ or $x = -\blacksquare$

g) Which solution for equation 2) is not a solution for equation 1)?

Thus, **squaring** the two sides of an equation **preserves the solutions.** Squaring, however, **creates the risk of introducing false solutions,** hence the importance of checking the resulting values.

These considerations allow us to outline the following steps for finding the zeros of a square root function or solving a radical equation.

1. Isolate the term containing the radical on one side of the equation.

2. State all the restrictions.

3. Square each side of the equation to eliminate the radical.

4. Solve the resulting equation.

5. Check that the resulting values respect the conditions of the given equation.

Below are some examples of algebraic solutions supported by a graphical method.

EXAMPLE 1

We want to find the zero of the function f defined by $f(x) = 2\sqrt{x-3} - 4$.

1. Establish $f(x) = 0 \Rightarrow 2\sqrt{x-3} - 4 = 0$

   or $2\sqrt{x-3} = 4$

2. Restrictions: $x - 3 \geqslant 0 \Rightarrow x \geqslant 3$

3. Solution: $2\sqrt{x-3} = 4$

   $\sqrt{x-3} = 2$

   $x - 3 = 4$ (By squaring each side of the equation.)

   $x = 7$

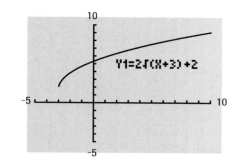

Since $7 \geqslant 3$ and 7 verifies the equation $2\sqrt{x-3} - 4 = 0$, 7 is the zero of the function.

EXAMPLE 2

We wish determine the zero of the function g defined by the rule $g(x) = 2\sqrt{x+3} + 2$.

1. Establish: $2\sqrt{x+3} + 2 = 0$

   or $2\sqrt{x+3} = -2$

2. Restrictions: $x + 3 \geqslant 0 \Rightarrow x \geqslant -3$

3. Solution: $2\sqrt{x+3} = -2$

   $\sqrt{x+3} = -1$ (Impossible)

There is no point in continuing since this equation states that a positive number equals a negative number. This function has no zero.

EXAMPLE 3

We want to solve the equation $2\sqrt{x+4} - 1 = x$.

The graphs of the functions on each side of the equation show that the equation has a single solution, which is 5.

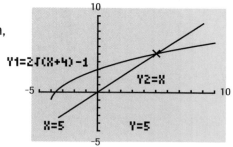

This solution is obtained algebraically as follows:

1. Isolate the term with the radical: $2\sqrt{x+4} - 1 = x$

$$\Downarrow$$

$$2\sqrt{x+4} = x + 1$$

2. Establish the restrictions: $x + 4 \geqslant 0 \Rightarrow x \geqslant -4$

and $x + 1 \geqslant 0 \Rightarrow x \geqslant -1$

Therefore a solution requires that $x \geqslant -1$.

3. Square each side of the equation: $4(x+4) = x^2 + 2x + 1$

4. Solve the quadratic equation: $4x + 16 = x^2 + 2x + 1$

$$x^2 - 2x - 15 = 0$$

Thus $x_1 = -3$ and $x_2 = 5$.

5. Check the results. Notice that -3 is rejected and that 5 is the solution to the equation.

h) Find the zeros of the following functions using algebra:

1) $f(x) = 2\sqrt{2x+4} - 6$

2) $g(x) = -2\sqrt{x-3} + 8$

i) Use algebra to solve the following equations in IR:

1) $8 - \sqrt{x-2} = 4$

2) $2\sqrt{2x+1} = 3\sqrt{x}$

SIGN AND INEQUALITIES

The stern of the ship

A naval architect uses a computer to design the blueprints for a ship. For a total length of 18 m, the stern follows the curve of the function $f(x) = -2\sqrt{x-3} + 4$. The waterline corresponds to the x-axis.

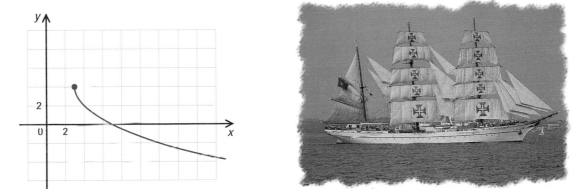

a) Which interval, along the x-axis, corresponds to the part of the ship's hull above the waterline?

b) What inequality has the previous interval as its solution set?

c) What are the two points whose coordinates play a key role in examining the signs of a square root function?

d) Give an example of the graph of a square root function in the form
$f(x) = a\sqrt{b(x - h)} + k$, whose sign over its entire domain is:

1) Positive.   2) Negative.

Once again, notice how helpful a visual aid can be in studying a square root function's signs and solving radical inequalities.

> To determine the sign of a square root function:
>
> 1.   Draw a graph using the coordinates of the vertex and the zero, if it exists.
> 2.   Read the intervals of the domain located on either side of the zero, if it exists.

Two evergreens

An 18.3 cm evergreen tree A is put in a flower pot as part of a study. Ten days later a 15 cm evergreen tree B is put in another pot. Different fertilizers are used on the trees. Over a seven-day period, the height of plant A varies according to the rule $y = 0.3x + 18.3$, and that of plant B, according to the rule $y = 3\sqrt{x - 10} + 15$, where x is the number of days since plant A was placed in the pot. For how many days was plant B taller than plant A?

a) What inequality must be solved to answer this question?

b) Solve this inequality using a calculator.

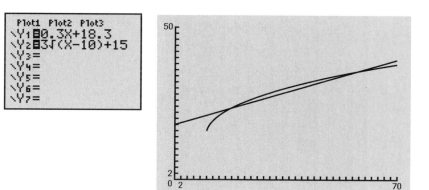

Reforestation has grown steadily in Québec over the past few years. By 1991 the province had planted a total of 221 000 000 new trees. Almost all the seedlings were conifers, spruces, larches and pines.

Note once again that solving an inequality consists of comparing the images of two functions.

The procedure for solving radical inequalities using a graph can be summarized in three steps:

> 1.   Define a function for each side of the inequality.
> 2.   Determine where the two curves intersect, if applicable.
> 3.   Determine the interval(s) of the domain over which the images of the first function are greater or less than those of the second, based on the given inequality.

FINDING THE RULE

Water slide

A water slide has the shape of a semi-parabola based on a square root function. This scenario is depicted in the graph below, with the axes scaled in metres. A series of vertical beams spaced at 5 m intervals support the slide. We want to find the length of each beam.

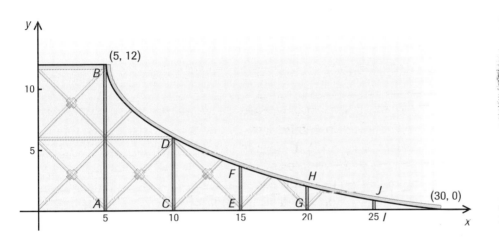

a) To what does the length of each beam in this graph correspond?

b) What must be known to calculate these lengths?

c) What is the standard form of the rule for this function?

d) What are the parameters of the rule with its current values?

e) How do you find the value of parameter **a**?

f) What are the lengths of the vertical beams supporting the slide?

It is easy to find the rule of a square root function when the coordinates of its vertex (h, k) and another point are known:

1. Substitute the values of **h** and **k** in the rule $y = a\sqrt{b(x - h)} + k$, where b — 1 if the semi-parabola is to the right of its vertex, and b = -1 if it is to the left.

2. Replace x and $f(x)$ with the coordinates of the other known point and calculate the value of parameter **a.**

Blackout

Between the 5th and 30th hours of a blackout, the temperature in degrees Celsius inside a house varies according to the function $f(t) = -2\sqrt{t-5} + 20$ where t is the time, in hours, since the start of the blackout.

Below are the graphs of the function f and its inverse f^{-1}.

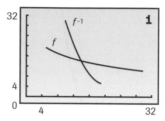

At the height of the ice storm of January 1998, almost half of all Québec residents were left without power.

a) For this situation, find:

   1) The domain of f.　　　　2) The range of f.

b) Find the rule for f^{-1}, which, by isolating t, allows us to calculate the time since the start of the blackout as a function of the temperature.

c) What type of function is f^{-1}?

d) Find the domain and range of f^{-1}.

> The inverse of a square root function is a restricted quadratic function.

Below are the **properties** of **transformed square root functions:**

Rule	$f(x) = a\sqrt{(x-h)} + k$ or $f(x) = a\sqrt{-(x-h)} + k$ with $a \neq 0$
Graph	Semi-parabola with vertex (h, k).
Dom f	$[h, +\infty[$ if b = 1 or $]-\infty, h]$ if b = -1
Ran f	$[k, +\infty[$ if a > 0 or $]-\infty, k]$ if a < 0
Zero	There is a zero if and only if a and k have opposite signs.
Extremes	k (maximum if a < 0 or minimum if a > 0)
Variation	Always increasing if a and b have the same sign; always decreasing if a and b have opposite signs.
Sign	Always the same sign if there is no zero.
Inverse	The inverse is a function (restricted quadratic function of a semi-parabola).

Square root functions can be added, subtracted, multiplied or divided. We may also find their composites with other functions.

e) If $f(x) = 2\sqrt{4(x - 1)} + 3$ and $g(x) = \sqrt{x - 1} - 3$, sketch the graph displayed by a graphing calculator for each of the following functions:

1) $f + g$ 2) $f - g$ 3) $f \cdot g$ 4) $\dfrac{f}{g}$

f) If $f(x) = \sqrt{x}$ and $g(x) = x^2 - 3x + 2$, state the rule for the following composites:

1) $f \circ g$ 2) $g \circ f$

INVESTMENT 11

1. Use a graphing calculator to find the zero, if it exists, of the following functions:

a) $f_1(x) = 2\sqrt{2x - 4}$ **b)** $f_2(x) = -2\sqrt{-(x - 3)} + 2$

c) $f_3(x) = -3\sqrt{2x - 1} - 2$ **d)** $f_4(x) = -\sqrt{-x}$

2. Solve the following equations using a graphing calculator.

a) $\sqrt{x - 2} = 3$ **b)** $4\sqrt{5 - 2x} = 12$ **c)** $5 + \sqrt{6 - 2x} = 3$

d) $2 - 3\sqrt{2 - x} = 5$ **e)** $\sqrt{x + 1} = 2x - 4$ **f)** $4\sqrt{2x - 3} = 12 - x$

3. Find the zero, if it exists, of each function using algebra.

a) $f(x) = 2\sqrt{2x + 4} - 6$ **b)** $g(x) = -2\sqrt{x - 3} + 8$ **c)** $h(x) = 4 - 2\sqrt{x - 3}$

4. Solve the following equations in IR:

a) $8 - \sqrt{x - 2} = 4$ **b)** $2\sqrt{2x + 1} = 3\sqrt{x}$ **c)** $\sqrt{x - 2} = \sqrt{x^2 + 4x}$

5. On earth, the period P of a pendulum, in seconds, is calculated using the formula $P = 2\pi\sqrt{\dfrac{l}{9.8}}$ where l is the length of the pendulum in metres. If a pendulum has a period of 4 s, what is its length?

A pendulum is a system that oscillates at a constant rate. It is usually a mass suspended from a fixed point so as to swing freely under the force of gravity.

6. The speed s of a ball depends on its mass m and the kinetic energy E with which it is thrown. This speed is expressed in metres per second and is based on the formula $s = \sqrt{\dfrac{2E}{m}}$ where E is in joules and m in kilograms. With how much energy was a 0.14 kg ball thrown if it reaches a speed of 20 m/s?

7. Given the functions $y = -4\sqrt{x - 2} + 8$ and $y = 3\sqrt{x + 6} - 5$:

    a) Solve the system formed by these two rules using a graphing calculator.

    b) What is the distance between the zeros of the two functions?

8. Show graphically that a transformed square root function has a zero only if parameters **a** and **k** are of opposite signs.

9. Given the function $f(x) = 2\sqrt{x - 1} - 4$, what is the distance between the vertex of its curve and its x-intercept?

10. What is the equation of the line that passes through the vertex and the x-intercept of the function $g(x) = -2\sqrt{-(x - 2)} + 6$?

11. Given functions f and g defined as follows:

    $f(x) = 2\sqrt{x - 2}$ $g(x) = \sqrt{x + 2}$

    For what value of x is $f(x) = g(x)$? (Solve algebraically.)

12. Over which interval of the domain are the images of the function $f(x) = 3\sqrt{x + 3} + 6$ positive?

13. For which values of the domain are the images of the function $f(x) = 3\sqrt{-(x + 3)} - 6$:

    a) Negative?   **b)** Between -3 and 3?

14. Solve the following inequalities:

    a) $\sqrt{x} \leqslant 4$ **b)** $\sqrt{x + 3} \geqslant 3$

    c) $\sqrt{-(x - 2)} + 4 < 8$ **d)** $2\sqrt{x + 3} - 4 \geqslant 13$

15. Solve the following inequalities using a graphing calculator:

    a) $\sqrt{x} \leqslant x$ **b)** $3\sqrt{x + 1} < 2x - 3$

    c) $2\sqrt{-(x - 2)} - 5 < x$ **d)** $\sqrt{x + 11} + 3 > x^2 - 4$

16. Two helicopters searching for the survivors of a shipwreck travel side by side at an altitude of 300 m. After receiving an order over their radios, one of the helicopters begins ascending such that its altitude, in metres, varies according to the equation $A_1(t) = 18t + 300$ where t is the time, in minutes, since the order was given. The second helicopter begins its ascent 4 min later and its altitude varies according to the rule $A_2(t) = 90\sqrt{t - 4} + 300$.

Helicopters are complex, delicate aircraft with a fairly limited range, requiring highly skilled pilots. Nonetheless, their particular capabilities, such as their maneuverability, make them ideal for a variety of applications: passenger and freight transport; mountain rescue operations; firefighting; farming; pipeline installation; inspection of precipitous terrain; power-line surveillance; etc.

a) At what time will the helicopters be at the same altitude?

b) Both helicopters halt their ascents 25 min after receiving the order. What is the difference in altitude between them?

17. Given the function $f:\ \mathbb{IR} \to \mathbb{IR}$

$$x \mapsto f(x) = 3\sqrt{x - 2} - 5$$

a) Draw the graphs of f and f^{-1}.

b) State the domain and range of f and f^{-1}.

18. In which quadrant is the graph of f^{-1} located if the graph of f is located entirely in:

a) The 1st quadrant?   **b)** The 2nd quadrant?

c) The 3rd quadrant?   **d)** The 4th quadrant?

19. State the rule for the inverse of the following functions:

a) $f(x) = 4\sqrt{-(x - 1)} + 3$ **b)** $g(x) = -2\sqrt{x + 7} - 10$

c) $h(x) = 4\sqrt{9x + 27} + 6$ **d)** $i(x) = 4\sqrt{-(x - 2)} - 8$

20. The braking distance and the coefficient of tire friction on the road are variables used to find the speed of an automobile at the moment the driver applies the brakes. The table of values below contains data compiled from tests on an asphalt road:

Braking distance (m)	0	4	11	22	36	44	65
Speed (km/h)	0	30	50	70	90	100	120

a) Plot these points and draw the curve passing through them.

b) Find the function rule for this mathematical model.

c) A police force uses the formula $v = 15.9\sqrt{df}$ where d is the braking distance in metres, and f is the coefficient of friction. What is the coefficient of friction in this example?

21. Given the functions $f(x) = 3\sqrt{x} + 5$ and $g(x) = -\sqrt{x} + 9$, find the rules for the following functions, then graph them:

a) $f + g$

b) $f - g$

22. The functions f and g are defined as $f(x) = 2\sqrt{x} + 3$ and $g(x) = -2\sqrt{x} + 3$.

a) Find the rule for $f \cdot g$.

b) Graph $f \cdot g$.

c) What is the domain of $f \cdot g$?

d) What is the range of $f \cdot g$?

23. The value of two automobiles is recorded over a 5-year period. The rules for their depreciation are $V_1 = -6.5\sqrt{x} + 25$ and $V_2 = -5\sqrt{x} + 20$ where x is the number of elapsed years, and V_1 and V_2 are expressed in thousands of dollars.

a) Find the rule for calculating the difference between the values of the two automobiles over this period.

b) What is the difference in their values after 5 years?

24. Two square root functions and their product are entered into a graphing calculator. Is the graph of the product function a ray? Justify your answer.

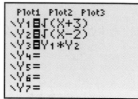

25. Find the rule for each square root function using the coordinates of the vertices V and the coordinates of a point P on its corresponding semi-parabola.

a)

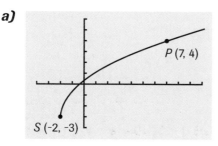

$P(7, 4)$

$S(-2, -3)$

b)

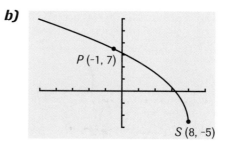

$P(-1, 7)$

$S(8, -5)$

c) $S(-4, -4)$ and $P(0, 0)$

d) $S(2, 3)$ and $P(5, -1)$

26. When a boat's motor is shut off, the time it takes for the boat to come to a complete stop depends largely on the shape of its hull. The table below lists a boat's speed from the moment its motor is shut off:

Time (s)	0	4	8	12	16	20	24	28
Speed (km/h)	48	32	25	20	16	12	9	6

a) Plot the graph that corresponds to this situation.

b) Find the function rule that can serve as a model for this situation.

c) How much time will it take for the boat to come to a complete stop?

27. In order to reinforce a dam, an engineer wants to build embankments that are both solid and aesthetically pleasing. The embankments are thus designed to follow the curve of a square root function. Find the function rule for this curve using the data supplied on the right.

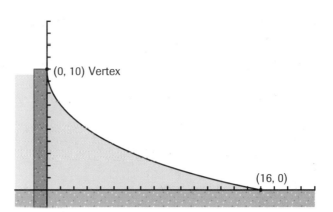

(0, 10) Vertex

(16, 0)

28. The letter "i" has been written using two square root functions with symmetric curves. Figure out their rules from the data on the graph.

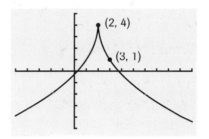

(2, 4)

(3, 1)

29. Find all the properties of the following functions:

a) $f(x) = 2\sqrt{x - 2} + 3$

b) $g(x) = 2\sqrt{-x + 3} - 1$

c) $h(x) = -2\sqrt{2x - 2} - 3$

d) $i(x) = -2\sqrt{-(x + 2)} - 5$

a) What are the possible signs of parameters **a, b, h** and **k** for the square root function:

1) Whose zero and y-intercept are strictly positive?

2) That has no zero or y-intercept?

3) That has a negative maximum?

4) That has a strictly positive maximum?

b) Point (3, 1) is the vertex of a semi-parabola that passes through point (7, 3).

1) Is there only one semi-parabola that satisfies these conditions? Justify your answer.

2) State the corresponding rule(s).

STEP
FUNCTIONS

CONCEPT OF STEP

Welcome to the real world

Two weeks ago Amy started her first job, a full-time position paying $8/hr for a 40 h week. Happy to have finally joined the labour force, Amy is really enjoying her work. Today is payday, and Amy can hardly wait to get her first pay cheque!

a) How much money should Amy expect to be paid?

When she saw the amount on her cheque, Amy thought she had only been paid for one week of work. The cheque stub, however, confirmed that it did indeed cover a two-week period. Amy was crestfallen; a large part of her first cheque had already been spent! An employee from human resources explained the various deductions to her.

First, there was federal income tax. The employee showed Amy the table and graph below:

Federal income tax

Taxable annual income ($)		Tax rate (%)
More than	Not exceeding	
0	- 29 590	17
29 590	- 59 180	26
59 180	-	29

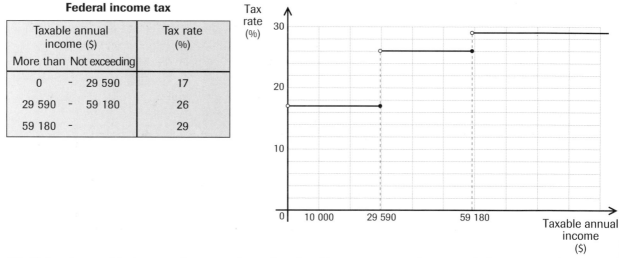

b) If Amy's taxable income is approximately 3/4 of her gross pay, how much federal income tax did she pay?

There were also deductions for provincial taxes, employment insurance, health insurance, pension plan, RRSP, union dues, etc. Almost 50% of her pay went towards these expenses.

c) What do the graph and table of values above have in common?

d) What do the solid and open circles on the graph represent?

e) Is this the graph of a function? Justify your answer.

A **step function** is a function that is constant at intervals, but changes abruptly for certain values of the independent variable, called **critical values.** The graph is formed of horizontal segments, usually closed at one end and open at the other. Since the graph cannot be drawn without lifting the pencil, the function is called **discontinuous.**

Hockey promotion

To boost his sales, a merchant offers his customers free hockey tickets to one of the local team's home games. Customers earn one free ticket for every $100 they spend at his store.

a) How many tickets will customers receive if they make purchases of:

   I) $275.99   2) $400.00

   3) $95.95   4) $1499.99

b) Rewrite the previous numbers, replacing all the digits after the hundreds column with zeros and eliminating all extra zeros.

c) A function that "truncates to the nearest hundred" is a function that associates a real number with another number whose digits after the hundreds column have been replaced by 0. Is this relation a step function? Explain your answer.

A function that truncates to the nearest integer, $Y_1 = $ iPart x, is displayed on a graphing calculator.

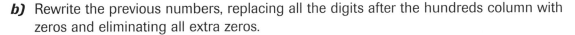

note: step from
–1 to 1 (length 2)
- also values of
neg.

d) Use a graph or calculator to find the value of:

  1) iPart 2.4   2) iPart -3.7   3) iPart -π   4) iPart -0.2

e) What happens to the number π if it is truncated to the nearest thousandth?

f) If $x = 12\ 456.789$, what is the value of $f(x)$ if f is a function that truncates to the nearest:

  1) Integer?   2) Hundredth?   3) Ten?   4) Thousand?

g) If $x = -12\ 456.789$, what is the value of $f(x)$ if f is a function that truncates to the nearest:

  1) Integer?   2) Hundredth?   3) Ten?   4) Thousand?

A **truncating** function associates a real number with another number that is generated by replacing the digits after a specified column with zeros. This function is a step function.

Budget check

MEMO

A company's financial services director issues a memo to all the departmental managers asking them to report the current state of their budgets. He asks them to round their totals to the nearest $10.

a) Indicate the amount a manager must report if her department's budget is:

1) $5678   2) $403.56   3) -$123   4) -$3478

b) Is the relation that associates the real amounts with the rounded amounts a step function? Explain your answer.

c) Describe the function f below in your own words.

d) Sketch the previous graph on a sheet of paper, this time taking the endpoints of the segments into account.

e) Find the value of:

1) $f(0.2)$ 2) $f(0.7)$ 3) $f(-0.2)$ 4) $f(-0.7)$ 5) $f(\pi)$

f) What happens to the number 45 678.934 if rounded to the nearest:

1) Integer?   2) Hundredth?   3) Ten?   4) Thousand?

g) What happens to the number -45 678.934 if rounded to the nearest:

1) Integer?   2) Hundredth?   3) Ten?   4) Thousand?

A **rounding** function associates a real number with the number having the required number of digits that is closest to it. This function is also a step function.

THE BASIC GREATEST INTEGER FUNCTION

How old do you think I am?

Several people were asked their age!

a) Who is telling the truth?

At certain stages of their lives, people pretend they are younger or older than they really are; at other times, they simply state their age. But even then, people are cheating somewhat, because when asked their age, they usually provide the greatest integer less than or equal to their actual age (their age at their last birthday). Only on their birthday are people actually stating their true age.

b) Give the greatest integer less than or equal to:

1) 25.5	2) 12.8	3) 5.2	4) 2
5) 0.1	6) -0.8	7) -1.2	8) -30.5

c) Given that [x] is the notation for the greatest integer less than or equal to x, find the value of:

1) [-4.1]	2) [-0.1]	3) [0.1]	4) [10.09]

The concept of **greatest integer less than or equal to** is used to define a step function, which is the most common example of this type of function.

The basic **greatest integer function** is defined as follows:

$$f: \ \mathbb{R} \longrightarrow \mathbb{R}$$

$$x \longmapsto f(x) = [x]$$

Its graph contains half-open segments that are 1 unit long and 1 unit apart.

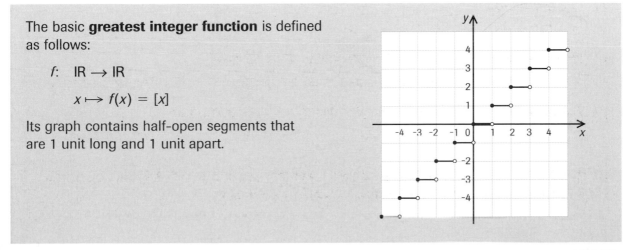

d) Shawn claims that if x is a positive number, the function $f(x) = [x]$ is the same as the function that truncates to the nearest integer. Is he right? Explain your answer.

e) Elise claims that the function $f(x) = [x]$ is similar to a rounding function, but one that always rounds down. Is she right? Explain your answer.

f) Complete the table of **properties** of the **basic greatest integer function.**

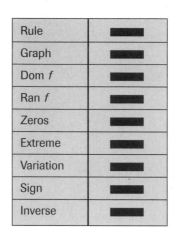

Rule	
Graph	
Dom f	
Ran f	
Zeros	
Extreme	
Variation	
Sign	
Inverse	

TRANSFORMED GREATEST INTEGER FUNCTIONS

Tough negotiations

A company's union and its management are in the process of negotiating a new collective agreement. The company is in serious financial difficulty. The previous collective agreement called for an annual job reclassification followed by a salary increase. Management is now proposing a new employee classification system that would have fewer categories and designate the first year of employment as a probationary period. Below are the two graphs presented at the bargaining table:

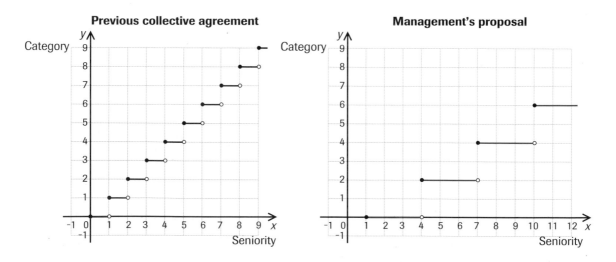

a) What geometric transformations were performed on the first graph to obtain the second graph?

b) If the function rule for the previous collective agreement is $f(x) = [x]$ where $f(x)$ is the category and x the seniority, find the function rule for the management proposal.

As with other functions, four parameters can be introduced into the rule for the basic greatest integer function to produce the rules for **transformed greatest integer functions.** These rules take the form $f(x) = a[b(x - h)] + k.$ The four parameters play the same role as in the other functions.

c) Parameter **a** is assigned different values. Describe their effects on the graph of the basic function.

$$f_1(x) = [x] \qquad f_2(x) = 2[x] \qquad f_3(x) = 0.5[x] \qquad f_4(x) = -[x]$$

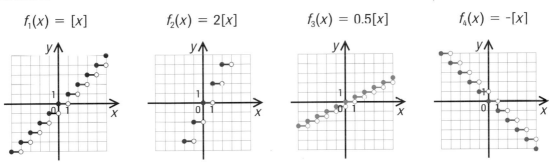

d) What geometric transformation has occurred as a result of changing parameter **a**?

e) Comparing the graphs in c), what can be said about:

1) The length of the segments?

2) The distance between two consecutive segments?

3) The "slope" of the step?

f) What happens if the value of **a** is negative? Check your answer.

g) Parameter **b** is assigned different values. Describe their effects on the graph of the basic function.

$$f_1(x) = [x] \qquad f_2(x) = [2x] \qquad f_3(x) = [0.5x] \qquad f_4(x) = [-x]$$

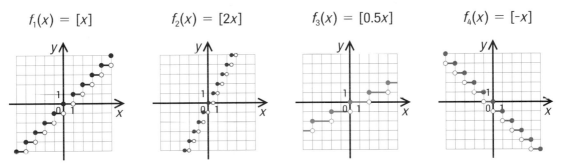

h) What geometric transformation has occurred as a result of changing parameter **b**?

i) In your own words, describe the effects of these transformations on the length of the segments, the distance separating each consecutive pair of segments, and the "slope" of the step.

j) What two changes occur to the segments in the graph of the basic function when the value of **b** is negative?

k) Parameters **h** and **k** are each assigned different values. Describe their effects on the graph of the basic function.

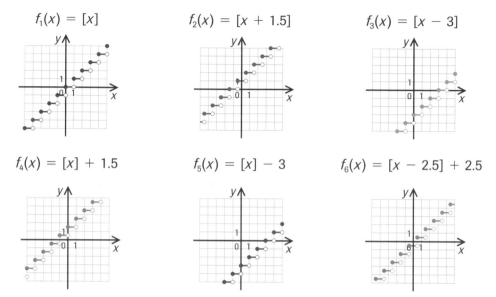

$$f_1(x) = [x] \qquad\qquad f_2(x) = [x + 1.5] \qquad\qquad f_3(x) = [x - 3]$$

$$f_4(x) = [x] + 1.5 \qquad\qquad f_5(x) = [x] - 3 \qquad\qquad f_6(x) = [x - 2.5] + 2.5$$

l) Analyse the table of values for the following functions, then state the impact of each parameter on each coordinate.

1) $f(x) = 2[x]$

X	Y₁	Y₂
-1.25	-2	-4
-1	-1	-2
-.75	-1	-2
-.5	-1	-2
-.25	-1	-2
0	0	0
.25	0	0

X=.25

2) $g(x) = [2x]$

X	Y₁	Y₃
-1.25	-2	-3
-1	-1	-2
-.75	-1	-2
-.5	-1	-1
-.25	-1	-1
0	0	0
.25	0	0

X=.25

3) $h(x) = [x - 2]$

X	Y₁	Y₄
-1.25	-2	-4
-1	-1	-3
-.75	-1	-3
-.5	-1	-3
-.25	-1	-3
0	0	-2
.25	0	-2

X=-1.25

4) $i(x) = [x] + 2$

X	Y₁	Y₅
-1.25	-2	0
-1	-1	1
-.75	-1	1
-.5	-1	1
-.25	-1	1
0	0	2
.25	0	2

X=.25

To graph a greatest integer function:

1. Find:
   1) The distance between the segments ($|a|$);
   2) The length of the segments $\left(\left| \dfrac{1}{b} \right| \right)$ and their endpoints (open or closed depending on the sign of b);
   3) The horizontal (h) and vertical (k) translations.

2. The images of the points (0, 0), (1, 0) and (1, 1) can also be found by performing calculations on the coordinates and generalizing the graph.

All the properties of these functions are determined from their graphs.

1. If a = 2.654 789, find the value of the following expressions:

    a) [100a]
    b) [a × 10⁶] − [4a]
    c) [a × 10⁻¹] + a × [10⁻¹] + [a] × 10⁻¹

2. Calculate the value of:

    a) $\left[\dfrac{2\sqrt{3}}{[2\sqrt{3}]}\right]$
    b) $\left[\dfrac{-\pi}{[-\pi]}\right]$
    c) $\left[\dfrac{\pi}{[-\pi]}\right]$

3. Indicate whether each of the following situations defines a step function.

    a) The cost of a taxi ride is $2.50 for the first fifth of a kilometre, plus 20¢ for each additional fifth of a kilometre travelled.

    b) The distance travelled by a car moving at a constant speed over a period of time.

4. A telephone company advertises the following long distance rates for calls made anywhere in North America: 50¢ for the first minute or part thereof, and 10¢ for each additional minute or part thereof.

    a) What is the cost of a long distance call lasting:

       1) 2.3 min?
       2) 1 h 12 min 10 s?

    b) Plot the graph of the function that associates the call's cost with its length.

    c) Does the graph of this function have:

       1) A minimum?
       2) A maximum?
       3) Any zeros?

5. Function g is an image of the basic greatest integer function following a vertical scale change of factor 5. Find the images of the segments joining the points whose coordinates are:

    a) (0, 0) and (1, 0)
    b) (1, 1) and (2, 1)
    c) (-1, -1) and (0, -1)

6. The functions below are transformed greatest integer functions.

    $f_1(x) = 4[x]$ $f_2(x) = \dfrac{1}{3}[x]$ $f_3(x) = [4x]$ $f_4(x) = \left[\left(\dfrac{1}{3}\right)x\right]$

    In each case:

    a) Determine if the scale change is horizontal or vertical.

    b) Indicate the size of the scale change.

    c) Plot the graph by calculating the coordinates of the images of the following points:
    (0, 0), (1, 0), (1, 1), (2, 1), (-1, -1) and (0, -1).

The first metal coins were minted in Lydia (modern Turkey) around 700 BC.

7. A country's legal tender is the "pekko." Due to inflation, no denominations less than 100 pekkos are printed. However, as the country's sales tax is 25%, the price paid by consumers is rarely in multiples of 100 pekkos. Merchants therefore round up the price to the nearest multiple of 100 pekkos.

   a) Plot the step function that relates the purchase price to the actual price.

   b) State the properties of this function in this context.

8. As an employee incentive, a store's manager offers his sales clerks a $50 bonus for every $1000 worth of merchandise they sell.

   a) Plot the bonuses as a function of total sales.

   b) State the properties of the function's mathematical model in the given context.

9. Frank's mother lends him $500 so that he can take part in a school trip. They agree that Frank will pay back $25 on the first of each month starting next January.

   a) How much will Frank still owe his mother on March 23rd of next year?

   b) Plot the graph of Frank's debt based on the time elapsed as of January 1 of next year.

10. Function f rounds to the nearest integer, function g truncates at the integer and function h is the basic greatest integer function. Which of these three functions associates the same image with x if x equals:

   a) 56.7?   **b)** -3.47?   **c)** $\sqrt{5}$?   **d)** -4π?

11. Find all the properties of function $y = 3[2x + 4] - 3$ over the interval [-10, 10].

12. Which geometric transformations associate the graph of the following transformed functions with the graph of the basic greatest integer function?

   a) $f_1(x) = [x - 5] + 6$ **b)** $f_2(x) = [x + 4] - 7$ **c)** $f_3(x) = -[x - 2]$

   d) $f_4(x) = [-x] + 3$ **e)** $f_5(x) = 5[-x]$ **f)** $f_6(x) = -[5x]$

13. Graph the functions defined in the previous exercise.

The works of Oresme (1323–1382) point to the general concept that one quantity varies along with another quantity. Leibniz is responsible for using the term "function" in its modern sense.

14. The rules below define step functions. Write them in the form $f(x) = a[b(x - h)] + k$.

   a) $f_1(x) = 5[2x - 6] + 1$ **b)** $f_2(x) = [3x + 5]$ **c)** $f_3(x) = \left[\dfrac{x}{2} - \dfrac{5}{2}\right]$

   d) $f_4(x) = \left[\dfrac{x - 20}{5}\right]$ **e)** $f_5(x) = \left[\dfrac{x}{5} - 20\right]$ **f)** $f_6(x) = 4(5 - 2[x]) + 1$

15. For the following functions, find the length of each segment forming the graph and state the distance between two consecutive segments:

   a) $f_1(x) = 5[x]$ **b)** $f_2(x) = [5x]$ **c)** $f_3(x) = \dfrac{1}{5}[x]$

   d) $f_4(x) = \left[\left(\dfrac{1}{5}\right)x\right]$ **e)** $f_5(x) = \dfrac{[x]}{5}$ **f)** $f_6(x) = \left[\dfrac{x}{5}\right]$

16. The function $f(x) = \dfrac{[10x + 0.5]}{10}$ is a greatest integer function corresponding to a function that rounds to the nearest tenth. State the rule for the greatest integer function used to round a number to the nearest:

a) Hundredth. **b)** Thousandth. **c)** nth decimal.

17. Can a function that truncates to the nearest integer be expressed using the greatest integer concept? If so, state the rule.

18. Describe what function f does if its rule is $f(x) = $ iPart $(100x) \div 100$.

19. A person's cardiovascular capacity can be calculated using the MaxVO$_2$ index, which stands for Maximum Volume of Oxygen. To measure the MaxVO$_2$ index of a 45-year-old man, the subject must take a test where he runs at the same speed on a treadmill for 30 min. At the start of the test, the treadmill is at a 10° angle relative to the ground. The angle is increased by 3° every 5 min. The data below are compiled during the test. Note that the subject's pulse is stable at each of the difficulty levels.

Period (min)	2	4	6	8	10	12	14	16	18
Pulse during period (beats/min)	90	92	102	106	120	122	123	136	136

a) Draw the step function that corresponds to this scenario.

b) What is the rule for calculating the pulse of the subject as a function of time?

c) State the rule for calculating the treadmill's angle as a function of time.

20. Is the function $f(x) = $ fPart x a step function?

21. Find the rule for a function that always rounds a number down to the nearest unit.

22. A store's accountant calculates the weekly commission paid to its sales staff using the rule $C(x) = 30\left[\dfrac{x}{1000}\right]$, where x is the weekly sales total of the salesperson and $C(x)$, the size of the commission. Both of these amounts are in dollars.

a) What is the minimum weekly sales total a salesperson must attain to earn a commission?

b) How much commission will a saleswoman earn if her weekly sales total is $12 354.45?

c) How much must a salesman sell in a week to earn a commission of at least $120?

d) Under what circumstances will a salesperson earn a commission of exactly $100?

e) In your own words, explain how the accountant calculates a salesperson's commission.

23. An insurance broker proposes a life insurance plan to a group of workers. The monthly premium P for a 27-year-old employee who smokes is based on the annual salary x using the formula $P(x) = 2.35\left[\dfrac{x}{1000}\right]$. In the event of death, the amount A of compensation follows the rule $M(x) = 1.75[x]$.

a) In your own words, explain how the broker calculates the premiums.

b) What is the yearly premium for a 27-year-old employee who smokes and whose salary is $28 657?

c) The broker also points out that, for non-smokers, the premium is reduced by 45¢ per month for every $1000 of annual income. What formula is used to calculate the monthly premium for a 27-year-old worker who does not smoke?

d) The amount of compensation doubles in the event of an accidental death. What happens to the rule in this case?

24. Given the functions $f(x) = \sqrt{x}$ and $g(x) = [x]$, find the rule for the required composite and state some characteristics that distinguish its graph from the graph of greatest integer functions in general.

a) $f \circ g$ **b)** $g \circ f$

25. Given the functions $f(x) = x$ and $g(x) = [x]$, describe the graph of the function:

a) $f + g$ **b)** $f - g$ **c)** $f \cdot g$ **d)** $\dfrac{f}{g}$

a) Consider the line passing through the closed endpoint of all the segments that form the graph of the transformed function $g(x) = a[b(x - h)] + k$.

1) State the slope of the line.

2) Find the y-intercept of this line using the same parameters.

3) Under what circumstances does this function have x-intercepts?

b) A function f is considered periodic with period p if $f(x + p) = f(x)$, for every value of x.

1) Is the function $h(x) = x - [x]$ a periodic function? If so, find the period; if not, explain why not.

2) In your own words, explain what is meant by a periodic function.

c) Use any of the functions studied up to now to find a composite whose graph is as original as possible.

d) Five students were asked to perform movements that a motion detector would pick up and represent as a graph of a greatest integer function. Describe these movements.

RATIONAL FUNCTIONS

| INVERSE VARIATION FUNCTION |
| THE BASIC RATIONAL FUNCTION |
| TRANSFORMED RATIONAL FUNCTIONS |
| SOLVING EQUATIONS AND RATIONAL INEQUALITIES |

INVERSE VARIATION FUNCTION

Don't try this at home!

We have all heard of fakirs who are able to walk on broken glass or nails. Their mysterious powers can be explained using a simple law of physics.

Imagine a fakir, whose mass is 50 kg (a weight of approximately 500 N), placing his feet, one by one, on a certain number of nails. The force F he puts on each nail depends on the number of nails he steps on.

a) State the rule for calculating the force on each nail if the fakir steps on x nails.

b) Enter this rule into a graphing calculator and describe the graph produced by the values in the display window on the right.

```
WINDOW
 Xmin=0
 Xmax=100
 Xscl=4
 Ymin=0
 Ymax=500
 Yscl=50
 Xres=1
```

c) Notice how the force on each nail varies as the number of nails increases. Use the table of values displayed on the calculator.

d) Describe the changes in the graph of the mathematical model for this scenario as x becomes very large.

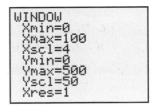

X	Y₁
80	6.25
90	5.5556
100	5
110	4.5455
120	4.1667
130	3.8462
140	3.5714
X=	

If the distance between a line and a curve continually decreases without ever reaching zero, the **curve is asymptotic to the line** and we call the line an **asymptote.**

e) Note how the force on each nail varies as the number of nails the fakir steps on becomes smaller and smaller.

f) What happens to the graph of the mathematical model as *x* approaches 0?

g) Which vertical line is an asymptote?

h) What happens in the table of values if we multiply the coordinates of the ordered pairs?

A function with this characteristic is called a **first-degree inverse variation function** and its rule takes the form $f(x) = \dfrac{a}{bx}$.

i) What key data must the fakir know if he wants to walk on the bed of nails safely?

The scenario involving the fakir corresponds to part of the graph of a mathematical model.

```
WINDOW
 Xmin=-100
 Xmax=100
 Xscl=10
 Ymin=-500
 Ymax=500
 Yscl=50
 Xres=1
```

j) What happens to the graph of this model if the domain is not restricted to positive numbers?

k) What value cannot belong to this function's domain?

Note that the graph is a special type of curve called a **hyperbola.** Moreover, any value that sets the denominator to zero is excluded from the function's domain. Since this curve cannot be drawn without lifting pencil from paper, the function is said to be **discontinuous.**

Augustin-Louis Cauchy (1789–1857) was primarily responsible for elaborating the concept of a function's continuity.

THE BASIC RATIONAL FUNCTION

The simplest inverse variation function has a rule where **a** and **b** each equal 1. This rule is $f(x) = \dfrac{1}{x}$ and it defines the **basic rational function.** The graph of the function is a **hyperbola** formed by two **branches** that are symmetrical about the lines $y = x$ and $y = -x$. There is a space between the two branches at the point where the denominator is equal to 0. Each branch of the graph is **asymptotic** to the axes; that is, the **axes** are **asymptotes.** The curve cannot be drawn without lifting the pencil and the function is therefore **discontinuous.**

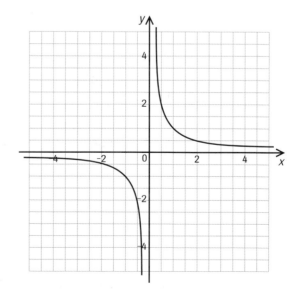

The **domain** of the function does not include the value that sets the denominator to zero. The domain is therefore **IR \ {0}** or IR*. Even if the independent variable is assigned very large or small values, the value of the dependent variable is never 0. Thus, the **range** of the function is also **IR \ {0}.**

The basic rational function has no x- or y-intercept. It therefore has no zero. It also does not have extremes (unless its domain is restricted).

Note that the function is decreasing and negative over $]-\infty, 0[$, and positive and decreasing over $]0, +\infty[$.

TRANSFORMED RATIONAL FUNCTIONS

Tragedy at Chernobyl

In addition to solar energy and fossil fuels, two of the most common energy sources are hydroelectricity and nuclear power. Nuclear power is viewed as a threat by environmentalists. One need only recall the tragedy that occurred at Chernobyl in 1986 when a nuclear reactor exploded, contaminating both the city's inhabitants and the surrounding environment. The rate of radioactivity is the ratio of the current radiation level to the initial radiation level. Experts have suggested that, one year after the explosion, the radioactivity rate in the area surrounding the Chernobyl reactor varied according to the function $f(x) = \frac{80}{x} + 5$, where x is the number of years since the reactor exploded.

Aerial view of the Chernobyl nuclear power plant after the explosion of a reactor on April 25, 1986.

a) How many years will it be before the radioactivity rate in the region is zero?

b) Describe the changes in the rate of radioactivity.

c) In the graph of the function's mathematical model, what is the equation of the asymptote that is:

   1) Vertical?   2) Horizontal?

Nuclear power plants, like traditional coal- or fuel-driven power plants, transform energy released by combustion into heat. This heat, which vaporizes water, is produced by the controlled fission of uranium in the reactor. Fission, or the splitting of a heavy atomic nucleus, is also the concept behind the atomic bomb.

Parameters can be introduced into the rule for the basic rational function. This results in transformed functions whose rules take the form $f(x) = \frac{a}{b(x - h)} + k$.

Once again, the parameters play the same role as in other functions, both with respect to the graph and the ordered pairs belonging to the basic function.

d) What is the effect of each parameter on:

   1) The graph of the basic function?

   2) The ordered pairs belonging to the basic function?

e) Given that the pairs (1/2, 2), (1, 1) and (2, 1/2) belong to the basic function, use the parameters to produce three ordered pairs belonging to the following functions:

   1) $g(x) = \frac{2}{x - 3}$ 2) $h(x) = \frac{1}{2(x + 1)} + 3$

*The **sievert** is the unit used to measure the amount of radiation absorbed by an organism.*

f) The asymptotes of the basic function intersect at (0, 0). Find the point of intersection of the asymptotes for the functions defined in *e)* and write the equations of these asymptotes.

g) Graph the two functions defined in *e)* using the asymptotes, the image of point (1, 1) of the basic function, and the symmetry of the branches of the hyperbola.

h) Which of the functions *g* and *h* defined in *e)* has a zero? What is this zero?

i) Referring to functions *g* and *h* defined in *e)*, find the values of the domain for which:
   1) $g(x) > 0$ 2) $h(x) \leq 0$

Thus, it is fairly easy to study functions whose rules have the form $f(x) = \dfrac{a}{b(x-h)} + k$.

Parameter **b** can be eliminated through a simple trick of arithmetic:

$$f(x) = \frac{a}{b(x-h)} + k \quad \Rightarrow \quad f(x) = \frac{a/b}{(x-h)} + k$$

Since **a/b** represents a value, this value can take the place of parameter **a.** We can therefore obtain a simplified form of the function:

$$f(x) = \frac{a}{(x-h)} + k$$

The rule $f(x) = \dfrac{a}{b(x-h)} + k$ can also be expressed as $f(x) = \dfrac{a_1 x + b_1}{a_2 x + b_2}$.

In fact, if both expressions in the first form are added using a common denominator, the result is a quotient of two linear functions:

$$\frac{a}{b(x-h)} + k = \frac{a + kb(x-h)}{b(x-h)} = \frac{kbx + a - kbh}{bx - bh} = \frac{(kb)x + (a-k)h}{(b)x + (-bh)}$$

By using the parameters of the linear function to represent the constants, we get:

$$f(x) = \frac{a_1 x + b_1}{a_2 x + b_2}$$

Homographic functions are rational functions that take the form:

$$f(x) = \frac{a}{b(x-h)} + k \quad \text{or} \quad f(x) = \frac{a_1 x + b_1}{a_2 x + b_2}$$

j) Using the division algorithm, write the rule $f(x) = \dfrac{4x + 2}{2x - 2}$ in standard form.

k) The vertical asymptote is a line whose points have an x-coordinate that sets the denominator to zero and is not part of the domain. Give the equation of the vertical asymptote of the following functions:

1) $f(x) = \dfrac{4x + 2}{2x - 2}$

2) $f(x) = \dfrac{a_1 x + b_1}{a_2 x + b_2}$

l) The horizontal asymptote is the line that the curve approaches when x becomes very large ($x \to +\infty$) or very small ($x \to -\infty$). The equation of this horizontal asymptote can be deduced using the parameters of the two linear functions and the reasoning below. Complete the reasoning:

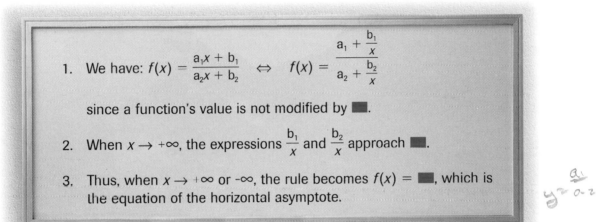

1. We have: $f(x) = \dfrac{a_1 x + b_1}{a_2 x + b_2}$ $\Leftrightarrow$ $f(x) = \dfrac{a_1 + \dfrac{b_1}{x}}{a_2 + \dfrac{b_2}{x}}$

   since a function's value is not modified by ■.

2. When $x \to +\infty$, the expressions $\dfrac{b_1}{x}$ and $\dfrac{b_2}{x}$ approach ■.

3. Thus, when $x \to +\infty$ or $-\infty$, the rule becomes $f(x) = $ ■, which is the equation of the horizontal asymptote.

m) State the equations of the asymptotes of the rational function defined by $h(x) = \dfrac{4x - 2}{3x + 1}$.

n) Explain why asymptotes play a key role in the graphs of homographic rational functions.

o) Is the inverse of a homographic rational function itself a function? If so, find the inverse of the function shown below.

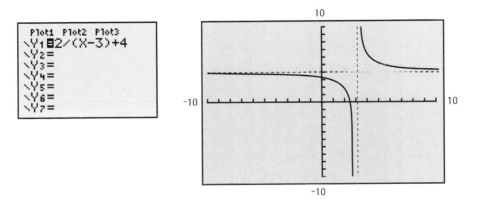

Operations and compositions can also be performed on rational functions.

p) Given the functions defined as follows:

$$f(x) = \frac{x+1}{x-1}$$

$$g(x) = \frac{1}{x+1}$$

$$h(x) = \frac{-2}{x+1} + 1$$

Find the function rule for:

1) $f + g$ 2) $g - h$ 3) $f \cdot h$ 4) $\frac{f}{g}$ 5) $f \circ h$

SOLVING RATIONAL EQUATIONS AND INEQUALITIES

Law of supply and demand

A company wants to start manufacturing golf clubs and asks a consulting firm to conduct some market research. This research consists of analysing the ratio of supply and demand over the years in order to observe market trends. The firm concludes that the rule governing this ratio is as follows:

$$f(x) = \frac{15}{0.5x - 12} + 3.$$

The company can then use this ratio to price its products and project its overall profits.

a) How long with it be before this ratio reaches zero?

b) For how long will the demand outpace the supply (ratio greater than 1)?

Since the 1930s, the rules of golf have limited the number of clubs allowed on a course to 14. A basic set of clubs consists of 3 drivers, 9 irons and 1 putter.

To answer these two questions, one must first solve a rational equation and a rational inequality, which raises the question of how such equations and inequalities are solved.

c) Taking the context into account, solve algebraically:

1) The rational equation used to calculate the moment when the ratio equals zero.

2) The rational inequality used to calculate the time period over which the ratio of supply and demand will be greater than 1.

d) In each case, justify the steps used to calculate the zero of a rational function or solve a rational equation.

1)
$$f(x) = \frac{a}{b(x-h)} + k$$

$$\frac{a}{b(x-h)} + k = 0$$

$$\frac{a}{b(x-h)} = -k$$

$$\frac{b(x-h)}{a} = \frac{1}{-k}$$

$$x - h = \frac{a}{-bk}$$

$$x = \frac{a}{-bk} + h$$

2)
$$f(x) = \frac{a_1x + b_1}{a_2x + b_2}$$

$$\frac{a_1x + b_1}{a_2x + b_2} = 0$$

$$a_1x + b_1 = 0$$

$$a_1x = -b_1$$

$$x = \frac{-b_1}{a_1}$$

e) Using the zero and the graph, explain how to solve an inequality in the form $\dfrac{a}{b(x - h)} + k \leqslant 0$ or in the form $\dfrac{a_1 x + b_1}{a_2 x + b_2} \geqslant 0$.

Thus, **homographic rational functions** have the following **properties:**

Rule	$f(x) = \dfrac{a}{b(x - h)} + k$ or $f(x) = \dfrac{a_1 x + b_1}{a_2 x + b_2}$
Graph	Composed of two branches of a hyperbola, asymptotic to two lines—one vertical, the other horizontal—whose equations are: Vertical asymptote: $x = h$ $\qquad\qquad$ $x = \dfrac{-b_2}{a_2}$ Horizontal asymptote: $y = k$ $\qquad\qquad$ $y = \dfrac{a_1}{a_2}$
Domain	$\mathrm{IR} \setminus \{h\}$ $\qquad\qquad$ $\mathrm{IR} \setminus \left\{\dfrac{-b_2}{a_2}\right\}$
Range	$\mathrm{IR} \setminus \{k\}$ $\qquad\qquad$ $\mathrm{IR} \setminus \left\{\dfrac{a_1}{a_2}\right\}$
Zero	Only if the horizontal asymptote is not the x-axis or $k \neq 0$.
Extreme	No extremes unless the domain or the range is restricted.
Variation	Decreasing over its two intervals or increasing over its two intervals.
Sign	Negative for that part of the domain below the x-axis on the graph and positive for the rest.
Inverse relation	The inverse is a homographic rational function.

INVESTMENT 13

1. Which of the rules below defines the basic rational function?

$f(x) = x^{-1}$ $\qquad$ $g(x) = x - 1$ $\qquad$ $h(x) = \dfrac{1}{x}$ $\qquad$ $i(x) = \dfrac{1}{\sqrt{x}}$

2. Which of the following functions are transformations of the basic function $f(x) = \dfrac{1}{x}$?

$f_1(x) = \dfrac{3}{x - 4}$ $\qquad\qquad$ $f_2(x) = \dfrac{4}{x - 5} + x$

$f_3(x) = \dfrac{7}{4x - 8} + 2$ $\qquad\qquad$ $f_4(x) = -\dfrac{5}{4x^2} + 2$

3. Determine the geometric transformation that associates the graph of the function $f(x) = \frac{1}{x}$ with each of the following functions:

a) $f_1(x) = \frac{1}{x} - 7$

b) $f_2(x) = \frac{6}{x}$

c) $f_3(x) = \frac{1}{5x}$

d) $f_4(x) = \frac{1}{x+4}$

4. The four graphs below correspond to functions in the form $f(x) = \frac{a}{x}$.
Place these functions in increasing order of **a**.

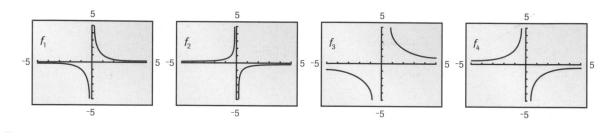

5. The graphs of the functions defined below are images of the graph of the basic function $f(x) = \frac{1}{x}$ after a composition of two or more geometric transformations. Describe these transformations.

a) $f_1(x) = \frac{-5}{x}$

b) $f_2(x) = \frac{1}{3x-6} - 2$

c) $f_3(x) = \frac{3}{x+4}$

d) $f_4(x) = \frac{3}{1-x} - 4$

6. Match the graph with its corresponding function.

$$f_1(x) = \frac{-3}{x-2} \qquad f_2(x) = \frac{1}{x+2} \qquad f_3(x) = \frac{-4}{2-x} \qquad f_4(x) = \frac{4}{-x} + 2$$

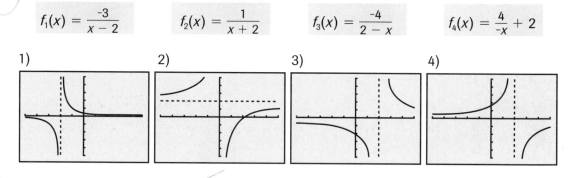

7. State the point of intersection of the asymptotes of the following functions:

a) $f(x) = \frac{2}{x-3} + 4$

b) $g(x) = \frac{-1}{x+5}$

c) $h(x) = \frac{3}{2x+4}$

d) $i(x) = \frac{3}{-x+6} - 5$

e) $j(x) = \frac{3x+4}{2x-1}$

f) $k(x) = \frac{2x-4}{3x-1}$

8. Explain why the graph of the function $f(x) = \frac{2x-4}{x-2}$ is not a hyperbola.

9. State the rule for the rational functions defined below using the form $f(x) = \dfrac{a}{b(x-h)} + k$, and find the domain in each case.

a) $f_1(x) = \dfrac{2x-3}{x-1}$

b) $f_2(x) = \dfrac{6x-15}{2x-8}$

c) $f_3(x) = \dfrac{-x+6}{2x-8}$

d) $f_4(x) = \dfrac{3x}{4x-5}$

10. Graph the following functions and find the equations of their asymptotes:

a) $f_1(x) = \dfrac{x-4}{x-5}$

b) $f_2(x) = \dfrac{4x-5}{2x-2}$

c) $f_3(x) = \dfrac{-6x+1}{2x+3}$

d) $f_4(x) = \dfrac{2x+1}{4x-3}$

11. A liquid solution that is 30% acidic is diluted with 50 mL of distilled water. The rule $C(x) = \dfrac{15}{x+50}$ represents the acidic concentration based on the quantity x of water added to the solution. The given quantities are in millilitres.

a) Graph this function for all the values of x up to 150 mL.

b) What is the y-intercept of this function?

c) How much water must be added to the solution so that the concentration is less than 1%?

d) What is the rule for calculating the concentration of an 80 mL solution that is 40% acidic, if we add x mL of water?

12. Financial institutions use "the rule of 72" to determine the approximate number of years required to double a principal invested at a given interest rate. This rule is $A(x) = \dfrac{72}{x}$, where x is the interest rate and $A(x)$ the number of years.

a) What was the interest rate if the principal doubles in 10 years?

b) Graph this function.

c) What would the domain of this function be if it were restricted to realistic interest rates?

d) What is the rule for determining the number of years left before the principal doubles if it has been invested for two years?

13. The point of intersection of a hyperbola's asymptotes is called the centre of the hyperbola. Find the centre of the hyperbolas belonging to the following functions:

a) $f_1(x) = 3 - \dfrac{5}{3x-12}$

b) $f_2(x) = \dfrac{5+2x}{2x-1}$

c) $f_3(x) = \dfrac{5-6x}{2-3x}$

d) $f_4(x) = \dfrac{-x}{4(x+3)}$

14. To go on a field trip to an insectarium, students must pay their share of the $300 transportation cost, plus an $8 admission charge.

a) State the rule for determining the amount each student must pay based on the number of students taking part in the activity.

b) What are the equations of the asymptotes to the curve defined by this function rule?

c) The bus cannot hold more than 45 students and no student is prepared to pay more than $28 for the field trip. Find the points where the function reaches a minimum and maximum.

15. Vanessa decides to sell her old records at a flea market. The cost of renting a stall is $25 and she sells each record for $2. The function $f(x) = \dfrac{2x - 25}{x}$ is used to express the average profit per record based on the number of records sold.

a) Graph this function.

b) What is the equation of the horizontal asymptote?

c) Explain the role of this asymptote in this example.

d) What would be the value of parameter **k** in the function rule if Vanessa sold each record for $3?

16. A merchant wants to launch an advertising campaign that will target her best customers. She has a number of flyers produced at a fixed cost of $400, plus $4 per flyer. Apart from 20 flyers that will not be distributed, she hopes each flyer will be read by at least two people. The merchant wants to know on average how much she is spending per customer for this campaign based on the number of flyers printed.

a) If x is the number of flyers printed, what expression represents the total cost of production?

b) What expression represents the number of customers that, in the merchant's opinion, will read the flyer?

c) State the function rule for calculating the average cost per customer of a flyer. What is the function's domain in this context?

d) Express the function rule in the form $f(x) = \dfrac{a}{b(x - h)} + k$.

17. Atmospheric pressure drops as altitude increases. The function $f(x) = \dfrac{530}{x + 5}$ is used to obtain the approximate atmospheric pressure in kilopascals based on the altitude in kilometres.

a) What is the atmospheric pressure at sea level according to this approximation?

b) At what altitude is the atmospheric pressure reduced by half?

c) What are the equations of the asymptotes of this function's curve?

d) Based on this approximation, at what altitude is the atmospheric pressure equal to zero?

18. The graph of function g is obtained by reflecting the graph of the basic rational function across the x-axis, following the translation $t_{(2, -3)}$. State the function rule for g as a quotient of two first-degree polynomials.

19. Find the solution set for the following inequalities:

a) $\dfrac{2x-4}{x-3} > 0$

b) $\dfrac{x-4}{2x+1} < 0$

c) $\dfrac{-2}{2x+1} + 3 \geq 0$

d) $\dfrac{2}{2x-6} - 3 \leq 0$

20. Provide the inverse of each function below.

a) $f_1(x) = \dfrac{3}{x-2} + 4$

b) $f_2(x) = \dfrac{x-4}{x}$

c) $f_3(x) = \dfrac{x+4}{x-2}$

21. State the rule for the function graphed on the right, using the given data.

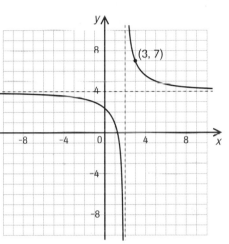

22. Functions f, g and h have the following rules:

$$f(x) = \dfrac{x-2}{x+3} \qquad g(x) = \dfrac{x-2}{2x+6} \qquad h(x) = \dfrac{x}{3x-6}$$

Find the rule for:

a) $f + g$

b) $\dfrac{f}{g}$

c) $g \cdot h$

d) $g - f$

e) $h \circ f$

23. Express the function $f(x) = \dfrac{x^2 - 4}{x^2 - 4x + 4}$ in the form $f(x) = \dfrac{a}{b(x-h)} + k$ and list its properties.

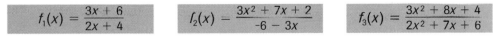

a) On the graph of the basic function $f(x) = \dfrac{1}{x}$, points $A(1, 1)$ and $B(-1, -1)$ are called the vertices of the hyperbola. For transformations, the hyperbola's vertices are images of the points A and B. Points $C(-1, 4)$ and $D(-5, 0)$ are the vertices of a hyperbola representing a function in the form $f(x) = \dfrac{a}{x-h} + k$.

   1) Are there one or more hyperbolas with vertices at points C and D?

   2) Find the equation(s).

b) The following three functions are very different, but do have one thing in common with respect to their domain and graph.

$$f_1(x) = \dfrac{3x+6}{2x+4} \qquad f_2(x) = \dfrac{3x^2 + 7x + 2}{-6 - 3x} \qquad f_3(x) = \dfrac{3x^2 + 8x + 4}{2x^2 + 7x + 6}$$

   1) Graph these functions.

   2) Find their common feature.

   3) State the rule for another function whose graph is a parabola, but possesses the same feature as the three previous functions.

Math Express 1

Functions represent a specific type of relation between two variables. They can be identified by the fact that each element of their domain has a single image. There are various types of functions in the domain of real numbers. The table below summarizes the main properties of the functions studied up to now.

Function	Rule	Graph	Number of zeros	Extremes	Is the inverse a function?
Constant	$f(x) = 1$ $f(x) = a$	Horizontal line	0 or an infinite number	Maximum $= a$ Minimum $= a$	No
Linear	$f(x) = x$ $f(x) = ax + b$	Oblique line	1	None	Yes
Quadratic	$f(x) = x^2$ $f(x) = a(b(x - h))^2 + k$ $f(x) = a(x - h)^2 + k$	Parabola	0, 1 or 2	Maximum or minimum: k	No
Absolute value	$f(x) = \lvert x \rvert$ $f(x) = a\lvert b(x - h) \rvert + k$ $f(x) = a\lvert x - h \rvert + k$	Angle	0, 1 or 2	Maximum or minimum: k	No
Square root	$f(x) = \sqrt{x}$ $f(x) = a\sqrt{b(x - h)} + k$ where $b = 1$ or $b = -1$ $f(x) = a\sqrt{x - h} + k$ $f(x) = a\sqrt{-(x - h)} + k$	Semi-parabola	0 or 1	Maximum or minimum: k	Yes
Greatest integer	$f(x) = [x]$ $f(x) = a[b(x - h)] + k$	Steps	0 or an infinite number	None	No
Rational (homographic)	$f(x) = \dfrac{1}{x}$ $f(x) = \dfrac{a}{b(x - h)} + k$ $f(x) = \dfrac{a}{x - h} + k$	Hyperbola	0 or 1	None	Yes

Only square root functions and rational functions do not have IR as their domain.

The study of these functions' signs is used to solve inequalities of each type from their graphs.

It is possible to create new functions by finding the composite of any two real functions or by performing different operations on each pair of functions.

All these functions are models for different kinds of scenarios, and the reason for studying them is to understand these scenarios better.

1 Which of the two fractions $\frac{3}{8}$ and $\frac{7}{13}$ is closest to $\frac{1}{2}$? Justify your answer.

2 How many decimal numbers are there between 1.23 and 1.24? Justify your answer.

3 How many irrational numbers are there between $\sqrt{2}$ and $\sqrt{3}$? Justify your answer.

4 Without calculating the exact answer, estimate the result of $\frac{12}{13} + \frac{7}{8}$.

5 Without calculating the exact answer, estimate the result of $72 \div 0.28$.

6 Which of the following sums is closest to 1?

$$\frac{5}{11} + \frac{3}{7} \qquad \frac{7}{15} + \frac{5}{12} \qquad \frac{1}{2} + \frac{4}{9} \qquad \frac{5}{9} + \frac{8}{15}$$

7 How many fractions are there between $\frac{2}{5}$ and $\frac{3}{5}$? Justify your answer.

8 Put the following numbers in increasing order: 0.595, 59%, $\sqrt{0.37}$ and $\frac{5}{8}$.

9 Give the sequence used to estimate the result of 72×0.46.

10 Calculate the value of the following expressions in your head:

a) $2|-4| + |5 - 3|$

b) $|-9| - |2.3|$

c) $|-0.25 \times 24.4| + |-\sqrt{0.16}|$

d) $|-0.125 \times 168|$

e) $|-4 \times -7| - \sqrt{225}$

f) $\sqrt{|6 \times 24|}$

g) $|-(452 \div 4)|$

h) $-2|20 \times 25| - |-600 \times 0.25|$

11 Solve the following equations in your head:

a) $|2x| = 25$

b) $|4x| = 680$

c) $|0.5x| = 4.2$

d) $|\sqrt{121}x| = 77$

e) $|x + 5| = 7$

f) $|x + 15| = 35$

g) $\left|x - \frac{1}{2}\right| = \frac{1}{4}$

h) $|2x + 0.4| = 7.6$

i) $4|0.75x| = 15.24$

j) $\left|\frac{3}{4}x\right| = 12$

12 Calculate the value of the following expressions in your head:

a) $[4\pi]$

b) $[\sqrt{120}]$

c) $[\sqrt{4.41}] + [\sqrt{5.76}]$

d) $\sqrt{[4.41] + [5.76]}$

13 Write an estimate of the following expressions by truncating after the first decimal place.

a) $5\sqrt{2}$ **b)** $\dfrac{\pi}{3}$ **c)** $\dfrac{6.3}{[2.5]}$ **d)** $\dfrac{[6.4]}{2.3}$

14 State which number is larger in each case.

a) $[\sqrt{\pi}]$ and $\sqrt{[\pi]}$ **b)** $[-\sqrt{7}]$ and $[-\pi]$

c) $\dfrac{1}{3+\sqrt{2}}$ and $\dfrac{1}{2+\sqrt{3}}$ **d)** $\dfrac{14}{\sqrt{15}}$ and $\dfrac{15}{\sqrt{14}}$

15 The graph below illustrates the speed of a cyclist in training.

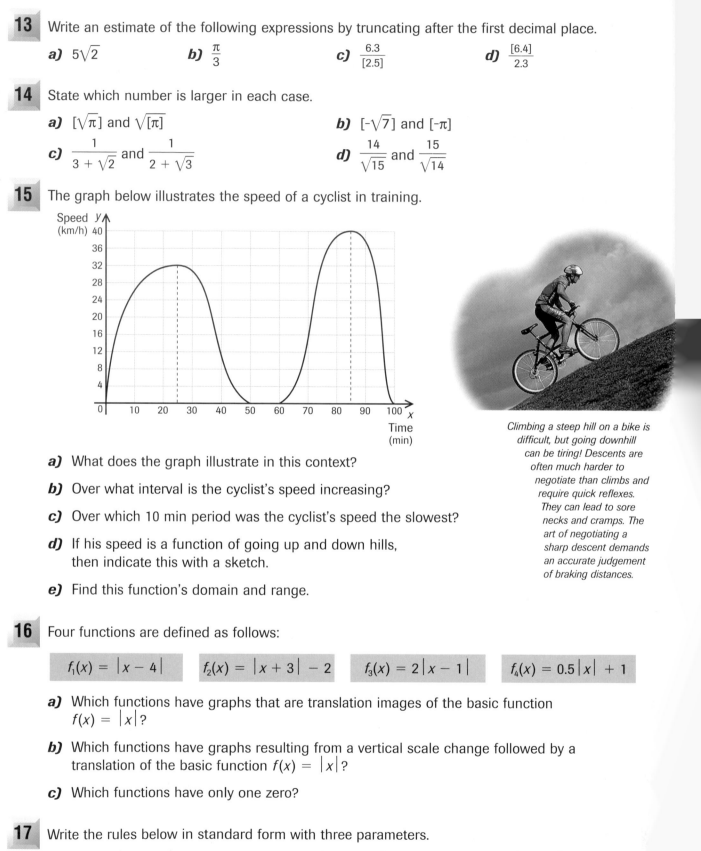

Climbing a steep hill on a bike is difficult, but going downhill can be tiring! Descents are often much harder to negotiate than climbs and require quick reflexes. They can lead to sore necks and cramps. The art of negotiating a sharp descent demands an accurate judgement of braking distances.

a) What does the graph illustrate in this context?

b) Over what interval is the cyclist's speed increasing?

c) Over which 10 min period was the cyclist's speed the slowest?

d) If his speed is a function of going up and down hills, then indicate this with a sketch.

e) Find this function's domain and range.

16 Four functions are defined as follows:

$f_1(x) = |x - 4|$ $f_2(x) = |x + 3| - 2$ $f_3(x) = 2|x - 1|$ $f_4(x) = 0.5|x| + 1$

a) Which functions have graphs that are translation images of the basic function $f(x) = |x|$?

b) Which functions have graphs resulting from a vertical scale change followed by a translation of the basic function $f(x) = |x|$?

c) Which functions have only one zero?

17 Write the rules below in standard form with three parameters.

a) $f(x) = |2x + 4| - 3$ **b)** $g(x) = 4|0.5x - 3| + 1$ **c)** $h(x) = -|2 - x| + 5$

18 Write the rule for the absolute value function whose curve has vertex A and passes through B.

a) $A(-4, 5)$ and $B(-1, 9)$ **b)** $A(2, -1)$ and $B(0, -4)$ **c)** $A(3, 0)$ and $B(-2, 4)$

19 The zeros of an absolute value function are -2 and 6, and the y-coordinate of the vertex is 4.

a) What is the function rule?

b) Find this function's domain and range.

c) Describe the variation of this function.

20 Which equations below have no solution?

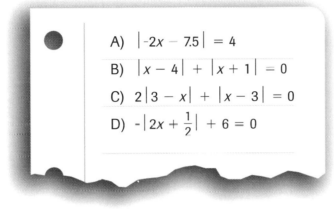

A) $\left| -2x - 7.5 \right| = 4$

B) $\left| x - 4 \right| + \left| x + 1 \right| = 0$

C) $2\left| 3 - x \right| + \left| x - 3 \right| = 0$

D) $-\left| 2x + \frac{1}{2} \right| + 6 = 0$

21 Solve the following equations in the set of real numbers algebraically.

a) $\left| 2x + 5 \right| = 10$ **b)** $4\left| 3 - 2x \right| - 7 = -3$

c) $\left| 5 - 4x \right| + 3\left| 5 - 4x \right| = 8$ **d)** $\left| x \right| = \left| -x \right|$

22 Solve the following equations using a calculator.

a) $2\left| 2x - \frac{6}{5} \right| + 6 = 11$ **b)** $\left| x^2 - 5x + 8 \right| = 2$

c) $\frac{2}{3}\left| 3x - 6 \right| - 4 = 2\left| x - 2 \right|$ **d)** $2\left| x - 1 \right|^2 + \left| x - 1 \right| = 3$

23 Examine the sign of the following functions:

a) $f(x) = \left| x + 3 \right| - 3$ **b)** $g(x) = -2\left| 3x + 12 \right| + 3$ **c)** $h(x) = \left| 0.5x \right| + 2.3$

24 Solve the following equations algebraically:

a) $\left| 3x - 8 \right| \leqslant 15$ **b)** $2\left| x - 5 \right| - 7 \geqslant -3$ **c)** $-4\left| x - 5 \right| < 11$

25 Solve the following inequalities in IR using a calculator:

a) $\left| 5 - 2x \right| \leqslant x + 3$ **b)** $\left| 2x - 4 \right| < 2\left| 1 - x \right|$

26 As part of a Physics assignment, students recorded the temperature outside their high school at 8:00 a.m. each day from October 1 to 20. They then established that the temperature, in degrees Celsius, varied according to the rule $T(x) = \frac{1}{2}|x - 7| - 3.5$ where x is the number of days since October 1.

In 1741 Swedish physicist Anders Celsius had a mercury thermometer built whose 0 corresponded to the freezing point of water and whose 100 corresponded to its boiling point.

In 1795 France defined a degree of temperature as "one one-hundredth of the distance between the freezing point and the boiling point of water"; hence the term degree centigrade, which became degree Celsius in 1948.

a) What was the temperature:

   1) On October 1?   2) On October 5?

b) What was the minimum temperature recorded during this period?

c) When were the recorded temperatures below freezing?

Mercury thermometers are popular because mercury boils at 674°C and solidifies at -38°C.

27 A stockbroker analyses the changes in a share's value over the past 12 months. The share's initial price was $16. After the fifth month, the share reached a minimum value of $3.50. The broker notices that the relation between the elapsed time, in months, and the value of the share, in dollars, is an absolute value function.

a) State the function rule.

b) What is the share worth now?

c) At what point does the value of the share return to its initial value?

d) What were the share's returns over this period?

28 An architect reproduces the model of a house's rafters on a Cartesian plane. The axes are scaled in metres and points C and D divide line segment OB into three congruent segments.

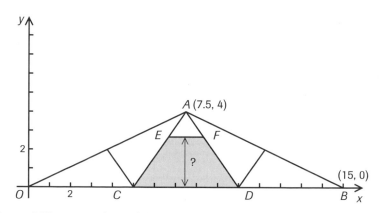

a) The roof is shaped like a section of the curve of an absolute value function. State the rule for this function.

b) Find all the properties of this function for this particular example.

c) If m $\overline{EF}$ = 2 m, what is the vertical clearance between beams EF and CD?

29 The functions *f* and *g* defined below are graphed on the right.

$$Y_1 = -1.5|x - 4| + 9 \qquad Y_2 = 0.5x - 1$$

Using algebra, find the solution set of:

a) $Y_1 = 0$ **b)** $Y_2 > 0$

c) $Y_1 = Y_2$ **d)** $Y_1 > Y_2$

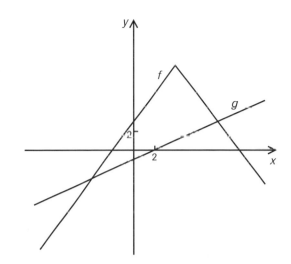

30 A maple syrup producer uses two identical pans to hold the maple sap needed to make his product. Today is Saturday and his daughter is helping him heat up the evaporator. The evaporation lasts 8 h. Every hour she records the level of the sap in the pans. On the right is a table of the data she gathered:

a) State the two function rules corresponding to the data and express the relation between the elapsed time and the level of the maple sap in the pans.

	Level of maple sap	
Time (h)	Pan 1 (dm)	Pan 2 (dm)
0	14	3
1	12	3.5
2	10	4
3	8	4.5
4	6	5
5	4	5.5
6	2	6
7	4	5.5
8	6	5

Traditional sugar shack at Rigaud

b) What is the range of each of these functions, given the restrictions of this case?

c) When was the level of the maple sap the same in both pans?

d) When was the level of the maple sap in the first pan higher than that in the second?

e) State the rule for the sum of these functions.

31 A function's graph is composed of two rays that have a common point P(a, b).

a) What property must the bisector of the angle formed by the two rays have for the graph to be that of an absolute value function?

b) What is this bisector's equation?

32 Sides AB and AC of triangle ABC located on the Cartesian plane correspond to the graph of the function $y = -\frac{5}{3}|x + 6| + 10$. Side BC is on the line $y = -5$. If the axes are scaled in centimetres, what is the area of triangle ABC?

33 Below are the rules for some square root functions. Find all the properties of these functions.

a) $y = \sqrt{-x + 3} - 1$

b) $y = -2\sqrt{16x - 48} + 2$

34 The coordinates of vertex S and a point P on the semi-parabola associated with a square root function are given below. State the function rule for each.

a) $S(-4, -3)$ and $P(5, 6)$

b) $S(6, 3)$ and $P(-10, -7)$

35 State the rule for the functions shown below.

a)

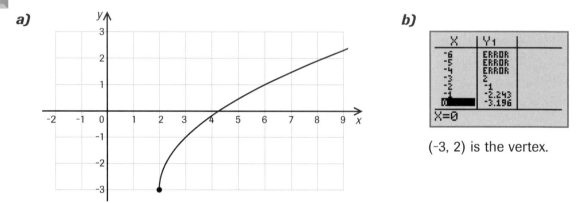

b)

(-3, 2) is the vertex.

36 Given functions f and g whose rules are $f(x) = 2\sqrt{x + 1} - 3$ and $g(x) = -\sqrt{4x + 4} - 3$:

a) What is the point of intersection of the graphs of the two functions?

b) Graph both functions.

c) Which transformation maps the graph of f onto the graph of g?

37 Solve the following equations using a calculator.

a) $\sqrt{x + 1} - 2 = -\frac{5}{3}\sqrt{x + 6} + 5$

b) $-2\sqrt{-(x - 8)} + 5 = 0.5x - 0.5$

c) $1.5|x - 4| - 4 = 2\sqrt{-(x - 8)} - 4$

d) $2\sqrt{x + 4} + 2 = 0.5(x - 4)^2 - 2$

38 State the restrictions and solve the following equations algebraically:

a) $\sqrt{x - 4} = 6$

b) $-3\sqrt{2x + 7} + 5 = 9$

c) $2\sqrt{3 - 2x} = 2 + x$

d) $\sqrt{-(x - 6)} + 2 = -x + 1$

39 Points (4, 2) and (8, 6) are, respectively, the vertex and a point on the semi-parabola represented by the quadratic function f whose domain is $[4, +\infty[$.

a) What is the rule for the inverse function f^{-1}?

b) What is the point of intersection of the curves associated with f and f^{-1}?

40 Solve the following equations using a graph:

a) $2\sqrt{x + 6} - 3 \geqslant 0$

b) $-2\sqrt{2x + 4} + 2 \geqslant 4 - 2x$

c) $\sqrt{x - 2} + 3 \geqslant -2\sqrt{-(x - 7)} + 5$

d) $x^2 - x - 12 \geqslant 1.5\sqrt{x + 5} - 4$

41 The weather forecast calls for freezing rain over the next 10 h. It has been raining for the past 5 h. Every hour a meteorologist records the thickness of ice formed by the freezing rain. The resulting data are presented in the table on the right. The meteorologist quickly realizes that the change in the ice's thickness can be approximated using a square root function.

Time (h)	Thickness (mm)
0	0
1	8
2	11
3	14
4	16
5	18

a) If the weather follows this rule for the next 10 h, how thick will the ice be?

b) Find all the properties of this function in the present context.

42 Jane has just started working for a life insurance company. She took a one-month training course to prepare for the job, and at the end of the fourth week, was paid $200 for having passed the course. Over the next 48 weeks, she collects premiums from her customers, and each week her salary varies approximately as a square root function. At right is the salary she earns in the first few weeks after taking the course.

Week	Salary ($)
4	200
5	240
6	255
7	270
8	280

a) How much will Jane earn in the 48th week?

b) When will Jane's weekly salary be more than $400?

43 A thin stream of water runs into a vase shaped like the one on the right. The water level is measured every few minutes. Given the shape of the vase, is it reasonable to assume that the relation between the elapsed time and the water level is that of a square root function? Justify your answer.

44 After travelling 500 m along the runway in 10 s, the pilot of a plane prepares for take-off using automatic pilot. Afterwards, the relation between the time since take off, in seconds, and the altitude, in metres, is established using the square root function $h(t) = 440\sqrt{t - 10}$.

Even the most basic automatic pilot feature will keep a plane on a steady course more accurately than a human being. Automatic piloting systems control the cruising speed, the speed of descent and the speed of the final approach to the runway.

a) How much time will it take the plane to reach an altitude of 10 225 m?

b) What is the rule for this function's inverse?

c) How long is the plane in the so-called "danger zone", created by the presence of birds at altitudes less than 1000 m?

45 When looking for the rule for a square root function, it is sometimes possible to find the parameters **a, h** and **k** using the function's graph or its table of values. Parameter **a** corresponds to the vertical scale change factor. Show that its value is:

$$a = f(h + 1) - f(h) \text{ if } b = 1$$

$$\text{and } a = f(h - 1) - f(h) \text{ if } b = -1$$

46 Function f is a basic greatest integer function, function g truncates to the nearest integer and function h rounds to the nearest integer. Use each of these functions and find the images of the following values:

a) $\sqrt{211}$

b) $-\dfrac{59}{17}$

c) $-345\,432\,167 \times 10^{-8}$

d) $504.35 - 0.354$

47 The rules for the three functions below were obtained by introducing parameters into the rule for the basic function $f(x) = [x]$:

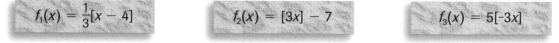

$$f_1(x) = \tfrac{1}{3}[x - 4] \qquad f_2(x) = [3x] - 7 \qquad f_3(x) = 5[-3x]$$

In each case find:

a) The composite of the geometric transformations involved in the graph.

b) The length of the segments forming the graph.

c) The distance between two consecutive segments in the graph.

48 Find the range of each of the following functions:

a) $f_1(x) = [3x] + 4$ **b)** $f_2(x) = 3[-x] - 4$ **c)** $f_3(x) = [x] - 4.5$

d) $f_4(x) =$ "x truncated to the nearest tenth"   **e)** $f_5(x) =$ "x rounded to the nearest hundred"

49 Find the length of the segments that make up the graph of the following functions:

a) $f_1(x) = [5x]$ **b)** $f_2(x) = -\left[\dfrac{x}{3}\right] + 3$ **c)** $f_3(x) = 3\left[\dfrac{x}{3}\right] + \dfrac{4}{3}$

d) $f_4(x) = $ "x truncated to the nearest integer"

e) $f_5(x) - $ "x rounded to the nearest integer"

50 Xiang's hourly wage is $12. He is paid for each complete quarter of an hour that he works.

a) What is the function rule that represents Xiang's salary based on the time, in hours, that he works.

b) Graph this function.

51 The composites of two basic functions are used to obtain the functions $h(x) = [\sqrt{x}]$ and $i(x) = -\sqrt{[x]}$.

a) Describe each composite using the basic functions.

b) Graph the composites.

c) Do both functions have the same domain?

d) Do both functions have the same range?

52 Contestants are penalized for arriving too early or too late at any of the checkpoints in a car rally. A car arriving early within the interval $]-5, -3]$ (in minutes) loses 2 points, and loses 1 point for arriving within the interval $[-3, -1[$. A car arriving late loses 1 point within the interval $[1, 3[$, 2 points within the interval $[3, 5[$, and so on.

a) How much time does a team have to make it to a checkpoint without being penalized?

b) The checkpoint official scores a -4 in Doris and Charlie's logbook. How many minutes were they early or late?

c) Write the rule in two parts for the function associating the number of penalty points with an early arrival time and a late arrival time.

53 Catriona has a digital stopwatch that records minutes and seconds. The numbers change at the end of each time interval.

a) If the actual time is 34.368 s, what does the stopwatch show?

b) What type of function is this: truncation, rounding or greatest integer?

c) According to Catriona's stopwatch, two speed skaters recorded a time of 5 min 20 s. If they finished the race at 50 km/h, what distance could have separated them at the finish line?

In 1736 an English clockmaker named John Harrison built the first marine chronometer out of wood. Modern chronometers are precision watches which can measure hundredths of a second.

54 Given the function $g(x) = [2x - 4]$, find the point or points where its curve intersects the curve of each of the following functions:

a) $f_1(x) = 3$ **b)** $f_2(x) = -2x$ **c)** $f_3(x) = 2x - 5$ **d)** $f_4(x) = 2\sqrt{x} - 2$

55 Function f is a basic greatest integer function and function g rounds every real number to the nearest integer.

a) Graph both functions on the same axes using two different colours.

b) What transformation maps the graph of g onto the graph of f?

c) Define g as a function of f.

56 Certain bank machines only allow customers to withdraw $20 bills.

a) What is the function rule for determining the number of $20 bills that can be withdrawn from the bank machine based on the amount of money in a person's account?

b) Mary is given a credit line of $500, meaning that she can withdraw money if her account balance is negative but is greater than -$500. What is the function rule for determining the number of $20 bills that Mary can withdraw based on her account balance?

57 Explain the difference between the graphs of the following functions:

a) $f(x) = 2\left[\dfrac{x}{3}\right]$ and $g(x) = 3\left[\dfrac{x}{2}\right]$ **b)** $f(x) = -[x]$ and $g(x) = [-x]$

c) $f(x) = [x]$ and $g(x) = -[-x]$

58 State whether or not the given function is a transformation image of the basic rational function.

a) $f_1(x) = \dfrac{1}{x} + x$ **b)** $f_2(x) = \dfrac{x + 1}{x - 1}$

c) $f_3(x) = \dfrac{-41}{2x - 1} + 5$ **d)** $f_4(x) = \dfrac{5x}{\pi - 3}$

59 State the function rule in the form $f(x) = \dfrac{a}{b(x - h)} + k$, if possible.

a) $f_1(x) = \dfrac{3x - 1}{x - 1}$ **b)** $f_2(x) = \dfrac{3x^2 - 4x + 1}{x - 1}$

c) $f_3(x) = \dfrac{4x - 5}{2x - 7} - 2$ **d)** $f_4(x) = \dfrac{3}{2x + 8} - \dfrac{2x + 3}{2(x + 4)}$

e) $f_5(x) = \dfrac{3x + 2}{2 - 4x} - \dfrac{2x - 3}{2(2x - 1)}$ **f)** $f_6(x) = \dfrac{x - 2}{x^2 - 4} + \dfrac{1}{2x + 4}$

60 Which of the functions below has a graph whose horizontal asymptote is closest to the x-axis? Justify your answer.

$$f(x) = \dfrac{4x + 2}{5x + 15}$$

$$g(x) = \dfrac{4}{x + 3} + 0.9$$

61 Michelle is playing basketball. She scores on 60% of her free throws. Indeed, out of 40 free throws, she has made a total of 24 baskets. The function $f(x) = \dfrac{24 + x}{40 + x}$ represents her average if she makes x baskets in a row starting now.

a) What type of function is this?

b) Graph the function.

c) How many consecutive free throws must she make to have an average of 75%?

d) What does the horizontal asymptote stand for in this situation?

62 A company pays its president an annual salary of $250 000, and each of its other x employees, $35 000.

a) State the function rule that represents the company's average salary, including the president's.

b) What happens to the function rule if the president decreases his salary by $25 000 and hires two more people at the same salary as the other employees?

c) In these examples, does the average indicate a general trend that accurately reflects the way salaries are distributed within the company?

63 A rational function f has its rule in the form $f(x) - \dfrac{a}{b(x - h)} + k$.

a) The graph of this function has a point of symmetry and two axes of symmetry. What are they?

b) Do the axes of symmetry remain the same if the sign of **a** changes in the original rule?

Leonhard Euler (1750) was the first to introduce the notation $f(x)$ to mean "function of x."

64 A merchant calculates that he must set the price of an item at $125 if he wants to get $100 by selling it at a 20% discount.

a) If the discount were 25%, at what price would the merchant have to sell the item to get $100?

b) Find the function rule for setting the sale price of the item if the merchant wants to get $100 for the item after selling it at a discount of $n\%$.

c) Is this function increasing or decreasing?

d) What does the vertical asymptote stand for in this case?

65 State the rule for a rational function whose graph is congruent (isometric) to the graph of the function $f(x) = \dfrac{2}{3x}$, and whose asymptotes are $x = 10$ et $y = -9$.

66 Students who are part of a Young Achievers Club calculate that they need an initial investment of $200 to finance their project. The cost of producing one of their "widgets" is $4 and they expect to sell them at $10 each.

a) How many "widgets" will they have to sell to make a profit?

b) State the function rule associating the profit on each item with the total number of "widgets" sold.

67 The manager of a real estate company studies the plans for a new shopping mall. In order for the mall to be viable, the average monthly rent for space must be $75 per square metre. Two very large retailers have each decided to rent spaces of 10 000 m² at $20 per square metre. Smaller stores will be expected to pay a monthly rent of $100 per square metre.

Suburban shopping mall.

a) State the function rule for expressing the average monthly rent per square metre for all the stores in the mall, based on the number of square metres reserved for the smaller stores.

b) How much space should be reserved for the smaller stores for the mall to be a profitable venture?

68 Using the concept of the greatest integer (less than or equal to), define the rule for the function that:

a) Truncates to the nearest integer.

b) Truncates to the nearest hundred.

c) Rounds to the nearest integer.

d) Rounds to the nearest tenth.

69 A rational function f is defined as $f(x) = \dfrac{4x - 6}{3x + 4}$.

For a long time the symbol $f(x)$ was used to designate the function itself; in the past 20 years, however, it has become common practice use a single letter, such a or g, to designate the function, and use the expression $f(x)$ to designate the function's images.

a) State the rule for the inverse of f.

b) What type of relation is the inverse?

c) What are the equations for the asymptotes to the curve of f^{-1}?

70 Given the rational functions defined as follows:

$$f_1(x) = \frac{3x - 1}{4x + 6} \qquad\qquad f_2(x) = \frac{7x - 5}{2x + 3}$$

Graph $f_1 + f_2$ after determining the function rule.

71 Given the rational functions whose rules are $f_1(x) = \dfrac{3x + 6}{4x - 12}$ and $f_2(x) = \dfrac{5x - 15}{4x + 8}$:

Find the domain, range and zeros of $f_1 \bullet f_2$.

72 The rules $f(x) = \dfrac{1}{\sqrt{x}}$ and $g(x) = \dfrac{\sqrt{x}}{x}$ define the same function. Justify this statement algebraically.

73 If the function f is the basic square root function, what is the function rule for $f \circ f$? Justify your answer using the properties of exponents.

74 Find the rules for two square root functions whose product has $h(x) = 6\sqrt{x^2 + 2x}$ as its rule.

75 The quotient of two square root functions has $j(x) = \sqrt{x - 1}$ as its rule. If one of the square root functions is $g(x) = \sqrt{x + 1}$, find the rule for the other.

76 An air show organizer wants two planes to fly towards each other while tracing the curve of the function $y = \dfrac{1600}{x - 20} + 1000$ where x and y are expressed in metres.

How close to each other will the planes fly?

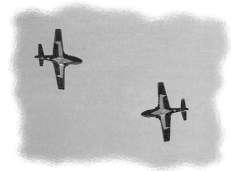

Snowbirds Air Show. The Snowbirds are the acrobatic airborne squadron of the Canadian Armed Forces.

77 If $f(x) = |x + 4|$ and $g(x) = |x - 2|$ define the functions f and g, determine, if possible, the minimums and the intervals over which the following increase:

a) $f + g$ **b)** $f - g$ **c)** $f \cdot g$ **d)** $\dfrac{f}{g}$

78 Carmen wants to take out a temporary life insurance policy. She contacts four companies which provide her with different ways of calculating the annual premium based on the client's age x. The offers are shown in the table at right.

Company	Rule
A	$p_1 = 17.70\sqrt{x}$
B	$p_2 = \dfrac{120x + 350}{x + 10}$
C	$p_3 = 9.10\left[\dfrac{x}{3}\right] + 4.50$
D	$p_4 = 3.50\,|x - 5| + 4.10$

Which company offers the lowest premium if Carmen is 32, and wants to take out an insurance policy for the next 3 years?

79 The table of values of six different types of functions involving real variables are provided below. Using the rate of change and a sketch of the graph, identify each type of function and find its rule.

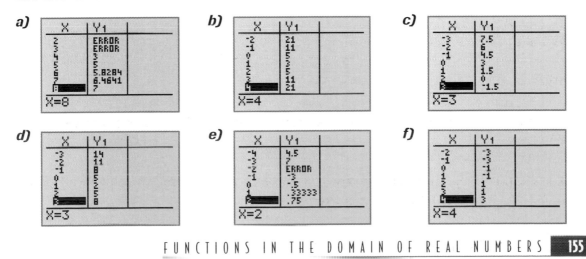

80 PRICE CODE

An electrician must submit a tender for the installation of electrical wiring in various types of factory-built homes. It takes him a ridiculous amount of time to make the necessary calculations. He records the floor area in square metres and the cost of the electrical installations for each type of home. The table of values at right shows some of the data he compiled. There are no homes with a floor area of less than 100 m².

a) Explain why the relation between the area and the cost might be a square root function.

b) Find the rule for a square root function that approximates this data.

c) What is the area of a home whose wiring costs $3255 to install?

d) What floor area gives a cost of at least $2500 for wiring?

e) If there is no house that has an area greater than 400 m², what is the maximum value of this function?

Area of the house (m²)	Installation cost ($)
100	2000
120	2670
140	2950
160	3160
180	3340
200	3500

81 ENGINE TEST

An auto technician tests the performance of a new car's engine. She initially programs the onboard computer so that the speed of the car increases by 12.5 km/h every second. After reaching a speed of 100 km/h, the car slows down at the same rate.

a) Graph the relation between the time, in seconds, and the speed of the car.

b) How long was the car in motion?

c) State the function rule that associates the time with the speed, and find all the properties of the mathematical model for this situation.

d) What distance did the car travel during the test?

Formula 1 car engine.

Automobile manufacturers use the data from tests run on racecar engines to improve the quality of the cars they produce.

82 HIGH-SEA BLACKOUT

A cruise ship has a power failure out at sea, which forces the passengers to extend their holiday by an extra 10 days. A civil suit is launched against the cruise ship company, which agrees to cover part of the lost wages that resulted from passengers missing work. The insurance company sets a maximum payout of $1000 per person. However, not all the passengers will automatically receive this amount. Those under the age of 20 will not be compensated. The amount of damages paid to those over 20 will be determined by the passenger's age (retired people over 60 will receive no money). Those passengers aged 20 will each receive $500. The vertical scale change factor will be 80.

a) Find the function rule used to calculate the amount to be paid out.

b) How much will a person over 50 receive?

c) How old are the passengers who will receive more than $800?

83 AERIAL PHOTOS

A small company specializes in aerial photography. During the summer its two employees fly over different cities and take aerial photos of certain properties. During the winter they contact the owners and offer to sell them the pictures of their land. Clearly, the higher the plane flies, the smaller the objects in the photo appear.

Using a 35 mm camera, they photograph a round lake, whose diameter is 1 km, from several altitudes. They then measure the lake's diameter as it appears in the photographs (5 cm by 8 cm format). The graph on the right represents these data.

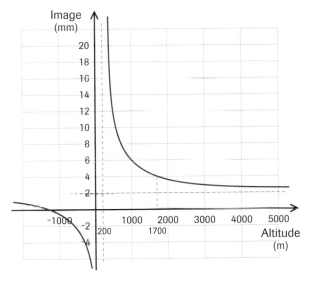

a) Find the rule for the function shown.

b) The diameter of the lake is 30 mm in one of the photos. At what altitude was the photo taken?

c) What would be the lake's diameter on a 15 cm by 24 cm photo?

1. Given the functions *f, g* and *h* defined as follows:

$$f(x) = x - 1 \qquad g(x) = 2x^2 + x - 3 \qquad h(x) = \sqrt{2x + 3} \qquad k(x) = \frac{x^2 - 1}{x + 3}$$

State the function rule that corresponds to:

a) $f + g$ **b)** $\dfrac{g}{f}$ **c)** $\dfrac{k}{f}$ **d)** $h - f$ **e)** $h \cdot h$

2. THE HERD

Over the past 30 years, biologists have noticed that the population of white-tailed deer in a hunting ground varies according to the function *P* defined as $P(t) = 18|t - 18| + 300$ where $P(t)$ represents the deer population and *t*, the number of years since the study began.

a) Graph the function used as the model for this situation.

b) State the domain and range of function *P* in this situation.

c) Examine the variation of function *P* in this context.

d) How long has the deer population been on the rise?

3. CREDIT LINE

A company has a $500 000 credit line that it uses when its account is overdrawn. The financial institution it deals with produces a transaction statement at the end of each week. Over the past year the company's weekly account balance has varied according to an absolute value function whose graph is shown on the right.

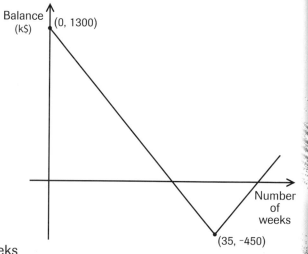

a) State the function rule that serves as a model for this scenario.

b) Examine the sign of this function.

c) Use algebra to find the number of weeks during which the company used its credit line.

d) State and solve the inequality used to determine the time after which the company's balance was less than $100 000.

4. FURNACE BREAKDOWN

Following a furnace breakdown, the temperature inside a house varies according to the rule $T(h) = -2\sqrt{h} + 20$ where $T(h)$ is the temperature in degrees Celsius and h, the number of hours since the start of the breakdown, which lasted four full days. Answer the following questions restricting the function T to the context of the question.

a) Graph function T.

b) What is the range of T?

c) State the rule for the inverse of T.

d) How long would the breakdown have to last for the temperature inside the house to reach the freezing point?

5. GOOD TRACK RECORD AN ASSET

A sales representative uses her car to visit her company's customers. At the end of each year, she records the number of kilometres travelled from the car's odometer. The table of values on the right contains some of these data rounded to the nearest thousand. She notices that the number of kilometres varies over the years according to a square root function. The vertex of the semi-parabola associated with this function has the coordinates (1, 25).

Number of years	Number of km × 1000
1	25
5	155
8	197
10	220

a) State the function rule that represents this scenario.

b) Find the function's range if the domain is restricted to [1, 10].

c) State the rule for the function's inverse.

d) Given that the number of kilometres always varies according to the same function, determine algebraically the number of years it will take for the odometer to reach at least 250 000 km.

6. CREDIT CARD PROMOTION

A retail store wants to promote its credit card and offers bonus points on purchases made with the card. Every $25 charged to the credit card earns two bonus points. The function rule for determining the total number of bonus points at the time of purchase is $f(x) = 2\left\lfloor \dfrac{x}{25} \right\rfloor$.

a) How many bonus points are awarded for a $146.75 purchase?

b) Describe the transformations that must be applied to the graph of the basic function $g(x) = \lfloor x \rfloor$ to produce the graph of the function f.

c) What is the range of the function f used as the model for this scenario?

d) Is it more profitable for customers to pay for all their purchases at once with their credit card, or to pay for each purchase separately? Justify your answer with an example.

7. TICKET SALES

Students in the school band purchase tickets for a raffle whose grand prize is a music course to be held over the summer. The students have the following amounts to spend: $1.75, $3.17, $2.25, $5.00, $6.45, $3.54, $4.00, $4.92, $8.25, $7.15 and $10.00. Each ticket costs $1.50.

a) State the rule for calculating the number of tickets each student can buy.

b) Graph the function used as the model for this scenario.

c) Find the maximum and the minimum of the function in this scenario.

d) How many tickets will the students be able to buy if they pool their money?

8. BUTTON SALE

The average profit p generated by a button sale varies according to the rule $p(x) = \dfrac{2x - 100}{x + 20}$ where x is the number of buttons sold.

a) What are the equations of the asymptotes of the function that is the mathematical model for this scenario?

b) Graph the function that is the mathematical model for this scenario.

c) Find the domain and range of function p in this example.

d) What minimum number of buttons must be sold to turn a profit?

9. EXCAVATION WORK

A construction company charges $75/h for excavation work plus $100 for transportation.

a) State the rule for calculating the average hourly rate of excavation work that lasts x hours.

b) How long must the work take so that the average hourly rate is less than $85?

c) The average hourly rate for one customer is $80. Determine algebraically the number of hours of excavation work required.

d) Can the average hourly rate be $75?

10. Given the functions defined as follows:

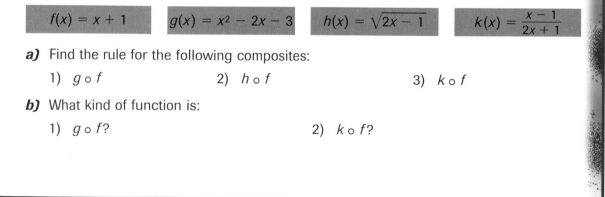

| $f(x) = x + 1$ | $g(x) = x^2 - 2x - 3$ | $h(x) = \sqrt{2x - 1}$ | $k(x) = \dfrac{x - 1}{2x + 1}$ |

a) Find the rule for the following composites:

    1) $g \circ f$ 2) $h \circ f$ 3) $k \circ f$

b) What kind of function is:

    1) $g \circ f$?   2) $k \circ f$?

Interview with...

Gottfried Wilhelm von Leibniz
(1646-1716)

Mr. von Leibniz, I was wondering if you could tell us what you thought about mathematics when you were 20?

At the time I considered mathematics to be an enjoyable hobby. I was more interested in politics, philosophy, theology, law and the invention of machines.

Yet you became the most well-known German mathematician of the 17th century! How did that happen?

When I was 26, I met the mathematician Huygens. This was a turning point in my life. He could identify my strengths and weaknesses in this field. He told me what material to read and advised me to pursue my mathematical studies. The following year one of Pascal's works led me to discover differential and integral calculus.

Tell us a little about the controversy that erupted between you and Newton over differential and integral calculus.

This controversy greatly affected my twilight years. I had published a summary of my work on the subject in 1684 and Newton published his in 1687. The controversy only really started in 1699. That year a Swiss mathematician declared Newton to be the inventor of differential and integral calculus. In his opinion, I had simply plagiarized Newton's work! This controversy created a rift in the mathematical community: the English rallied behind Newton, while the rest of Europe defended me.

you think this controversy affected the progress of mathematics in the following century?

Indubitably! For about a century, exchanges between mathematicians in rival factions ground to a halt. At that point the English mathematicians, being quite a conservative lot, suffered a setback. They were unable to benefit from the progress and enhancements that other mathematicians on the Continent brought to my work.

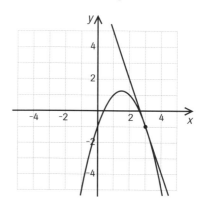

You were the first mathematician to coin the term "function." When did that happen?

The date was August 1673. I coined the term in a manuscript that dealt with derivatives and functions, while I was explaining the relations between coordinates.

One last question, Mr. von Leibniz. Why go to all the trouble of inventing a calculating machine in 1671 when Pascal had already done it in 1642?

My calculating machine was based on a new concept and differed from Pascal's in that it could perform the four basic arithmetical functions mechanically. My invention aimed to help astronomers avoid doing long calculations. I presented my prototype to the members of the Royal Society in 1673, and they found it superior to Pascal's invention.

In addition to his work in mathematics, Gottfried Wilhelm von Leibniz dedicated his life to pursuing a wide range of activities. He was not only one of the greatest philosophers of his time, but was also a linguist, a logician, a pioneer in geology, etc. He started a scientific journal and was one of the founding members of the Academy of Sciences in Berlin. His discovery of differential and integral calculus surprised even the most skillful mathematicians of his day.

Leibniz worked on numerous problems throughout his life.

a) Among other things, he came up with a number of different ways to divide a triangle into four parts of equal area with a minimum number of lines. Find one way of doing this.

He invented differential and integral calculus. One of its basic concepts is the derivative. A function's derivative provides the rule for calculating the slope of a tangent to a curve at a given point. The derivative f with respect to x is written as $\frac{d(f(x))}{d(x)}$.

b) Given the function f defined by $f(x) = -x^2 + 3x - 1$:

Find the slope of the tangent at $(3, -1)$

by replacing x with 3 in $\frac{d(f(x))}{d(x)} = -2x + 3$.

c) Two polynomial functions and their derivatives are given. Find the derivative of the third polynomial function.

1) If $f(x) = 4x^2$, then $\frac{d(f(x))}{d(x)} = 8x$.

2) If $g(x) = 4x^2 + 3x + 1$, then $\frac{d(f(x))}{d(x)} = 8x + 3$.

3) If $h(x) = 2x^3 + 5x^2 + 3x - 4$, then $\frac{d(f(x))}{d(x)} = $ ■■■.

MY PROJECTS

PROJECT 1 Movement

The goal of this project is to reproduce, as much as possible, the movement(s) that would cause a motion detector to generate the graphs below. In each case, one or more students standing in front of the motion detector must move in such a way as to produce the given graphs. Write a full report of the experiment, describing the movements in each case.

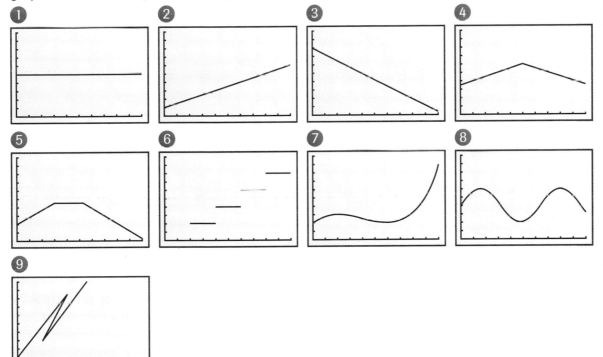

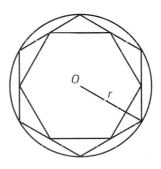

PROJECT 2 Nothing but hexagons!

A regular hexagon has been drawn inside a circle whose radius is r. Using the midpoints of this hexagon as vertices, a second regular hexagon has been drawn. We can continue using this method to create other hexagons.

a) Complete the second line of the table of values below by finding the area of each hexagon as a function of r.

b) Complete the third line of the table by comparing the area of each hexagon to the area of the first.

c) Use the same method with an equilateral triangle, a square or other regular polygons.

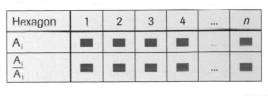

Hexagon	1	2	3	4	...	n
A_i	■	■	■	■	...	■
$\dfrac{A_i}{A_1}$	■	■	■	■	...	■

I KNOW THE MEANING OF THE FOLLOWING EXPRESSIONS:

Absolute value: Real number written as $|x|$ and equivalent to x if $x \geq 0$ and to $-x$ if $x < 0$.

Basic function: A function that is the simplest of its type and from which other functions are generated by introducing parameters into its rule.

Change of a function: Increasing and decreasing intervals of a function.

Composition of functions: Operation where one function follows another.

Domain: Set of values belonging to the source set that have at least one image.

Extreme: Largest or smallest number in the range of a relation.

Function: Relation between two variables in which one and only one image is assigned to each element of the domain.

Greatest integer: Greatest integer less than or equal to x written as $[x]$.

Image: Value of the target set associated with a value in a source set.

Inverse of a function: Relation obtained by reversing the variables.

Maximum: Largest number in the range.

Minimum: Smallest number in the range.

Range: The values belonging to the target set that are the image of at least one value of the source set.

Relation: Association between the elements of a source set and the elements of a target set.

Rounded number: Number obtained when the original number is replaced by the number with the required number of digits that is closest to it.

Sign of a function: Sign of the y-coordinates of a function's ordered pairs.

Square root: Real number written as $\sqrt{x}$ or $-\sqrt{x}$ such that its square is x.

Transformed function: Function obtained by introducing one or more parameters into the rule for a basic function.

Truncating: Operation whereby the digits after a specified position are replaced with zeros, and unnecessary zeros are ignored.

Zero: Value of the domain associated with a range value of 0.

Reflection 2

OPTIMIZATION .....

THE MAIN IDEAS

- ▶ First-degree inequalities in two variables
- ▶ Systems of linear inequalities
- ▶ Polygon of constraints
- ▶ The function rule
- ▶ Interpretation and decision making

TERMINAL OBJECTIVE

- ▶ To solve problems using systems of inequalities.

INTERMEDIATE OBJECTIVES

- ▶ **To represent** a situation by an inequality in one or two real variables.
- ▶ **To graph** first-degree inequalities in two real variables.
- ▶ **To graph** the solution set of a system of first-degree inequalities in two real variables.
- ▶ **To represent** the function to be optimized algebraically.
- ▶ **To determine** which possibility offers the best solution or solutions in a given situation.
- ▶ **To justify** the choice of values that optimize the function rule.
- ▶ **To find the optimum solution** in a given situation, considering the various constraints.

SYSTEMS OF FIRST-DEGREE INEQUALITIES

REPRESENTING INEQUALITIES
GRAPHING
SYSTEMS OF EQUATIONS
SYSTEMS OF INEQUALITIES
POLYGON OF CONSTRAINTS

REPRESENTING INEQUALITIES

Evacuation plan

Flooding occurs when snow melts too rapidly or pack ice jams a river. A small municipality situated on an island established an evacuation plan in case of flooding. It will use a helicopter that can hold 5 passengers and a boat that can hold 12 people. It expects it will have to evacuate no more than 100 people during this operation. To cut down on costs, the helicopter and the boat will have to be filled to capacity.

Flooding at La Baie, in the Saguenay region, July 1996.

a) If *x* represents the number of trips made by the helicopter, and *y* the number of trips made by the boat, give the expression that represents the number of people that can be evacuated.

b) Give the inequality that can be stated using this expression.

The Canadian army conducted numerous rescue and supply operations when floods hit the Saguenay region in 1996.

To **represent a situation** by an **inequality**:

1. **Identify one or more variables** in the example.

2. Find the algebraic expressions that must be compared.

3. **Write the inequality** with the proper inequality symbol.

Once the inequality is stated, it is a good idea to use numerical values to check that it represents the information accurately.

c) For the situation described, is it possible to make:

1) 4 helicopter trips and 3 boat trips?

2) 8 helicopter trips and 5 boat trips?

3) 5 helicopter trips and 8 boat trips?

A solution for an inequality in **two variables,** *x* and *y*, consists of the value of *x* and the value of *y* that satisfy this inequality and is represented by an **ordered pair.** The solution set contains all the **pairs (*x*, *y*) that satisfy this inequality.**

d) Many expressions are used to describe inequalities between two variables *x* and *y*. Represent each of the following expressions algebraically using an inequality symbol.

1) *x* is less than or equal to *y*.

2) *x* is greater than *y*.

3) *x* is smaller than *y*.

4) *x* is greater than or equal to *y*.

5) *x* is not greater than *y*.

6) *x* is at least equal to *y*.

7) *x* is at least *y*.

8) *x* is less than *y*.

9) *x* is at most *y*.

10) *x* is not less than *y*.

11) *x* is at least equal to *y*.

12) *x* is at most equal to *y*.

> Expressions representing inequalities were found in the writings of Eudoxus (c. 408-355 BC)

e) For each of the preceding cases, find two ordered pairs that satisfy it.

INVESTMENT 1

1. Express the following inequalities in words.

   a) $-9 < 5$

   b) $x \geqslant 33$

   c) $3 < \pi \leqslant 3.5$

   d) $-9.25 \leqslant x < 0$

   e) $a < b < c$

   f) $0 \leqslant x \leqslant 0$

2. Jeremy loves music, especially rock music. His compact disc collection consists of at least 5 times as many rock CDs as jazz CDs.

   a) Find the number of variables contained in this situation.

   b) Does Jeremy own more rock CDs or jazz CDs?

   c) State the inequality that describes this situation.

   d) Check the inequality for accuracy by replacing the variables with appropriate numerical values.

Dizzy Gillespie

Jazz was invented in the United States by black musicians towards the end of the 19th century. It has had a great influence on contemporary music in the West.

3. Represent the following information by linear inequalities.

a) The maximum temperature *t* recorded yesterday was 29.3°C.

b) Andrea's age *a* is no more than twice Diana's age *d*.

c) Fabian's Chemistry test score *c* is at least 15 marks lower than his Math test score *m*.

d) The sale of tickets for a show brought in over $1250. A child's ticket costs $4 and an adult's, $7. Let *c* represent the number of tickets for children and *a* the number of tickets for adults.

4. The cost of using a cellular phone varies according to the time of day. One company offers the following rates: 50¢/min during peak hours and 10¢/min at any other time. Consider a bill that is greater than $80.

a) Let *x* represent the duration, in minutes, of the calls made during peak hours and *y* the calls made any other time. Represent this situation by an inequality in two variables.

b) Give three ordered pairs that belong to the solution set.

The cellular phone is "cellular" because it operates within a zone of the telephone network. A region is divided into smaller units, or cells, each equipped with a radio transmitter that has a range of 13 to 19 km.

5. A school bus is carrying both students *s* and monitors *m*. Translate the following information into algebra:

a) There are at least 40 people on the bus.

b) There are at least 5 times more students than monitors.

c) There are no more than 55 people on the bus.

6. An accountant calculates that a company needs to pay less than 35% of its income in salaries to remain competitive.

a) If *i* represents the company's income, what expression corresponds to 35% of this income?

b) If *s* represents the total amount of salaries paid by the company, translate the statement made by the accountant into an inequality in two variables.

7. In a car show, 10% of the cars are sports cars and 18% are sedans. There are over 60 vehicles in these two categories.

a) Using *n* as the number of cars, determine the total number of cars at the auto show.

b) If *x* is the number of sports cars and *y* the number of sedans, state an inequality using the information given.

THINK TANK

a) Explain the ambiguity of the following expression that we often hear in TV and radio ads: "Take advantage of our super sale! All merchandise reduced by up to 50% or more!"

b) Using only the number 2 and variables x and y, write an inequality that would have the following pairs in its solution set.

1) (1, 2), (2, 5), (5, 8), (10, 20)

2) (5, 10), (5, 11), (10, 20), (10, 21)

3) (0, 2), (2, 4), (5, 7), (5, 10)

4) (-9, -4), (0.1, 0), (17, 8), (100, 20)

GRAPHING

A dense forest

Forestry technician measuring the diameter of a tree.

Forestry engineers sometimes classify forests by density. A forest is "dense" when it has over 1000 trees per hectare. To classify a forest in northern Abitibi, we need to know the number of coniferous trees x and deciduous trees y per hectare.

a) What condition must be met for this forest in Abitibi to be classified as "dense"?

This condition is stated by the inequality $x + y > 1000$.

b) Write the inequality in the form $y > ax + b$ and give at least five ordered pairs that satisfy this inequality.

The equation $y = -x + 1000$ is shown here by a dotted line in the first quadrant of a Cartesian plane. It divides the quadrant into three regions: the points on the dotted line, the points above the dotted line and the points below the dotted line.

c) Which of the points A, B, C, D, E or F have coordinates that are solutions of the inequality $y > -x + 1000$?

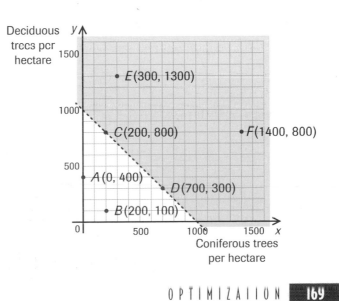

Deciduous trees per hectare y

Coniferous trees per hectare x

This situation refers to the mathematical model shown below.

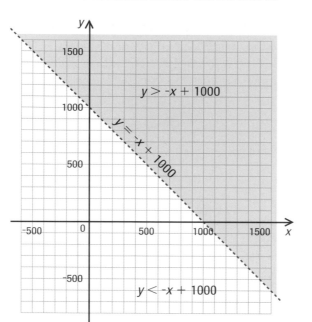

$y > \text{-}x + 1000$

$y = \text{-}x + 1000$

$y < \text{-}x + 1000$

The larch is a special type of coniferous tree. Unlike other conifers, it sheds its leaves (needles) when winter approaches.

d) Is it true that:

1) All the points on the line have coordinates that satisfy the equation $y = \text{-}x + 1000$?

2) All the points above the line have coordinates that satisfy the inequality $y > \text{-}x + 1000$?

3) All the points below the line have coordinates that satisfy the inequality $y < \text{-}x + 1000$?

All the points whose coordinates satisfy an inequality are on the same side of the line as the equation that comes from the inequality. These points form a **half-plane** and show the **solution set** of the inequality.

The boundary of the half-plane is a solid straight line when the "equal to" symbol is part of the inequality ($\leq$ or $\geq$). It is a dotted straight line when "equal to" is not included ($<$ or $>$). We usually shade the half-plane.

A half-plane is **closed** when its boundary is a solid line and **open** when the boundary is a dotted line.

Fleet of airplanes

A fleet of airplanes owned by React-Air is made up of twin- and three-engine aircraft that can carry, respectively, 40 and 80 passengers. On a certain holiday, all the company's flights were sold out. That day at least 4800 people flew with React-Air. We are interested in the number of flights made by each type of aircraft owned by the company.

Mirabel Airport, northeast of Montréal.

a) If *x* represents the number of flights made by the twin-engine aircraft and *y* the number of flights made by the three-engine aircraft, represent the situation as a linear inequality.

b) Using the rules for transforming inequalities, rewrite this inequality in the form $y \geq ax + b$.

Writing an inequality as $y \gtrless ax + b$ **immediately** gives the **slope, a,** and the **y-intercept, b,** of the boundary of the half-plane.

c) Refer to the inequality in the previous example.

1) Is an equality included in the inequality?

2) Give the slope and the initial value of the boundary equation.

3) Graph the boundary line of the equation.

4) Shade the half-plane for the inequality, taking into account the inequality symbol.

d) The half-plane representing an inequality is easy to identify. Here are the half-planes for four inequalities in the form $y \leq \blacksquare$, and the half-planes for four inequalities in the form $y \geq \blacksquare$. Study the diagrams and develop a hypothesis.

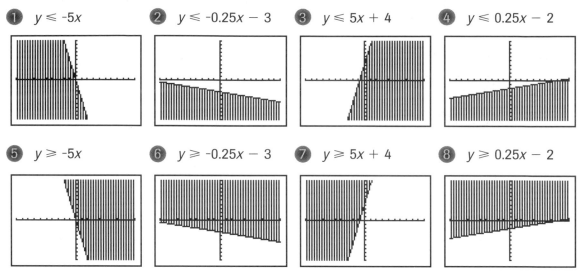

① $y \leq -5x$ **②** $y \leq -0.25x - 3$ **③** $y \leq 5x + 4$ **④** $y \leq 0.25x - 2$

⑤ $y \geq -5x$ **⑥** $y \geq -0.25x - 3$ **⑦** $y \geq 5x + 4$ **⑧** $y \geq 0.25x - 2$

Here is a way of expressing the hypothesis: For points with the same *x*-coordinate as a point on the line, the *y*-coordinate is greater if the point is above the line and smaller if the point is below the line.

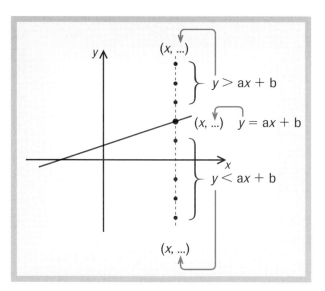

The examples above suggest the following procedure to find the solution set of a first-degree inequality in two variables.

1. Write the inequality in the form $y \geq ax + b$.

2. Draw the boundary for the equation $y = ax + b$ using a **solid** or a **dotted** line, depending on whether or not an equality is included in the inequality.

3. Shade the half-plane below the line if the symbol is $<$, or above the line if the symbol is $>$.

We can also solve linear inequalities using a graphing calculator.

e) Here are two sequences of screens that show how to solve a linear inequality. If you have a different model of calculator, find out how to use it to solve an inequality.

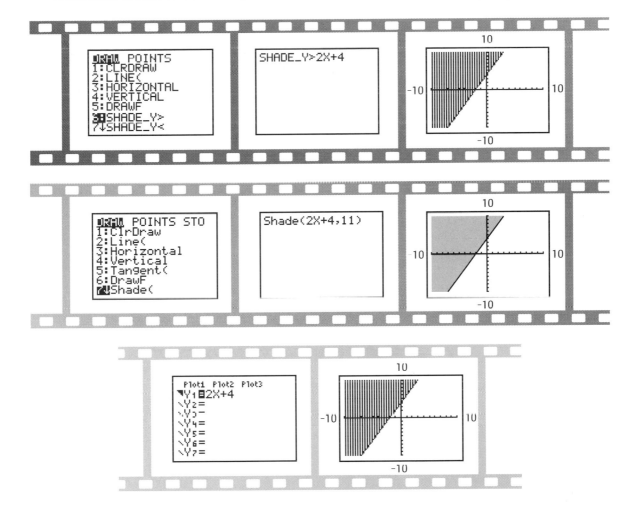

Note that you have to decide whether the half-plane is open or closed.

f) Using a graphing calculator, solve the following inequalities. State whether the half-plane is open or closed.

1) $y < 5x - 2$ 2) $y \geqslant -2.5x - 4$

3) $y > x + 7$ 4) $y \leqslant -4x$

The graphing calculator rapidly displays the solution set of a linear inequality.

1. Using the form $y = ax + b$, write the equation of the boundary of each of the following inequalities:

a) $0 \geqslant 12x - 3y$

b) $\dfrac{y - 10}{3} \leqslant x$

c) $-3x + 1.5y + 6 < 0$

d) $\dfrac{x}{6} + \dfrac{y}{7} > 1$

e) $\sqrt{2}(x - y) + 8 > 0$

f) $2x - 7.5 < y$

2. For each of the inequalities in question 1, state whether the boundary is a solid line or a dotted line.

3. Find the inequality that represents each of the solution sets shown below.

a)

b)

c)

d)

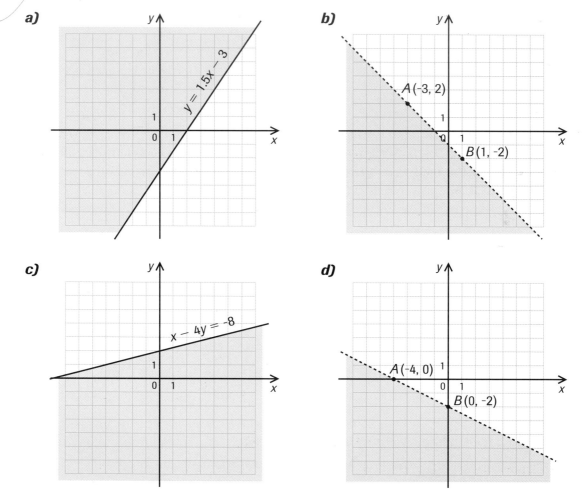

4. If $x < 2$ defines the half-plane shown on the right, graph the half-plane for:

a) $x < -3$

b) $x \geq 4$

c) $y > -2$

d) $y - 3 \leq 0$

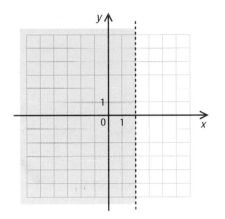

5. Determine whether or not the ordered pair $(2, 8)$ is included in the solution set of the following inequalities:

a) $y \leq 4x - 2$

b) $5x - y < 10$

c) $-6x + 3y < 12$

d) $0 \geq 4x - y$

e) $x > 5$

f) $y > 5$

6. A wallpaper distributor sends his best customers discount coupons that can be applied to their next purchase. Sending these coupons by courier costs 50¢ locally and $1.50 long-distance. The maximum budget available for all the mailings is $120. The following graph represents this scenario:

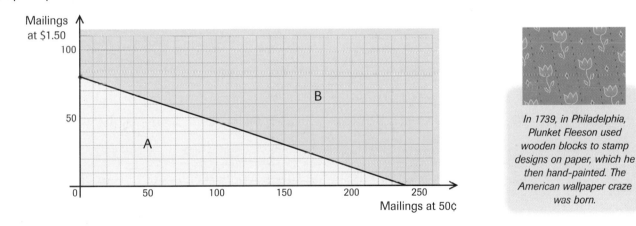

In 1739, in Philadelphia, Plunket Fleeson used wooden blocks to stamp designs on paper, which he then hand-painted. The American wallpaper craze was born.

a) Give the inequality that represents this example.

b) Determine the slope and the y-coordinate at the origin of the boundary.

c) Explain why the points on the boundary belong to the solution set.

d) Which region, A or B, represents the solution set for the inequality in this situation?

7. Solve the following inequalities by graphing their solution sets.

a) $y \leq x$

b) $y < -2x + 6$

c) $y \geq 5x - 5$

d) $-5x + 2.5y > 0$

e) $9 \geq 12x - 3y$

f) $6x + 1.5y - 9 < 0$

8. State the inequality representing each of the following situations:

a) The slope and the *y*-coordinate at zero for the boundary are respectively 8 and -4. The boundary is a solid line and the region below the line is shaded.

b) Point (0, 0) belongs to the solution set. The pairs (-8, -4) and (2, 6) are both solutions of the inequality and satisfy the equation for the boundary.

c) The *x*-coordinate at zero of a vertical dotted line is 3. The half-plane for the inequality corresponds to the region on the left side of the boundary.

d) The graph for the solution set is an open half-plane. The *x*-coordinate for all the points in the half-plane is greater than twice the *y*-coordinate.

9. Represent each of the following examples as a linear inequality and graph the solution set of the mathematical model of this inequality on paper or with a graphing calculator.

a) Mike owns a truck that runs on diesel fuel and a car fuelled by unleaded gas. Diesel fuel costs 40¢/L and unleaded gas costs 60¢/L. In one month, he spends over $72 for both types of fuel. Let *x* represent the number of litres of diesel fuel and *y* the number of litres of unleaded gas consumed in one month.

A diesel eng (named after its inventor, Rudolph Dies is economica because of its low consump of a fuel oil th costs less tha gasoline.

b) The perimeter of a rectangle is at least 80 cm. Let *x* represent the length of the rectangle and *y* the width.

c) A company manufactures white ping-pong balls and orange ping-pong balls. The white sell for 15¢ apiece and the orange for 25¢ each. A sporting-goods store buys at most $300 worth of balls. Let *x* represent the number of white balls and *y* the number of orange balls.

Ping-pong, or tennis, was fir played in Eng around 1880.

d) In a local swimming pool, a mixture of chlorine and bromine is used to purify the water. A litre of chlorine costs $8 and a litre of bromine costs $16. The pool manager buys a total of at least $240 worth of these products. Let *x* represent the number of litres of chlorine and *y* the number of litres of bromine.

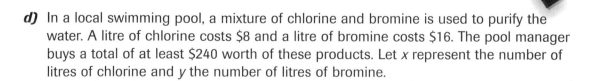

10. Match each of the screens below with one of the inequalities shown on the right.

$$y_1 \geqslant 2x + 3 \qquad y_2 \geqslant -3x - 2 \qquad y_3 \geqslant -2$$
$$y_4 \leqslant 2x + 3 \qquad y_5 \leqslant -3x - 2 \qquad y_6 \leqslant -2$$

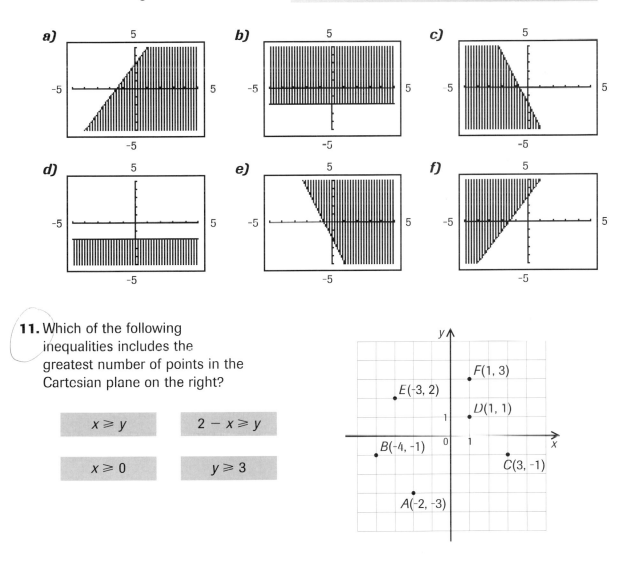

a)

b)

c)

d)

e)

f)

11. Which of the following inequalities includes the greatest number of points in the Cartesian plane on the right?

$x \geqslant y$

$2 - x \geqslant y$

$x \geqslant 0$

$y \geqslant 3$

F(1, 3)

E(-3, 2)

D(1, 1)

B(-4, -1)

C(3, -1)

A(-2, -3)

a) How many inequalities have a boundary with the equation $y = 4x - 2$? Graph the half-planes representing each inequality.

b) Give two inequalities with half-planes whose intersection is an empty set and whose union corresponds to the entire Cartesian plane.

c) Look again at the examples in exercise 8. If we reverse the order of the variables in these situations, would we obtain the same solution set? Use a graph to justify your answer.

SYSTEMS OF EQUATIONS

Olympic dreams

Mary-Sue is a good swimmer. She dreams of competing in the Olympics some day. Every week she trains at the pool to develop her technique and at the gym, to improve her physical condition. Last week she trained 8 times at the pool and 4 times at the gym, for a total of 20 h. This week she plans to train 6 times at the pool and 6 times at the gym, for a total of 21 h.

Swimming has been practised in all civilizations, at all times. The ancient Greeks held competitions in the Mediterranean, though these were not included in the Olympics.

a) Let x be the hours spent training at the pool and y the hours spent training at the gym. Determine the two equations that express this situation.

Two or more equations derived from a single situation and that use the same variables form a **system of equations.**

The following graph represents the system of equations for this situation.

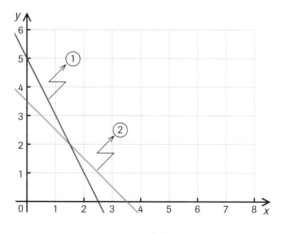

A Japanese imperial edict of 1603 prescribed that swimming be part of the school curriculum and that competitions be held between schools.

b) Match up each line with its corresponding equation.

c) Give the coordinates of the point that satisfies the two equations simultaneously.

The x- and y-coordinates of the point of intersection of two lines are the **solution** for the system of linear equations illustrated above. Generally, the solution is expressed as an **ordered pair (x, y).**

At the point of intersection of the two lines, the y variable in the first equation has the same value as the y variable in the second equation. This makes the right hand sides equal.

$$y = -2x + 5 \atop y = -x + 3.5 \quad \Rightarrow \quad -2x + 5 = -x + 3.5$$

d) Solve the equation obtained.

e) How long is one training session:

1) At the pool? 2) At the gym?

We can use a graph to solve systems of equations, but for a more precise solution we use an **algebraic** method.

The choice of the most appropriate method for solving a system of equations algebraically often depends on the type of equations that make up the system. The methods are as follows:

Comparison	Substitution	Elimination
$y = 3x - 5$	$y = 30 + 5x$	$3x + 6y = 21$
$y = 7x - 13$	$-10x + 3y = 25$	$5x + 8y = 29$
$\Downarrow$	$\Downarrow$	$\Updownarrow$
$3x - 5 = 7x - 13$	$-10x + 3(30 + 5x) = 25$	$15x + 30y = 105$
$-4x = -8$	$-10x + 90 + 15x = 25$	$15x + 24y = 87$
$x = 2$	$5x = -65$	$\Downarrow$
$\Downarrow$	$x = -13$	$6y = 18$
$y = 3 \times 2 - 5$	$\Downarrow$	$y = 3$
or	$y = 30 + 5 \times -13$	$\Downarrow$
$y = 7 \times 2 - 13$	or	$3x + 6 \times 3 = 21$
$\Downarrow$	$-10 \times -13 + 3y = 25$	or
$y = 1$	$\Downarrow$	$5x + 8 \times 3 = 29$
	$y = -35$	$\Downarrow$
		$x = 1$

The **comparison** method is usually used when the same variable has been isolated in both equations.

The **substitution** method is usually used when a variable is isolated in only one equation.

The **elimination** method is usually used when no variable has been isolated.

SYSTEMS OF INEQUALITIES

Four Seasons but no "Winds"

An orchestra conductor feels that the tone of Vivaldi's *Four Seasons* is perfect for an orchestra with at least twice as many string instruments as wind instruments. To play this suite at a concert, the conductor must select no more than 30 musicians to play both types of instruments.

This situation can be expressed using the inequalities

$$x \geq 2y \quad \text{and} \quad x + y < 30 \; .$$

a) What do the variables x and y represent in each of these inequalities?

b) Isolate y in each of these inequalities.

Two or more inequalities derived from a single situation and that use the same variables form a **system of inequalities.**

c) A graph of the solution set for each of these inequalities is shown. The solution set consists of all ordered pairs that satisfy the inequality. Match each graph to one of the inequalities of the system.

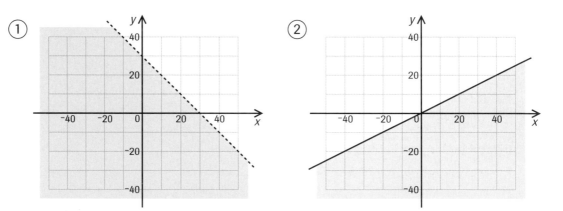

d) Complete the following table showing whether the coordinates of the given points are solutions for either of the inequalities.

	$y \leq \dfrac{x}{2}$	$y < 30 - x$
$A(20, 20)$	▬	▬
$B(40, 10)$	▬	▬
$C(10, 10)$	▬	▬
$D(20, 5)$	▬	▬

e) Find the coordinates of five points that satisfy both equations simultaneously.

The solution set of a first-degree system of inequalities in two variables consists of all ordered pairs that **simultaneously** satisfy all the inequalities of the system.

Since x and y represent the same quantities in both inequalities, they can be represented on a single Cartesian plane.

The two lines divide the plane into four regions.

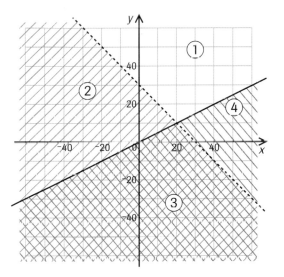

f) Which region, or regions, contain the points with coordinates that satisfy:

1) The inequality $y \leqslant \dfrac{x}{2}$?

2) The inequality $y < 30 - x$?

3) Both the inequality $y \leqslant \dfrac{x}{2}$ and the inequality $y < 30 - x$?

g) Is the point of intersection of the two boundaries included in the solution set of this system of inequalities? Justify your answer.

On a graph, the solution set of a first-degree system of inequalities in two variables corresponds to the **region of the plane that is common to the solution sets** of all the inequalities making up the system.

1. Give an approximate solution for each of the following systems of equations after graphing the system.

    a) $y = x$

        $y = -x + 2$

    b) $y = 3x + 1$

        $y = 7x$

    c) $y = 5$

        $y = 3x - 13$

    d) $-4x + y = 10$

        $x - 2y = -6$

2. Solve the following systems of ~~inequalities~~ *equations* using the comparison method.

    a) $y = 5x - 2$

        $y = -3x - 2$

    b) $y = -x + 18$

        $y = 3x - 6$

    c) $y = -3.5x + 10$

        $y = 0.5x$

3. Solve the following systems using either the substitution or the elimination method.

    a) $-2x + 2y = 28$

        $4x - 3y = -29$

    b) $-x + y = 10$

        $5x + 3y = -10$

    c) $3x - y = 3$

        $\dfrac{(2x + y)}{2} = -8$

    d) $-x - y = -5$

        $-3x - y = 15$

    e) $y = 3(x - 3) + 10$

        $x = 3y - 7$

    f) $y = \sqrt{8}x + 5$

        $-\sqrt{18}x + 3y = 9$

4. The graph below shows the boundaries of a system of two inequalities. Give the system of inequalities for each lettered region of the plane.

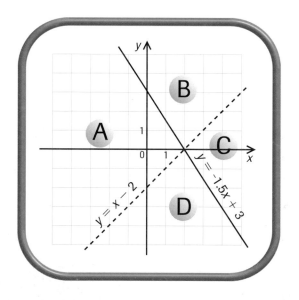

5. Graph the solution set for each system of inequalities below.

    a) $y \leq x$

        $y \geq -x$

    b) $y < -2x + 3$

        $y > x - 5$

    c) $y \geq 0$

        $y < -5x + 20$

    d) $-2x + y \leq 0$

        $8x - 2y > -6$

6. Which of the systems in question 5 have the ordered pair (2, 3) in their solution set?

7. Represent the system of inequalities on the right algebraically.

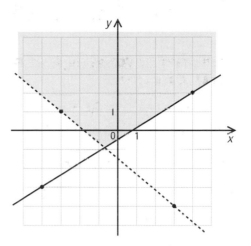

8. Each graph below represents the solution set for a system of two inequalities.

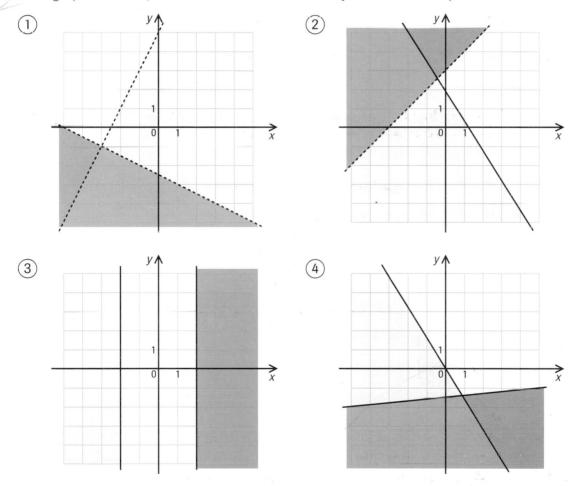

① ② ③ ④

a) Which system has an empty set as a solution set?

b) In which system are the coordinates of the point of intersection of the boundaries included in the solution set?

c) Which system has a solution set that is the region common to two open half-planes?

9. Represent each of the following examples as a system of inequalities, then graph the system.

a) A municipal garden grows black tulips and white tulips. There are over 4000 tulips in total. The number of white tulips increased by 500 is greater than twice the number of black tulips.

b) The length of a rectangle is at least twice as long as its width, and its perimeter is less than 100 cm.

c) A golf bag contains two types of clubs: drivers and irons. In Sheila's bag, fewer than one third of the clubs are drivers. She usually carries a total of fewer than 16 clubs in her bag when she plays golf.

The tulips that bloom on Parliament Hill in Ottawa are a lovely gift from the Netherlands.

10. After a natural gas leak is detected, the surrounding area is evacuated as a safety precaution. The chief of operations determines the area to evacuate from a map of the district. This area is defined by the graph of the system of inequalities shown on the right.

$$y_1 \geqslant -x - 2$$
$$y_2 \leqslant x + 4$$
$$y_3 \leqslant -3x + 8$$

a) Each graph shown below represents a solution set for one of the inequalities. Match up each graph with the corresponding inequality.

1)   2)   3)

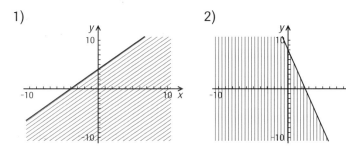

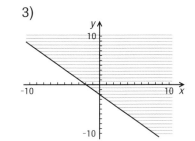

b) Superimposing the three graphs gives us one region on the plane that is shaded three times. What does this region represent?

c) Give the coordinates of three points that are:

1) Inside the region to be evacuated.

2) On the boundary of the region to be evacuated.

3) Outside the region to be evacuated.

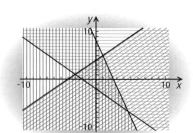

a) What is the system of inequalities whose solution set corresponds to:

1) The first quadrant of the Cartesian plane? 2) The second?

3) The third?   4) The fourth?

b) Compare the solution for a system of equations to that for a system of inequalities. What is common to both? How do they differ?

c) One of the two inequalities forming a system is $y \le 4x + 3$. What is the expression of the other inequality if the graph of the solution set is:

1) A line?   2) An empty set?

d) In a system of inequalities, if the boundaries of the two half-planes are parallel, what are the possible solution sets?

POLYGON OF CONSTRAINTS

An airplane with class!

To design an airplane, several requirements must be taken into account. Some involve the number of passenger seats. The model DC-W has two sections: business class and economy. Given the dimensions of the airplane, the total number of seats must be less than or equal to 100. To meet the demand for seats in each class, there must be at least 4 times more seats in economy than in business class.

a) For this type of airplane, list the seating requirements that need to be met.

In mathematics, the conditions that must be met in a situation are called **constraints.** Constraints are generally expressed as inequalities.

To represent constraints as inequalities, we must first **identify the variables.** Generally we use the variables x and y.

b) If x represents the number of seats in business class, what does y represent?

We must then **find all the constraints** expressed in the situation and **represent them as inequalities.**

Book V of Euclid's Elements uses expressions such as "exceeds," "equals" and "smaller" to compare given dimensions.

c) Here are the main constraints in this situation. Express them as inequalities.

1. The total number of seats must be less than or equal to 100.

2. There must be at least 4 times as many seats in economy as in business class.

Moreover, in real-life situations, variables rarely assume negative values. Two other inequalities, called the **"non-negative" constraints,** are therefore added.

3. $x \geqslant 0$

4. $y \geqslant 0$

Thus, we obtain a system made up of four inequalities.

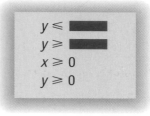

The solution set of this system of inequalities corresponds to the region illustrated below. When the inequalities of the system represent constraints, the solution set is called a **polygon of constraints.** A polygon of constraints may be closed or open.

d) Consider the coordinates of the vertices of this polygon, which is a triangle.

1) Estimate the coordinates of vertices A and C.

2) Find the coordinates of the third vertex using algebra.

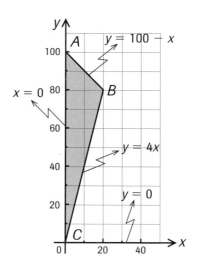

To make a precise calculation of the coordinates of one of the vertices of a polygon of constraints, we have to **solve the system of two equalities** for the boundary lines intersecting at this vertex.

Operation car-wash

A group of young people organized a wash-a-thon to raise funds for charity. They charged $4 to wash the exterior of a car and $6 for a full inside-and out car-wash. During the morning, Arif took in $28 at most. He did at least as many full car-washes as twice the number of outside car-washes minus 6. From this information, how many car-washes of each type did he do?

a) Identify the variables in this situation.

b) Use words to express the constraints of the situation and represent them as inequalities.

c) Adding the non-negative constraints, give the complete system of inequalities and determine its solution set.

d) Give the coordinates of the vertices of the resulting polygon of constraints.

You can find the solutions for a system of inequalities derived from constraints by following this procedure:

1. Clearly identify the variables.
2. State all constraints, including the non-negative constraints.
3. Represent the constraints as inequalities and isolate the y variable.
4. Graph the solution set of the system.
5. Determine the coordinates of the vertices of the polygon by solving the systems of equations for the polygon's boundaries.

INVESTMENT 4

1. Draw the polygon of constraints for each system of inequalities.

a) $y \leqslant -x + 10$
$y \geqslant -x + 5$
$x \geqslant 0$
$y \geqslant 0$

b) $y \geqslant 4x$
$y \leqslant 2x + 10$
$x \geqslant 0$
$y \geqslant 0$

c) $x \geqslant 0$
$y \geqslant 0$
$x \leqslant 5$
$y \leqslant 5$

d) $-4x + y \leqslant 20$
$4x + 2y \leqslant 20$
$x - y \leqslant 0$

2. Find the coordinates of all the vertices for each of the following polygons of constraints using an algebraic method.

a)

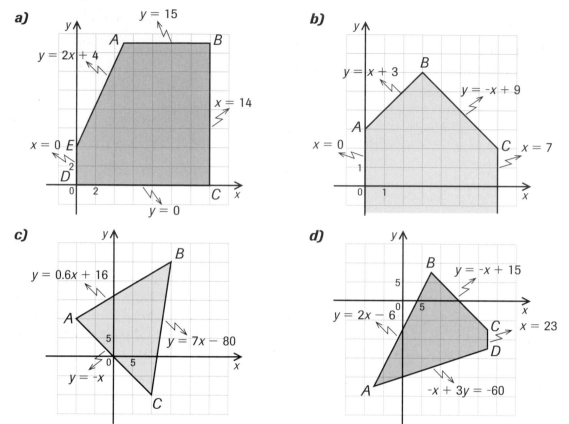

b)

c)

d)

3. A graphing calculator shows a polygon of constraints in the form of a triangle.

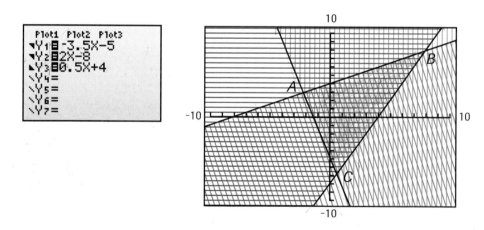

a) Match up each of the equations on the editing screen with one of the sides of the polygon of constraints on the display screen.

b) Give the system of inequalities shown.

c) Find the coordinates of vertices *A*, *B* and *C*.

4. Graph each system of inequalities and determine algebraically the coordinates of the vertices of the polygon of constraints.

a)
$$y \leq -x + 10$$
$$y \geq -0.5x + 5$$
$$x \geq 0$$
$$y \geq 0$$

b)
$$-x + y \geq 3$$
$$x + y \geq 3$$
$$2x + y \leq 7$$

c)
$$y \geq x$$
$$y \leq 5x$$
$$y \leq -3x + 16$$

5. For each of the following systems, identify the inequality that can be excluded from the system without affecting the polygon of constraints.

a)
$$y \geq -\frac{x}{3}$$
$$y \leq -2x + 6$$
$$y \geq -3x - 3$$
$$x \geq 0$$

b)
$$x + y \geq -4$$
$$2x + 8 \geq y$$
$$x \leq 0$$
$$y \leq 0$$

c)
$$y \leq x$$
$$y \leq -x$$
$$y \leq 8$$
$$y \leq -8$$

6. A truck carries individually packed mattresses and pillows. The truck driver earns $1.50 per pillow and $17 per mattress. There are no more than 75 boxes in the truck. If 8 pillows are added, the number of pillows is at least 3 times the number of mattresses. The truck driver has to earn at least $330 for his trip. If x represents the number of pillows and y the number of mattresses, represent the following constraints as inequalities.

a) The number of pillows and the number of mattresses must be positive numbers.

b) There are no more than 75 boxes in the truck.

c) If 8 pillows are added, the number of pillows is at least 3 times the number of mattresses.

d) The truck driver must earn at least $330 for the trip.

7. The Mauricie region publishes a travel guide every year. This year the committee in charge of designing the guide plans to produce a booklet containing at least 30 colour pages and a certain number of black-and-white pages. The committee estimates that the guide will contain at least 60 pages. Because of a limited budget, however, there will be no more than 100 pages.

a) What are the two variables in this example?

b) Represent the non-negative constraints as inequalities.

c) Use inequalities to express the following restrictions:

1) The guide will contain at least 30 colour pages.

2) The guide will contain at least 60 pages.

3) The guide will contain no more than 100 pages.

Les Forges du Saint-Maurice,
*an historic site in the
Mauricie region, Québec.*

8. Geraldine owns an orchard. In the fall, once the apples have been picked, she takes the least attractive to make juice that is sold in 1 L and 2 L containers. This year she produced at least 100 L of juice. Geraldine found that the 1 L size is at least 5 times more popular than the 2 L size. In all, she has a maximum of 94 containers she can use. How is the juice distributed among the 1 L and 2 L containers that she sells?

Apple-picking in Rougemont, in the Montérégie region. There are about 290 apple growers in this region.

a) Represent the constraints of this situation as a system of inequalities.

b) Graph the solution set of this system.

c) Find the coordinates of the vertices of the resulting polygon of constraints.

The McIntosh apple is probably the most well known. It is one of the main varieties produced in Québec, along with the Cortland, the Empire and the Lobo.

9. An electrical appliance technician bills her customers by mail. If x is the number of envelopes and y the number of stamps used, express in words the constraint for each of the following inequalities:

a) $x \geqslant 0$ *b)* $y \geqslant 0$ *c)* $x + y \geqslant 120$

d) $y \leqslant 2x$ *e)* $y \geqslant x - 30$ *f)* $x + y \leqslant 180$

In a 1634 treatise, Pierre Herigone was one of the first to use a symbol to represent an angle. He used the symbols < and ∠ interchangeably, despite the fact that the symbol < was already being used for the expression "less than."

a) Give a system of inequalities whose polygon of constraints is an isosceles trapezoid.

b) Can the graph of the solution set for a system of inequalities be a concave polygon of constraints? Explain.

c) A polygon of constraints has three boundaries with positive slopes. State whether this polygon can be:

1) Closed?   2) Open?

A **first-degree** inequality **in two variables** can always be written in the form $y \gtrsim ax + b$. The solution set contains all the ordered pairs (x, y) that satisfy the inequality.

To translate the inequalities from words into algebraic expressions, we need to:

1. **Identify the variable or variables** in the given situation.

2. **Establish the algebraic expressions** to be compared.

3. **Write the inequality** by choosing the appropriate inequality symbol.

To graph the solution set for a first-degree inequality in two variables:

1. Isolate y in the inequality:

   $$y \gtrsim ax + b$$

2. Draw the boundary line with equation $y = ax + b$ using a **solid** or **dotted** line, depending on whether or not the equality is included in the inequality.

3. Shade in the half-plane below the line if the inequality symbol is $<$, or the half-plane above the line if the inequality symbol is $>$.

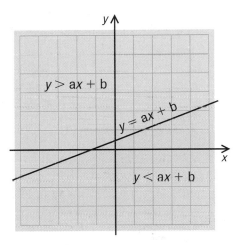

The set of these points forms an **open** or **closed half-plane** that shows the solution set for the inequality.

Two or more inequalities derived from a single situation form a **system of inequalities.** The solution set for such a system is the **region of the plane that is common** to both half-planes.

When a system of inequalities represents a set of constraints, the graph of the solution set is a **polygon of constraints.** We find the coordinates of the vertex of the polygon of constraints by solving the system of equations for the boundary lines forming this vertex.

1 In a magic square, the sum of each line, each column and each diagonal is the same. Here, the sum is -10. Copy and complete this magic square.

5		-8	
-6	0	-1	-3
-2	-4	-5	1
-7		4	

2 Replace the triangles with the numbers 3, 4, 5 and 6 to obtain the highest result.

a) $\frac{\triangle}{\triangle} + \frac{\triangle}{\triangle}$ b) $\frac{\triangle}{\triangle} - \frac{\triangle}{\triangle}$ c) $\frac{\triangle}{\triangle} \times \frac{\triangle}{\triangle}$ d) $\frac{\triangle}{\triangle} \div \frac{\triangle}{\triangle}$

3 Replace the triangles with the numbers 2, 4, 6 and 8 to obtain the lowest result.

a) $\frac{\triangle}{\triangle} + \frac{\triangle}{\triangle}$ b) $\frac{\triangle}{\triangle} - \frac{\triangle}{\triangle}$ c) $\frac{\triangle}{\triangle} \times \frac{\triangle}{\triangle}$ d) $\frac{\triangle}{\triangle} \div \frac{\triangle}{\triangle}$

4 Find which results do not make sense.

A) $2 \div 0.5 = 4$ B) $\frac{2}{3} \div \frac{1}{6} = 4$ C) $\frac{1}{2} \div 2 = 4$ D) $\frac{3}{2} \div 0.5 = 4$

5 Find which of these operations yields the result closest to 2.

A) $2 \div 4$ B) $\frac{1}{2} \div 1$ C) $1 \div \frac{1}{2}$ D) $0.5 \div \frac{1}{2}$

6 Find which division has a quotient of 1.

A) $0.5 \div 2$ B) $2 \div \frac{1}{2}$ C) $\frac{1}{2} \div 2$ D) $\frac{1}{2} \div 0.5$

7 Perform these operations mentally.

a) 12×24 b) 18×16 c) 54×46 d) 62×58

8 Provide a strategy for calculating the following in your head: "An egg producer has 1354 eggs divided into cartons of a dozen each. If the cartons must be completely filled, find how many eggs he has left."

9 Without calculating, find each of the following linear relationships.

a)

x	y
0	3
1	5
2	7
3	9
4	11
...	...
10	23
x	...

b)

x	y
0	4
1	0
2	-4
3	-8
4	-12
...	...
10	-36
x	...

c)

x	y
0	-2
1	2
2	6
3	10
4	14
...	...
10	38
x	...

10 If x is an even number and y is an odd number, represent each of the following statements as an inequality.

a) The sum of both numbers is less than or equal to 45.

b) Twice the even number is less than three times the odd number.

c) The sum of both numbers is at most 50.

d) The odd number is at least twice the even number.

e) The even number is greater than one third of the odd number.

f) The sum of both numbers multiplied by three is at least 100.

11 Take $x - y < 6$, a linear inequality in two variables.

a) In one sentence, describe the characteristic that an ordered pair must have to be included in the solution set of this inequality.

b) State two ordered pairs that are not in the solution set.

c) Is the ordered pair (-17, -23) a solution for this inequality? Explain.

12 Yoda has a card collection. During the winter, he is mostly interested in hockey cards, but in the summer, he prefers baseball cards. If x is the number of hockey cards and y is the number of baseball cards, translate each of the following inequalities into words:

a) $2x \geqslant 3y$ **b)** $x > y + 30$ **c)** $\frac{x}{2} < y$ **d)** $2(x + y) < 1000$

13 Of the ordered pairs (0, 0), (-4, 8), (5, 11) and (1, 20), find which one satisfies all of the following inequalities:

| $x > -4$ | $y \leqslant 20$ | $2x < y$ | $x + 7 > y - 3$ |

14 A house has a dual-energy heating system. Depending on the outside temperature, the system activates either electric heat or oil heat. After using the heating system for a whole winter, we notice that it activates the electric heat at least 5 times as often as the oil heat.

a) If x represents the number of days of electric heating and y the number of days of oil heating, represent this situation as an inequality in two variables.

b) State two ordered pairs that satisfy this inequality.

15 The graph of a linear inequality is shown below.

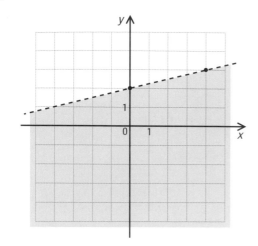

a) Does the solution set illustrated in the graph correspond to one of the following inequalities? If so, to which one?

$$2x + y > 4$$

$$x - 4y > -8$$

$$y < 2x + 0.25$$

$$y < x^2 + 2$$

b) Determine whether the following points are included in the solution set of each of the inequalities above.

1) $A(-3.5, 1)$ 2) $B(0, 2)$ 3) $C(3, 2.5)$

16 Graph the solution set of the following inequalities.

a) $y > 3x + 8$

b) $3y \geq 4(1.5x - 9)$

c) $10x + 5y < 5$

d) $49x - 11y \leq 121 - 6x$

17 A conference room's lighting system includes both incandescent light bulbs and fluorescent tubes. Because fluorescent tubes consume less energy than light bulbs, the room has at least 10 more fluorescent tubes than three times the number of light bulbs.

a) State the linear inequality that represents this situation.

b) Find the equation for the boundary of this inequality.

c) Determine if the solution set for this inequality corresponds to the half-plane above or below the boundary.

American invento_
Thomas Edison
perfected the
carbon filament
lamp around 187_
The marketing o_
these lamps
encouraged Edis_
in 1882 to creat_
the first electric
distribution netw_
the Edison
Company, in Ne_
York. This comp_
later became th_
General Electri_
Company.

18 The graph of the solution set for the system below is a triangle.

a) Graph this system on a plane.

b) Determine the coordinates of the vertices.

c) State the length of the triangle's sides to the nearest centimetre.

d) Calculate the distance between each vertex and the side opposite it.

e) Calculate the triangle's area.

$$y \geq 2x - 2$$

$$3y \leq -2x + 26$$

$$y \geq -6x + 14$$

19 During the summer, Leah offers a pool-cleaning service. She charges $10 for an in-ground pool and $12 for an above-ground pool. During a particular week, she chooses to clean more than 4 in-ground pools and a maximum of 6 above-ground pools. In total, she expects to clean at most 12 pools during the week and to make at least $120.

a) Represent this situation as a system of linear inequalities.

b) Using a graphing calculator, graph this system of inequalities.

c) Using tables of values, determine the coordinates of the vertices in the resulting polygon.

20 A cruise ship carries vacationers as well as crew members. To provide adequate services, the size of the crew must be at least one-tenth of the total number of people on board. In all, there are fewer than 600 people on board the cruise ship.

a) Represent each of the following conditions as an inequality:

1) The size of the crew must be at least one-tenth of the total number of people aboard.

2) In all, there are fewer than 600 people aboard the cruise ship.

b) Graph the solution set of this system of inequalities.

21 Describe a situation in everyday life that can be expressed by:

a) The inequality $x > 18$.

b) The inequality $x - 33 \geqslant 50$.

c) The double inequality $-4 < x \leqslant 10$.

d) The inequality $x + y < 56.5$.

22 The boundary lines for a system formed by two inequalities are shown on the right.

a) Match up a region of the graph with each of the following screens.

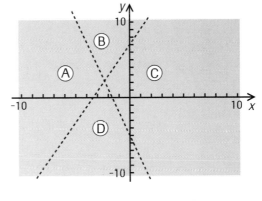

1)

2)

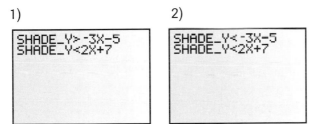

b) Check your answers with a graphing calculator.

c) State the systems of inequalities with solution sets that match the two other regions of the graph.

23 Just like systems of equations, a system of inequalities sometimes has no solution. Think about a system formed by two inequalities.

a) Do the half-planes for the system have a common region:

1) If their boundaries intersect?

2) If their boundaries are parallel and each half-plane is the region above the boundary?

3) If their boundaries are parallel and each half-plane is the region below the boundary?

b) When does a system of two inequalities have no solution?

24 A ferryboat transports cars and buses. The area reserved for vehicles is no greater than 1056 m². An area of approximately 12 m² is needed for a car and approximately 48 m² for a bus.

a) Represent this example as a linear inequality in two variables.

b) Graph the solution set of this inequality.

c) For one crossing, it is expected that approximately 24 cars will board the ferry. What is the maximum number of buses that can be taken on board?

d) Can 76 cars and 3 buses board the ferry? Explain.

Ferryboats link certain municipalities in Québec that are separated by the St. Lawrence River, such as Rivière-du-Loup and Saint-Siméon. Many do not operate in the winter.

25 Solve the following systems of equations using the most appropriate algebraic method.

a) $y = -2x - 7$
$y = -(2.5 + 3x)$

b) $2x + 4y = 10$
$x = 3(2y - 1)$

c) $x + y = -7$
$100x + y = -7$

26 Ally organizes a roofing "bee" to fix her roof. More than 6 people have already said they will come. For lunch, she expects to order out for spaghetti or poutine. An order of spaghetti costs $6 and poutine costs $4. She has no more than $80 to pay the restaurant bill.

a) Represent this situation as a system of linear inequalities.

b) Ignoring the reality of the situation, graph the solution set of the system.

c) Find the coordinates of the point of intersection of the two boundaries.

d) Are these coordinates a solution for the system? Justify your answer.

e) How can you determine whether or not an ordered pair is included in the solution set of a system of linear inequalities? Explain the graphic and algebraic methods.

27 On weekends Mark does baby-sitting to earn pocket money. He charges $4/h in the daytime and $5/h at night. Next month Mark expects to be able to baby-sit for a maximum of 18 h during the day and a maximum of 15 h at night. He hopes to earn a minimum of $120.

a) Represent the non-negative constraints as inequalities.

b) What other constraints does Mark have to take into account?

c) Graph the set of inequalities derived from these constraints.

d) Find the coordinates of the vertices of the resulting polygon of constraints.

28 RIGHT-HANDED, LEFT-HANDED OR AMBIDEXTROUS?

In a school of at least 670 students, 8% of students are strictly left-handed and 90% are strictly right-handed. We are interested in the number of students who are either left-handed or ambidextrous. Represent this situation as a linear inequality in two variables.

Leonardo da Vinci (1452-1519)

Leonardo da Vinci was left-handed. He wrote from right to left and, to be read, his writings had to be placed in front of a mirror.

29 JUMP IN!

A municipality has a maximum of $45 000 to hire students for summer jobs at its outdoor swimming pools. Lifeguards can expect to make $4500 for the summer and people working on maintenance will earn $1500.

a) Using x as the number of lifeguards and y as the number of people on the maintenance staff, represent this situation as an inequality.

b) Show algebraically that the equation for the boundary of this inequality is equivalent to $y = -3x + 30$.

c) Determine if this line belongs to the half-plane representing the solution set and explain your answer.

d) Is the solution set situated above or below the boundary? Justify your answer.

30 OUTING ON THE LAKE

The neighbourhood recreation committee has a maximum of $840 to spend on organizing a rowboat outing in a provincial park. It can reserve wooden or aluminum boats. It costs $40 to rent a wooden boat and $60 for an aluminum boat. To get such low rates, at least 6 rowboats have to be rented. Taking into account the number of people registered, the committee decides to rent at least twice as many wooden boats as aluminum boats.

Mount Richardson, Gaspé Provincial Park.

a) Write a realistic system of linear inequalities for this example, then graph the system.

b) Find the coordinates of the vertices of the resulting polygon of constraints.

31 GOLFING TO PLAY POOL

Billiards was first played in the 14th century—on the ground. Today, many versions of the game exist, such as American billiards, or "pool," which is popular all over the world.

A youth centre wants to set up a pool room, so a golf tournament and benefit supper are planned to raise the necessary funds. Registration for the supper alone costs $10 while registration for both the supper and the tournament costs $20. The hall where the supper will be held can accommodate no more than 60 people and the golf club can register a maximum of 80 players. The centre needs a minimum $1100 to set up the pool room.

a) Represent each constraint of this problem as an inequality.

b) Graph these inequalities, then find the coordinates of the vertices of the polygon of constraints.

1. Graph the solution set for each of the following inequalities.

   a) $2y > 4x + 7$ **b)** $-2(y + 2) \leqslant 2x$ **c)** $3x - 2y > 0$

2. Express each of the following situations as an inequality in two variables and graph the solution sets.

   a) A pair of leather boots costs at least 75% more than a pair of vinyl boots.

   b) At least 2.5 times more men use electric razors than safety blades.

3. Graph the solution set for each of the systems of inequalities derived from the following situations:

   a) A hair dressing salon sells at least 100 more bottles of conditioner than of shampoo each year. In all, the salon sells more than 500 bottles per year.

   b) A bus carries teenagers and adults. There are at least 8 teenagers and the number of adults is no greater than 3 times the number of teenagers.

   c) In a high school of no more than 600 students, the difference between the number of non-smokers and four times the number of smokers is greater than 50.

4. **THE POWER OF CALCIUM**

   A nutrition guide indicates that teenagers need at least 1260 mg of calcium per day to grow healthy bones. The amount should not exceed 1800 mg, however. A cup of partly skimmed milk has 300 mg of calcium and a bowl of ice cream has 180 mg. According to the guide, how many portions of each should a teenager consume each day if these are her only sources of calcium?

   a) Give the system of linear inequalities that represents the constraints in this example.

   b) Plot the polygon of constraints for the situation.

5. **WHEELCHAIR FRIENDLY**

   An engineer drew up blueprints for a railway passenger car. She estimates the area taken by a seat to be 1.5 m², and the area required for each wheelchair to be 2 m². The area for passengers must be at least 255 m² and at most 340 m² in the passenger car, and space for at least 3 wheelchairs must be provided. The engineer, however, must also keep in mind that the demand for seats is at least 10 times greater than the demand for wheelchair space.

   a) Represent the constraints for this situation as a system of inequalities.

   b) Graph the solution set for this system.

   c) Find the coordinates of the vertices of the resulting polygon of constraints.

OPTIMUM SOLUTIONS

Onward and upward

Vitrex specializes in manufacturing both summer and winter windows. A summer window consists of a pane of glass and a screen, while a winter window consists of two panes of glass spaced several millimetres apart. To meet the demand, Vitrex has to manufacture at least 10 summer windows and 30 winter windows per week. The company can make no more than 100 windows in one week.

If x represents the number of summer windows and y the number of winter windows, we obtain the following system of inequalities:

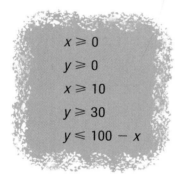

$$x \geq 0$$
$$y \geq 0$$
$$x \geq 10$$
$$y \geq 30$$
$$y \leq 100 - x$$

"Float glass," now called plate glass, was invented in 1958 by the Englishman Alistair Pilkington, and enabled architects to build towering glass office buildings. Its arrival transformed traditional glassmaking into a heavy industry.

The polygon of constraints for this system is shown on the right.

It is easy to figure out that Vitrex's target objective in manufacturing windows is to turn a profit. The profit on a summer window is $70 and the profit on a winter window is $85.

a) Does a weekly output of 25 summer windows and 65 winter windows satisfy the production constraints? Justify your answer.

We know that the coordinates of the points forming this polygon of constraints are solutions for the system of constraints. Each of these solutions generates a profit.

b) What rule allows us to calculate the profit P?

Vitrex's **objective** is to make the greatest possible profit. The fonction rule is used to place a value on this objective.

c) Complete this table showing the profit generated by each of the given pairs:

Calculation of profit

POINTS	PROFIT
(10, 30)	$P = 70 \times 10 + 85 \times 30 = \$3250$
(10, 60)	$P = 70 \times 10 + 85 \times 60 = \$$ ▬
(10, 90)	$P = 70 \times 10 + 85 \times$ ■ $= \$$ ▬
(20, 40)	$P = 70 \times$ ■ $+ 85 \times$ ■ $= \$$ ▬
(30, 60)	$P = 70 \times$ ■ $+ 85 \times$ ■ $= \$$ ▬
(60, 40)	$P = 70 \times$ ■ $+ 85 \times$ ■ $= \$$ ▬
(70, 30)	$P = 70 \times$ ■ $+ 85 \times$ ■ $= \$$ ▬

Note that each ordered pair generates a particular profit and that this profit varies from one pair to the next. Some **ordered-pair solutions are more profitable** than others.

d) For the preceding pairs, which generates the highest profit?

e) How many windows of each type must Vitrex manufacture to achieve this highest profit?

In some cases, the target objective is a **maximum** while in others, it is a **minimum.**

Dark and white chocolate

Keeping their different tastes in mind, Macha wants to give at least 12 chocolates to her friends for Easter. At least two of them love white chocolate. Even though dark chocolate costs more, Macha intends to buy at least twice as many dark chocolates as white chocolates, but no more than 20 dark chocolates. One white chocolate costs $2 and one dark chocolate costs $4.

François-Louis Cailler made the first chocolate bar in 1819 in Switzerland. The production of hand-made chocolate began in Europe after the Spanish brought the recipe for chocolate back from the Americas. At the time it was a drink made from the roasted and ground beans of the cacao tree.

The green candies are angelica flavoured. Angelica is an aromatic plant whose stem and petiole are used in confectionery.

If x represents the number of white chocolates and y the number of dark chocolates, we obtain the following system of inequalities and the resulting polygon of constraints.

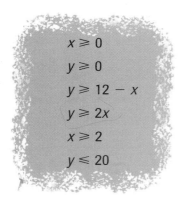

$$x \geqslant 0$$
$$y \geqslant 0$$
$$y \geqslant 12 - x$$
$$y \geqslant 2x$$
$$x \geqslant 2$$
$$y \leqslant 20$$

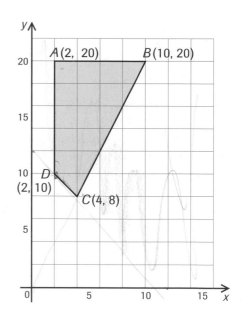

a) In this case, besides wanting to please her friends, what is Macha's objective?

b) Complete the rule used to place a value on Macha's objective.

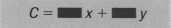

$$C = \blacksquare x + \blacksquare y$$

c) Using this rule, complete the following table.

Calculation of cost

POINTS	COST
(2, 10)	$C = 2 \times 2 + 4 \times 10 = \$44$
(2, 15)	▬▬▬▬▬▬▬▬▬
(2, 20)	▬▬▬▬▬▬▬▬▬
(4, 8)	▬▬▬▬▬▬▬▬▬
(5, 15)	▬▬▬▬▬▬▬▬▬
(8, 16)	▬▬▬▬▬▬▬▬▬
(10, 20)	$C = 2 \times 10 + 4 \times 20 = \$100$

d) Which ordered pair results in the minimum cost?

e) How many chocolates of each type should Macha buy to meet her objective?

Depending on the situation, the optimum solution can be the one that produces:

• The **highest value,** called the **maximum.**

• The **lowest value,** called the **minimum.**

The maximum or minimum can be calculated with a rule that represents the target objective.

FUNCTION RULE

Tonnes of snow

During a snow-removal operation, a city uses two types of trucks: one that can haul 3 t and the other 5 t of snow. There are at least 5 times as many 3 t trucks as 5 t trucks. The city expects to haul between 300 t and 600 t of snow during this operation. The cost of a 3 t truck is $20 per trip and a 5 t truck costs $35. We want to know the number of trips that must be planned to minimize the cost of the snow removal.

t is the symbol for tonne.

a) Describe the target objective for this example.

b) State the function rule that the city can use in evaluating costs if:

x is the number of 3 t trucks.

y is the number of 5 t trucks.

c) Describe the constraints in this situation.

d) From the vertices of the polygon of constraints shown below, which has coordinates that meet the city's objective?

This situation has two major elements:

- The **objective.**

- The **constraints.**

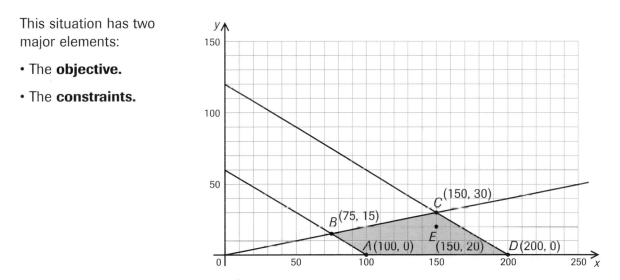

The objective can be either a maximum or a minimum and is calculated using a rule called the **function rule.**

The function associated with this rule is called the **objective function.**

In a problem, it is very important to distinguish between the constraints and the function rule. Generally, the function rule is found at the end of the problem and is not involved in constructing the polygon of constraints. It is represented by an **equation,** not an inequality.

There are many situations with constraints in which we look for a maximum or a minimum. Such problems are known as **optimization problems.**

Examples of optimization problems are part of daily life: companies that strive for higher profits, producers that work to lower costs and farmers determined to maximize yields, all face them in their work.

Solving an optimization problem means looking for a solution that

Mathematicians became interested in optimization problems during the Second World War (1939–1945) when the U.S. armed forces experienced problems supplying and distributing military provisions.

maximizes or minimizes

INVESTMENT 5

1. Each of the following graphs represents a polygon of constraints. Each table lists the ordered pairs for certain points of the polygon and a rule that represents the objective. Determine which ordered pair produces a maximum and which produces a minimum for the target objective.

a)

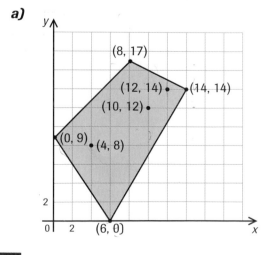

POINTS	$M = 5x + 3y$
(0, 9)	
(4, 8)	
(6, 0)	
(8, 17)	
(10, 12)	
(12, 14)	
(14, 14)	

b)

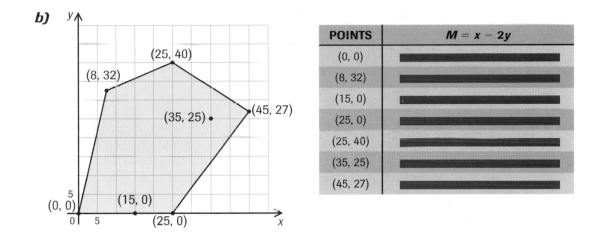

POINTS	$M = x - 2y$
(0, 0)	
(8, 32)	
(15, 0)	
(25, 0)	
(25, 40)	
(35, 25)	
(45, 27)	

2. A polygon of constraints is graphed below. The points shown are integer coordinates.

a) Evaluate the rule $M = 4x + y - 10$ for each of these points.

b) Determine which pair generates:

1) The highest value.

2) The lowest value.

c) Explain why the coordinates of the identified pairs cannot generate a value for M of:

1) -12   2) 7.5   3) 30

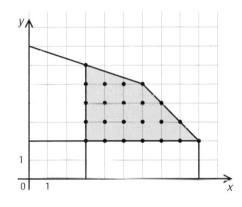

3. A company specializes in manufacturing single-seater and double-seater kayaks. It builds up to 40 kayaks a day. It must build at most four times as many singles as doubles to meet the demand. Every day the company must build a minimum of 5 doubles and at least 10 singles. The profit is $300 for a single and $180 for a double. We want to know how much profit the company can earn daily.

a) If x represents the number of single-seaters and y the number of double-seaters, find the rule used to calculate the company's profit.

Ocean kayaks, Ile Verte,
ower St. Lawrence. The
ginal Inuit kayak was a
g, narrow fishing boat
made of seal skin. A
"roll" is a boating
anoeuvre in which the
kayaker is completely
immersed in the water
ile flipping the kayak
ver sideways in a full
revolution.

b) From the ordered pairs defining the points given in the polygon of constraints shown, find which one maximizes the objective; that is, the one that generates the highest profit.

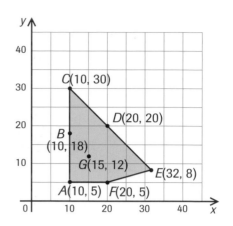

4. A builder is contracted to construct an apartment building of three- and four-room units. Before breaking ground, he must take into account the following constraints: the building has to have at least 10 apartments of each type, and there must be a minimum of 40 apartments in all. To comply with a municipal by-law, three times the number of three-room apartments added to twice the number of four-room apartments must not exceed 170. It costs approximately $25 000 to build a three-room unit and $30 000 for a four-room unit. Naturally, the contractor wants to keep construction costs to a minimum.

a) If x represents the number of three-room units and y the number of four-room units, state the rule used to find the construction costs of the building.

b) From the polygon of constraints shown below, find the point whose coordinates result in the minimum cost.

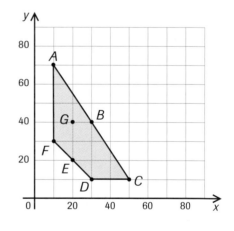

5. New cars are shipped by train from a car factory to a dealership. Some flat-cars can carry 12 cars and others can carry 20. At least 200 cars will be shipped at a time. The railway company, however, does not accept more than 14 flat-cars per train. It charges $3000 per 12-unit flat-car and $5000 per 20-unit flat-car. We have to minimize shipping costs.

a) If x represents the number of 12-unit flat-cars and y the number of 20-unit flat-cars, state the rule used to calculate shipping costs.

b) From the ordered pairs for the points on the polygon of constraints shown below, find the one(s) whose coordinates result in the minimum cost.

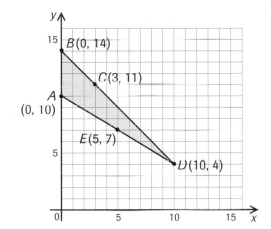

6. The triangle shown on the right is a polygon of constraints:

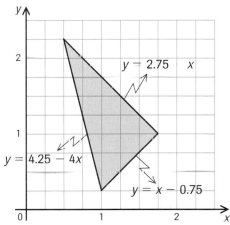

a) On your graphing calculator, enter the equations for the lines representing each side of the polygon.

b) Display the graph so that the polygon of constraints can be clearly seen.

c) Position the cursor at the centre of the triangle and write down the coordinates to the nearest tenth.

d) Moving the cursor, identify three other points in the polygon of constraints whose coordinates generate for the rule $M = x + 2y$:

   1) A value greater than the one generated by the pair in c) above.

   2) A value that is less than the one generated by the pair in c) above.

e) Starting from the centre of the triangle, describe in words the cursor movements giving coordinates that generate:

   1) Increasing values for the rule $M = x + 2y$.

   2) Decreasing values for the rule $M = x + 2y$.

7. A recreation night is being planned in a multi-ethnic neighbourhood to promote inter-cultural goodwill. The guests have asked that there be at least 6 h of continuous music during the evening. The organizers hire a reggae band that charges $150/h, and an MC to host the evening at $70/h. The band wants a contract of at least 3 h and expects to be on stage at least twice as long as the MC. We want to know how to divide the time between the reggae band and the MC so as to minimize the cost, but still meet the expectations of the guests and the musicians.

a) What are the two variables in this example?

b) Represent each of the constraints as an inequality.

c) What is the target objective of the organizing committee? Is it a minimum or a maximum?

d) What is the function rule?

Reggae is a musical style that originated in Jamaica, specifically in the underprivileged districts of Kingston, the capital city.

8. To increase sales, the owner of a "dépanneur" wants to install new shelves in his store. According to his plans, he has a surface area of 70 m² to display his products. His sales permit stipulates that no more than 50 m² can be set aside for foodstuffs and no less than 10 m², for non-food products. In addition, the space allotted for non-food products must not exceed one third of the space occupied by foodstuffs. According to his projections, he must make weekly profits of $10/m² for foodstuffs and $12/m² for non-food products.

a) What is the owner's target objective?

b) Identify each of the variables in this example.

c) State the rule that allows the merchant to calculate his profits.

d) State the inequalities that represent the constraints on redesigning the store.

The word "dépanneur," which refers to a store selling a limited range of convenience products, is specific to the province of Québec.

9. A farmer grows both green beans and carrots. This year she wants to reserve at least twice as much land for beans as for carrots. In the spring, she needs 2 d to sow one hectare of green beans and 3 d for one hectare of carrots. She has a maximum of 24 d in which to complete the job. To meet her needs, she must sow at least 6 ha of green beans and at least 2 ha of carrots.

a) Identify the two variables in this situation.

b) Think up a realistic objective for the farmer.

c) Represent the objective as a function rule.

d) State the inequalities that represent the constraints to be considered.

The green bean is an herbaceous plant first cultivated in Central America. It was first introduced in Europe in 1529 for Pope Clement VII.

*The hectare is a unit for measuring land area and is equivalent to 10 000 m². The symbol for hectare is **ha**.*

10. In a textile factory, full-time employees contribute $30 a week to the pension plan and part-time employees contribute $10 a week. We want to know the maximum sum that the factory workers could pay into the pension plan each week.

a) What are the values of x and y if the function rule is $R = 30x + 10y$?

b) Express in words the constraint represented by each of the following inequalities:

1) $x \geqslant 0$ 2) $y \geqslant 0$ 3) $x + y \leqslant 150$

4) $x \geqslant 4y + 60$ 5) $x \leqslant 120$ 6) $y \geqslant 20$

c) In this example, are we looking for a maximum or a minimum?

a) In exercises 1, 2, 3, 4 and 6, find the points in each polygon of constraints whose coordinates represent the optimum solutions.

b) In exercise 5, find the point in the polygon of constraints whose coordinates give the lowest shipping cost.

c) From these answers, what can you conjecture about the location of one or more points that define the optimum solution in a polygon of constraints?

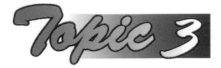

Topic 3 DECISION MAKING

SCANNING LINE
OPTIMIZATION PROBLEMS

SCANNING LINE

Chips and cola go hand in hand

According to a study on eating habits, chips and cola are inseparable. A dépanneur sells a bag of chips at a very low price to attract customers. The price is so low that the owner loses 10¢ per bag. On the other hand, he makes a 50¢ profit on the sale of each cola. In one day, he usually sells at least as many bags of chips as he does colas, at least 10 colas and up to 40 bags of chips. He sells no more than 60 of these products in all, however.

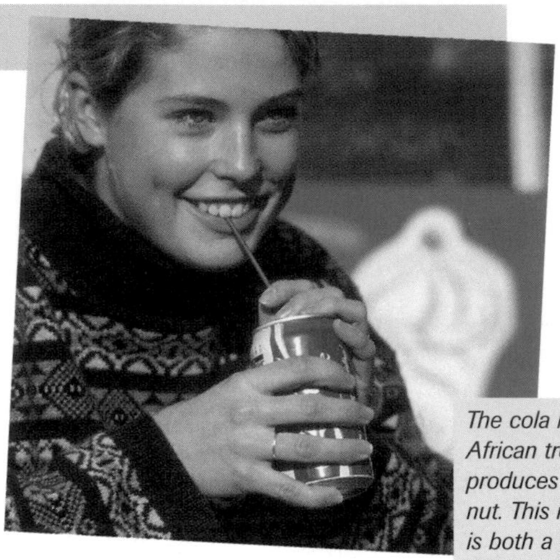

The cola is a tall African tree that produces the co nut. This ingredie is both a tonic a a stimulant, and used in making cola-based products.

CONSTRAINTS

a) If the number of colas sold is represented by x and the number of bags of chips sold by y, provide the system of inequalities that represents the dépanneur owner's constraints and that corresponds to the polygon of constraints shown on the right.

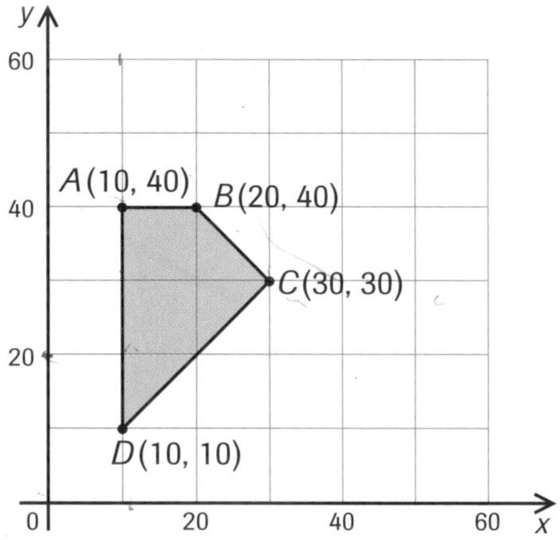

OBJECTIVE

The dépanneur owner wants to maximize the profit from the sale of these two products.

b) State the rule that enables the owner to calculate the profit P from the sales of the two products.

The dépanneur owner is looking for a **graphical method** that will allow him to determine the number of colas and bags of chips that will **maximize** his profit.

c) In this context, explain the meaning of each of the following rules and write them in function form.

1) $0 = 0.5x - 0.1y$ 2) $5 = 0.5x - 0.1y$

3) $10 = 0.5x - 0.1y$ 4) $15 = 0.5x - 0.1y$

The polygon of constraints, the lines corresponding to these rules, and some points in the polygon are illustrated in the graph on the right.

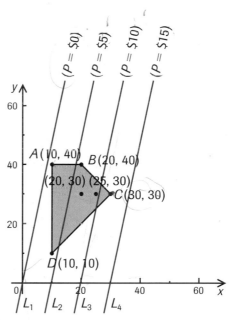

d) What characteristic is common to all of these lines?

e) How can you explain this characteristic?

f) By earning a 50¢ profit per cola and losing 10¢ per bag of chips, can the dépanneur owner expect to earn the following profits within the constraints?

 1) $0   2) $5   3) $10   4) $15

g) Find the profit for each of the following ordered pairs:

 1) (10, 40)   2) (10, 10)   3) (20, 40)

 4) (20, 30)   5) (25, 30)   6) (30, 30)

The parallel lines appearing on the graph can be considered as paths left behind by a scanning line with a slope of 5.

A **scanning line** is a line that is translated across the Cartesian plane. To define a particular scanning line, we assign a value to the objective in the equation of the objective.

h) Describe how the profit varies when the line shifts from L_1 to L_4.

i) What are the first and last points of the polygon of constraints touched by the line as it shifts from L_1 to L_4?

j) Which point of the polygon of constraints generates:

 1) The maximum profit? 2) The minimum profit?

Note that the coordinates of the **first** and **last** points of the polygon of constraints touched by the scanning line generate a **maximum** or a **minimum.**

Boating on the St. Lawrence

To make some money with his yacht, Martin decides to give boat tours on the St. Lawrence. He must comply with the relevant regulations. Because of the dimensions of the yacht, the number of children increased by twice the number of adults cannot exceed 140. To meet the demand, Martin estimates that there must be at least 30 children on board. At the same time, because of security standards, the number of adults must be at least one third the number of children.

CONSTRAINTS

a) If the number of children is represented by x and the number of adults by y, state the system of inequalities that represents the constraints Martin must work with and that corresponds to the polygon of constraints shown on the right.

OBJECTIVE

Naturally, Martin would like to maximize his profits! He studies various price combinations for a boat tour.

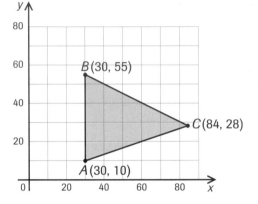

First attempt

b) Based on the prices shown on the right, provide the rule to calculate Martin's revenue R, in dollars, for each boat tour.

Child: $3
Adult: $10

Martin is looking for a **method** that will allow him to **find out the number of children and the number of adults** that will **maximize** his profits. He can use a **graphical method.**

c) For this problem, explain the meaning of each of the rules:

1) $100 = 3x + 10y$ 2) $300 = 3x + 10y$
3) $500 = 3x + 10y$ 4) $700 = 3x + 10y$

The graph below represents the polygon of constraints and the lines corresponding to these rules.

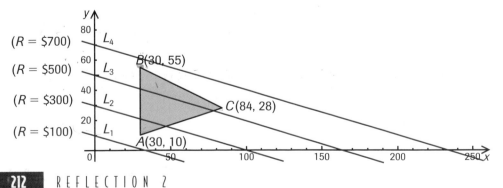

d) What is the slope of each of these lines?

e) By charging $3 per child and $10 per adult, can Martin earn the following amounts within the constraints?

1) $100   2) $300   3) $500   4) $700

f) Describe how the revenue will vary when the line is shifted from L_1 to L_4.

g) Identify the vertices that correspond to the first and last points touched by the scanning line as it goes from L_1 to L_4.

h) Which point has the coordinates that produce:

1) A maximum revenue?   2) A minimum revenue?

Once again, we note that the coordinates of the first and last points of the polygon of constraints touched by the scanning line generate a **maximum** or a **minimum.**

Second attempt

i) Given the rates shown on the right, what will be the rule of Martin's objective?

j) Complete the table of the rules obtained for various revenues:

Revenue	$R = \blacksquare + \blacksquare$	$y = \blacksquare$
100	$100 = \blacksquare x + \blacksquare y$	$L_1: y = 10 - \dfrac{x}{2}$
300	$\blacksquare$	$L_2: y = \blacksquare$
500	$\blacksquare$	$L_3: y = \blacksquare$
700	$\blacksquare$	$L_4: y = \blacksquare$

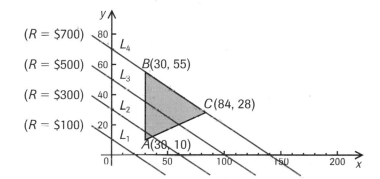

The graph on the right shows the polygon of constraints and the lines corresponding to these equations.

k) Which point has coordinates that produce:

1) A maximum revenue?

2) A minimum revenue?

l) Do all the coordinates of the points of line segment BC generate a maximum revenue?

These two attempts allow us to observe the following:

1. The values that optimize (maximize or minimize) an objective are the coordinates of the first and last vertices of the polygon of constraints that the scanning line meets.

2. Sometimes the coordinates for all the points of a side of the polygon of constraints optimize the function rule.

The scanning line in action

With the following program, we can clearly visualize how the scanning line moves, regardless of its slope. Let's look at a polygon of constraints with the following vertices: (2, 4), (6, 7), (8, 2).

a) Enter the program at right on a graphing calculator.

```
PROGRAM:SCAN
:Input A
:ClrDraw
:Line(2,4,6,7)
:Line(6,7,8,2)
:Line(8,2,2,4)
:For(B,1,9+10abs
(A),1)
:If A<0:Then
:Line(0,B,10,10A
+B)
:Else
:Line(0,-10A+B,1
0,B)
:End:Pause :End
```

b) Define the values displayed on the editing screen.

```
WINDOW
 Xmin=0
 Xmax=10
 Xscl=1
 Ymin=0
 Ymax=10
 Yscl=1
```

c) Start the SCAN program.

You must begin by giving the slope of the scanning line you want to generate.

```
prgmSCAN
?-1
```

d) By pressing ENTER, you can see the movement of the scanning line.

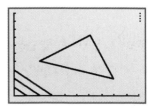

e) Answer the following questions using the SCAN program:

1) Find the coordinates of the point that generates a maximum for $M = 2x + 4y$?

2) Find the coordinates of the point that generates a minimum for $M = x + 10y - 5$?

3) What is particular about the maximum generated by $M = 10x + 4y$?

1. Each of the following graphs shows a polygon of constraints as well as the scanning line for a function rule.

For each graph, indicate which points in the polygon of constraints have coordinates that optimize (maximize or minimize) the function rule.

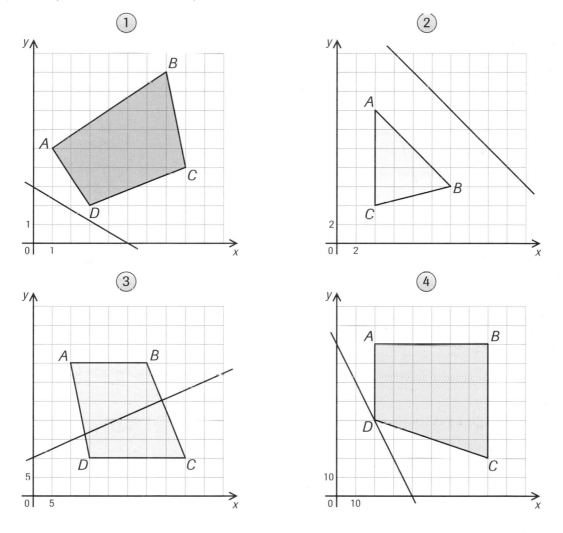

2. Give the slope of the scanning line for each of the following functions.

a) $M = 18x + 30y$ **b)** $M = 40x + 20y$ **c)** $M = -7x + 21y$

d) $M = 7.5x + 2.5y$ **e)** $M = 5x - 12y$ **f)** $M = 3x + 3y - 10$

3. Copy the polygon of constraints shown on the right. Draw a scanning line for the function rule and for which:

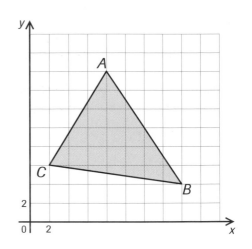

a) The coordinates of point *A* produce a maximum.

b) The coordinates of point *C* produce a minimum.

c) The coordinates of the points on side *AB* produce a maximum.

4. The function rule $R = 5x + 3y$ corresponds to the revenue from the sale of two products. The vertices of the polygon of constraints are $A(19, 20)$, $B(24, 30)$, $C(40, 25)$ and $D(30, 22)$.

a) Graph the polygon of constraints.

b) Draw a scanning line.

c) Which ordered pair generates the maximum revenue?

5. The rule $C = 5x + 3y$ corresponds to the production costs for two products, and the vertices of the polygon of constraints are $A(50, 50)$, $B(50, 100)$, $C(90, 120)$ and $D(100, 100)$.

a) Graph the polygon of constraints.

b) Draw a scanning line.

c) Which ordered pair produces the minimum cost?

6. Copy the scanning line below onto a grid. Draw a polygon of constraints *ABC* with coordinates that generate:

a) A maximum for all points on side *AB*.

b) A minimum for all points on side *AB*.

c) A maximum for point *A*.

d) A minimum for point *A*.

e) A minimum for point *A* and a maximum for point *C*.

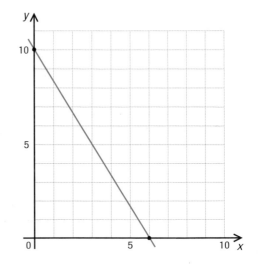

7. In a polygon of constraints $ABCD$, what can be said about boundaries AB and CD if the coordinates of all the points on these boundaries produce, respectively, the minimum value and the maximum value of a function to be optimized?

8. Determine all the points with integer coordinates on a line segment whose endpoints have the following coordinates:

a) $(0, 0)$ and $(8, 4)$ **b)** $(-1, 3)$ and $(7, -5)$ **c)** $(-12, 5)$ and $(38, 10)$

9. If $A(0, 0)$, $B(5, 8)$ and $C(2, 17)$ are the vertices of a polygon of constraints and m is the slope of a scanning line, find all the possible values of m that produce a maximum for the following, if m is a negative number:

a) All points on line segment BC.

b) The point $(5, 8)$.

c) The point $(2, 17)$.

a) Four students made the following statements about optimization problems:

1) The coordinates of the highest point of a polygon of constraints always maximize the function to be optimized.

2) In a polygon of constraints, the coordinates of the point closest to the origin always minimize the function to be optimized.

3) The coordinates of the lowest point of a polygon of constraints always minimize the function to be optimized.

4) In a polygon of constraints, the coordinates of the point farthest from the origin always maximize the function to be optimized.

Prove that each of these statements is false by providing a counter-example.
Use a scanning line.

b) On the right is the graph for a system of linear-quadratic inequalities. The common region, shown in green, is like a polygon of constraints. We want to maximize the rule of the function $M = 3x + 4y$.

1) Draw a scanning line.

2) Visualizing the line as it moves, estimate the coordinates of the point that generates the highest value for M.

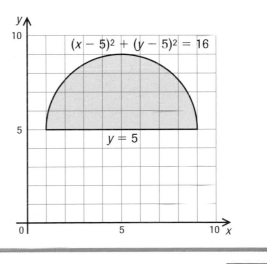

OPTIMIZATION PROBLEMS

Fasten your seat belt!

A driving school offers a program that includes a minimum of 5 theory classes and 5 practical classes. The number of theory classes is less than or equal to the number of practical classes and no one can register for more than 20 classes in all. A practical class costs $25 while a theory class costs $20. What is the minimum sum that must be spent to take this program?

a) If *x* represents the number of theory classes and *y* the number of practical classes, find the rule for objective *C*.

b) Represent the system of constraints for this example as a system of inequalities.

The graph of the polygon of constraints for the system is given below.

We know that the ordered-pair solution that optimizes the objective corresponds to one of the vertices of the polygon of constraints. But which one? To answer this question, draw the scanning line.

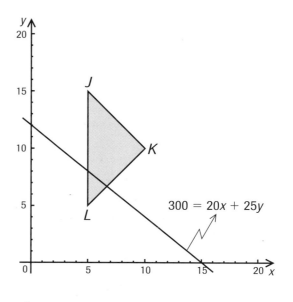

By replacing *C* with a meaningful value such as $300, we can represent the line with equation $300 = 20x + 25y$ or $y = 12 - \dfrac{4x}{5}$.

c) In which direction must we move the scanning line in this case, so that the value of *C* decreases?

d) By scanning the polygon of constraints with this line, find the vertex that produces the minimum cost.

e) Find the coordinates of this vertex using an algebraic method.

f) What is the minimum cost of the program offered by the driving school?

The method used to solve an optimization problem is:

1. Identify the x and y variables.
2. Determine the objective and its equation $M = ax + by + c$.
3. Represent the constraints as a system of inequalities.
4. Graph the polygon of constraints and the scanning line.
5. Find the vertices that optimize the function rule.
6. Determine the coordinates of one of these vertices.
7. Calculate the value of the objective at this vertex.
8. Compare the value obtained at other vertices to check the solution.

While still in school, George Dantzig was the first to develop a method for solving problems that involved various inequalities and variables. This method is known as the "simplex method."

Vanished into thin air

Each year nearly 500 boats are reported missing around the world. Imagine an uncharted island whose port can accommodate a maximum of 20 ships. The cruise ships and merchant ships that come to this port are boats that have vanished. Although there are always at least 5 merchant ships in port, there are always more cruise ships than merchant ships. On average, a cruise ship carries 750 people and a merchant ship 250. How many ships of each type should be anchored in the port to ensure the greatest possible number of people on the island?

a) If x represents the number of cruise ships, what does y represent?

b) Use words to describe the objective of this problem.

c) What is the function rule for this objective?

The graph of the polygon of constraints representing this situation is shown on the right. A scanning line is also shown.

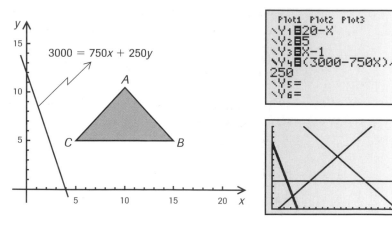

d) On the graph, find the vertex of the polygon whose coordinates generate the maximum value.

e) Find the coordinates of this vertex algebraically.

f) What is the maximum number of people that might be found on the island?

g) Find the maximum number of people that might be found on the island by completing the following table:

VERTEX	COORDINATES	NUMBER OF PEOPLE
A		
B		
C		

Calculating the rule at each vertex of the polygon of constraints is another way to solve an optimization problem.

INVESTMENT 7

1. Let $A(5, 1)$, $B(10, 6)$ and $C(3, 15)$ be the vertices of a polygon of constraints. Which of these points has coordinates that generate:

    a) A maximum for the function rule $M = 4x + 10y$?

    b) A minimum for the function rule $M = 3x + 2y$?

2. For each polygon of constraints defined by the following systems of inequalities, find the coordinates of the points that satisfy the given objective.

a)

$$x \geqslant 0$$
$$y \geqslant 0$$
$$y \leqslant 10 - 2x$$
$$y \geqslant \frac{x}{2}$$

Rule: $M = x + 10y$

Objective: maximize.

b)

$$x \geqslant 1$$
$$y \geqslant 6$$
$$y \geqslant 2x + 4$$
$$y \leqslant -2x + 20$$

Rule: $M = 2x + 6y$

Objective: minimize.

c)

$$y \leqslant 5x - 12$$
$$y \geqslant x$$
$$y \leqslant -3x + 36$$

Rule: $M = 3x + 4y$

Objective: maximize.

3. A furniture manufacturer makes either maple or oak cabinets. It can complete up to 90 cabinets per month. Depending on the orders, it will make at least 50 maple cabinets and at least 20 oak cabinets each month. Because the supply of oak is limited, however, the company must produce at least twice as many maple cabinets as oak cabinets. There is a profit of $150 on the sale of a maple cabinet and $275 on the sale of an oak cabinet. We want to know the number of cabinets of each type that the company must deliver monthly in order to maximize its profits.

a) Identify each of the variables.

b) Describe the objective and state the rule.

c) Represent each of the constraints as an inequality.

d) Graph the polygon of constraints and draw a scanning line.

e) Find the vertices whose coordinates optimize the function rule.

f) How many cabinets of each type must the cabinet company deliver each month to meet its objective?

g) How much is its profit?

A cabinetmaker is someone who specializes in making high-quality wood furniture.

4. A municipality in the Laurentians wants to produce a book on its history. To cover some of the production costs, it must find a maximum of 30 sponsors. A sponsor can choose either a half-page colour advertisement that costs $75 or an $80 full-page black-and-white advertisement. At least 20 pages have to be set aside for advertisements. At least twice as many sponsors choose the half-page colour advertisement as the black-and-white page. We want to know the number of advertisements of each type that must be sold to yield the maximum advertising revenue.

a) What are the two variables?

b) State the equation that translates the objective.

c) Provide the system of inequalities derived from the constraints of the problem, and graph the system.

d) Using the method of your choice, determine the number of advertisements of each type that must be sold in order to yield the maximum advertising revenue.

e) What is the maximum revenue?

5. At a fund-raising benefit for a youth centre, the donations received are in $10 and $20 bills. At the beginning of the day, at least three $20 bills have been donated. By the end of the day, the amount raised is estimated to be at least $120 and at most $240. We also know that the number of $10 bills is greater than or equal to the number of $20 bills.

a) If the number of $10 bills is x and the number of $20 bills is y, find the function rule.

b) What is the maximum amount raised at the fund-raiser?

c) What is the largest possible number of $20 bills? In that case, how many $10 bills are there?

d) What is the largest possible number of $10 bills? In that case, how many $20 bills are there?

6. The card game *Magic* is very popular among teenagers. Because some cards are common and others rare, they do not all have the same value. Before a trade, Roger has at least as many rare cards as he has common cards. The difference between the number of cards of each type does not exceed 20. In all, Roger has between 60 and 80 cards. If he receives 5 common cards in exchange for one rare card, how many cards of each type should he have at the start of trading to finish with the largest number of cards once trading is over?

A cross between card games and role-playing games, Magic was invented in 1993 by Richard Garfield, an American mathematician specializing in combinatorial mathematics.

7. The vertices of a polygon of constraints have points $A(0, 0)$, $B(10, 0)$, $C(15, 5)$ and $D(10, 15)$. Determine one or more ordered pairs that generate the maximum value for the objective defined by the rule $M = 4x + 2y$.

a) Graph the polygon of constraints *ABCD*.

b) Determine the value of the objective using the coordinates of each vertex.

c) Find the coordinates of all the points whose coordinates have integral values and generate the maximum.

8. We want to maximize $M = 2x + 4$ according to the constraints given in the system of inequalities shown on the right.

a) Display the polygon of constraints on a graphing calculator.

b) Choose a reasonable value for M, and draw the scanning line on the same display screen.

c) Display the table of values and find the coordinates of the point that maximizes the objective.

d) If the inequality $y \leqslant 17 - x$ is added to the system, do we obtain the same ordered-pair solution? Explain your answer.

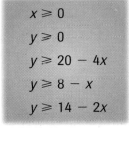

$y \geqslant 4$

$y \geqslant 20 - 4x$

$y \leqslant \dfrac{35 - x}{4}$

9. The system of inequalities at right represents a set of constraints. The graph is found below.

a) What is different about this polygon?

b) What are the coordinates of the point that minimizes the following function rules?

  1) $M = 10x + y$

  2) $M = x + 10y$

c) Can we find a function rule that has a maximum, given the same constraints?

$x \geqslant 0$

$y \geqslant 0$

$y \geqslant 20 - 4x$

$y \geqslant 8 - x$

$y \geqslant 14 - 2x$

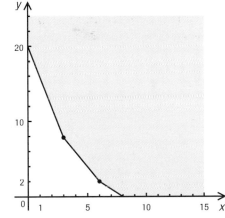

An expert must find forgeries in a collection of paintings. The difference between the number of originals and forgeries is greater than 1, and there are no more than 8 paintings in all. Without hesitating, the expert claims that at least 2 are forgeries. Determine the maximum number of forgeries:

1) If the expert's claim is true.

2) If the expert's claim is false.

A **polygon of constraints** is the illustration, on a Cartesian plane, of the solution set of the system of inequalities that represents the constraints of a problem. This region is composed of all the points whose coordinates satisfy each of the inequalities of the system.

Generally, problems composed of constraints have a precise **objective.** This objective may be a maximum or a minimum and is represented by a function in the form **$M = ax + by + c$.**

If the target objective is:

• The **highest** value, we must look for a **maximum.**

• The **lowest** value, we must look for a **minimum.**

To solve an **optimization problem** is to look for the **solution that generates a maximum or a minimum value for the objective within the constraints.**

The solution of an optimization problem may be **the coordinates of one of the vertices** or the coordinates of **the points forming a side** of the polygon of constraints.

Once we know the coordinates of the vertices of a polygon of constraints, we can simply calculate the value of the function rule at each of these vertices. This determines at which vertex the objective is optimized.

Generally, it takes considerable time to find the coordinates of all the vertices of a polygon of constraints. By sketching a **scanning line** upon the graph of the polygon of constraints, we can **quickly** find the vertex or side whose coordinates generate the optimum value.

Follow this procedure systematically:

1. Identify the x and y variables.

2. Determine the function rule $M = ax + by + c$.

3. Represent the constraints as a system of inequalities.

4. Graph the polygon of constraints and show the scanning line.

5. Find the vertices that optimize the function rule.

6. Find the coordinates of one of these vertices.

7. Calculate the value of the function rule at this vertex.

8. Compare the value obtained by the scanning line at other vertices to check the solution.

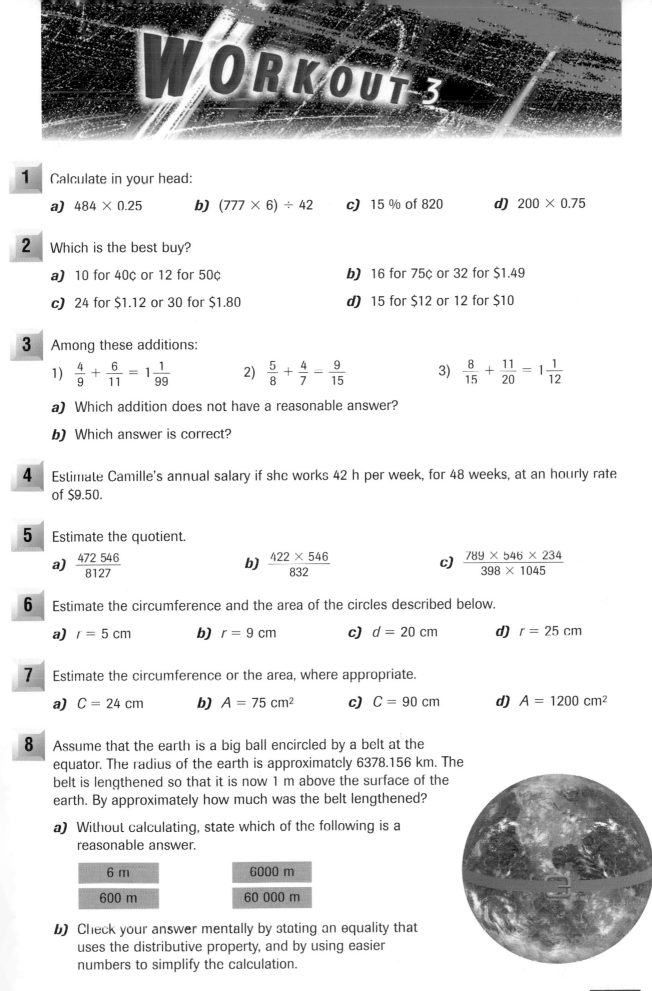

WORKOUT 3

1 Calculate in your head:

a) 484×0.25 **b)** $(777 \times 6) \div 42$ **c)** 15 % of 820 **d)** 200×0.75

2 Which is the best buy?

a) 10 for 40¢ or 12 for 50¢ **b)** 16 for 75¢ or 32 for $1.49

c) 24 for $1.12 or 30 for $1.80 **d)** 15 for $12 or 12 for $10

3 Among these additions:

1) $\frac{4}{9} + \frac{6}{11} = 1\frac{1}{99}$ 2) $\frac{5}{8} + \frac{4}{7} = \frac{9}{15}$ 3) $\frac{8}{15} + \frac{11}{20} = 1\frac{1}{12}$

a) Which addition does not have a reasonable answer?

b) Which answer is correct?

4 Estimate Camille's annual salary if she works 42 h per week, for 48 weeks, at an hourly rate of $9.50.

5 Estimate the quotient.

a) $\frac{472\ 546}{8127}$ **b)** $\frac{422 \times 546}{832}$ **c)** $\frac{789 \times 546 \times 234}{398 \times 1045}$

6 Estimate the circumference and the area of the circles described below.

a) $r = 5$ cm **b)** $r = 9$ cm **c)** $d = 20$ cm **d)** $r = 25$ cm

7 Estimate the circumference or the area, where appropriate.

a) $C = 24$ cm **b)** $A = 75$ cm² **c)** $C = 90$ cm **d)** $A = 1200$ cm²

8 Assume that the earth is a big ball encircled by a belt at the equator. The radius of the earth is approximately 6378.156 km. The belt is lengthened so that it is now 1 m above the surface of the earth. By approximately how much was the belt lengthened?

a) Without calculating, state which of the following is a reasonable answer.

6 m	6000 m
600 m	60 000 m

b) Check your answer mentally by stating an equality that uses the distributive property, and by using easier numbers to simplify the calculation.

9 In a major hotel, guests can use several elevators. An elevator takes a maximum load of 1560 kg. It is assumed that a man's average mass is 75 kg and that a woman's is 60 kg. At one point, the elevator contains twice as many women as men and there are at least 3 men. We want to know the minimum load of the elevator at that moment.

a) What are the two variables in this example?

b) Describe the target objective.

c) Determine the function rule.

d) Provide the system of inequalities for the constraints of the problem, then graph the system.

10 During an archaeological dig, Mahmoud finds a rock on which there is information and a map. After he decodes the information, he realizes that it is a list of inequalities that define a region on the map. The inequalities are shown on the right.

A point in a set of axes is seen on the map. What are its coordinates if it is the farthest point from the origin in the polygon of constraints?

An archaeological dig.

11 Let $A = \{(x, y) \mid 3 \leqslant x \leqslant 8 \wedge 2 \leqslant y \leqslant 6\}$ and $B = \{(x, y) \mid 2 \leqslant x \leqslant 6 \wedge 3 \leqslant y \leqslant 8\}$ the set of points obtained by interchanging x for y in A.

a) Graph set A and set B.

b) Provide the coordinates of the vertices of the region common to A and B.

c) If this region is a polygon of constraints, what inequalities express these constraints?

d) Which point of the polygon of constraints maximizes $M = 2x + 3y$?

12 A machine shop produces propellers and gear systems for boats. It takes about 2 h to make a propeller and 3 h for a gear system. A regulation on noise pollution limits machine operation to 98 h per week. The space set aside for storage is 200 m³. A box containing a propeller occupies a volume of 1 m³ and a gear system needs 3 m³. A market survey concludes that the shop must make at least twice as many propellers as gear systems. If a propeller sells for $40 and a gear system for $60, find the maximum revenue.

a) What are the two variables in this example?

b) Find the equation of the function rule.

c) State the system of inequalities that describes the constraints of the problem, then graph the system.

d) Find the number of propellers and the number of gear systems that the shop should make to maximize its revenue.

e) How much is this revenue?

13 The graph on the right shows a polygon of constraints and the coordinates of each vertex are indicated. We want to optimize function $M = ax + by$. Assign values to the parameters **a** and **b** in the function rule such that:

a) Only the coordinates of vertex A produce a maximum.

b) Only the coordinates of vertex B produce a maximum.

c) The coordinates of vertices A and B both produce a maximum.

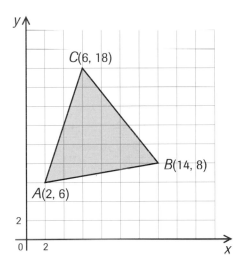

14 Danny earns a little money by offering guided tours in a horse-drawn buggy. The buggy can hold no more than 10 people, excluding the driver. The total mass of the passengers cannot exceed 500 kg. The average mass of an adult is 65 kg and that of a child is 30 kg. He expects to charge $7 per adult and $4 per child for a guided tour. He estimates that each time he gives a tour it will cost him $20. State the rule that Danny can use to calculate the profit for each tour.

A calèche ride outside Bonsecours Market in Old Montréal.

15 Among the ordered pairs (-2, 11), (0, 13), (7, 7) and (2, 12), we are looking for the one that will generate a maximum for the rule $M = 5.25x + 7.15y$. William suggests the following steps:

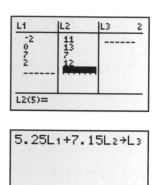

1. Enter each ordered pair.
2. Multiply the x-coordinates of the ordered pairs by 5.25 and the y-coordinates by 7.15, then add the results.
3. Look for the highest value among the results.

Using this method, find which of the ordered pairs (-5, -3), (7, 11), (3, 20) and (12, 4) has coordinates that generate a minimum for the following rules:

a) $M = 0.25x + 0.5y$ **b)** $M = 2x - 3y$ **c)** $M = 4x + 7y + 7.5$

16 The lines with equations $y = -2x + 16$ and $y = -\frac{x}{2} + 7$, which form four regions in the first quadrant, are shown on the graph at right.

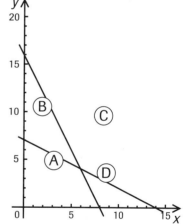

a) Match up each system of inequalities with one of the regions on the above graph.

1)
$x \geqslant 0$
$y \geqslant 0$
$y \geqslant -2x + 16$
$y \geqslant -\frac{x}{2} + 7$

2)
$x \geqslant 0$
$y \geqslant 0$
$y \leqslant -2x + 16$
$y \geqslant -\frac{x}{2} + 7$

3)
$x \geqslant 0$
$y \geqslant 0$
$y \geqslant -2x + 16$
$y \leqslant -\frac{x}{2} + 7$

4)
$x \geqslant 0$
$y \geqslant 0$
$y \leqslant -2x + 16$
$y \leqslant -\frac{x}{2} + 7$

b) Which of these regions corresponds to an unbounded polygon of constraints?

c) Provide the coordinates of the point common to all of these regions.

17 The system of inequalities shown on the right represents the constraints of a situation:

$$x \geqslant 0$$
$$y \geqslant 0$$
$$x \geqslant 10$$
$$y \geqslant 2x + 5$$
$$y \leqslant 80 - x$$

a) Graph the solution set of this system of inequalities.

b) Find the coordinates of the vertices of the resulting polygon of constraints.

c) Find the coordinates of three other points belonging to the polygon of constraints.

d) Which point:

   1) Minimizes the objective with the rule $M = 10x + 5y$?

   2) Maximizes the objective with the rule $M = 3x + 5y$?

18 The Aquadive Club offers scuba-diving lessons for teenagers. No more than 30 are allowed per class and each lesson costs $10. To meet security standards, there must be at least one monitor per 5 teens. The 5 monitors available each charge $20 per lesson. The class will be cancelled, however, if there are fewer than 10 teens registered. Determine the number of registrations and the number of monitors for the Aquadive Club to maximize its income within the various constraints.

Diver and Napoleon wrasse.

19 We want to determine the type of plane figure that, for a fixed perimeter, produces a maximum area. For example, if we have a 60 cm rope, what figure should we create with it to maximize the area?

a) Calculate the area of:

   1) An equilateral triangle with a perimeter of 60 cm.

   2) A rectangle with a length of 20 cm and a width of 10 cm.

   3) A square with a perimeter of 60 cm.

   4) A circle with a circumference of 60 cm.

b) What conjecture can you make from these results? Explain your answer.

20 The equations for 4 boundaries of a system of inequalities representing constraints were entered on the editing screen. The fifth equation corresponds to a scanning line for a given objective. On the graph, the scanning line is thicker.

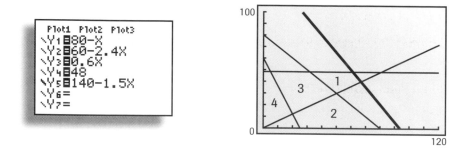

Determine the ordered pair that generates:

a) The maximum value for the polygon of constraints labelled 1.

b) The minimum value for the polygon of constraints labelled 2.

c) The minimum value for the polygon of constraints labelled 3.

d) The maximum value for the polygon of constraints labelled 4.

21 We want to solve an optimization problem with a graphing calculator. The system of inequalities that represents the constraints of the situation is shown on the right.

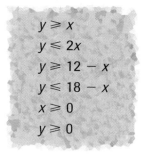

$$y \geqslant x$$
$$y \leqslant 2x$$
$$y \geqslant 12 - x$$
$$y \leqslant 18 - x$$
$$x \geqslant 0$$
$$y \geqslant 0$$

a) Display the boundaries associated with each inequality of the system using the following window.

```
WINDOW FORMAT
Xmin=0
Xmax=20
Xscl=2
Ymin=0
Ymax=20
Yscl=2
```

b) Find the region on the screen that corresponds to the polygon of constraints.

c) If the coordinates of the vertices are integers, find the coordinates using the cursor.

d) Find the ordered pair that produces a maximum if $M = 0.5x + y$.

22 Make up an optimization problem whose aim is to:

a) Maximize the profits from the sale of two products.

b) Minimize the manufacturing costs of two products.

23 A moving company has six-wheel and ten-wheel trucks. Before the first snowfall, the trucks need winter tires. The company has at most 150 of these tires. At that time of year, six-wheelers are in demand at least twice as often as ten-wheelers. However, the company must have at least 3 ten-wheelers ready for large moves. The profit is $175 per day from a six-wheeler and $210 per day from a ten-wheeler. We are looking for the number of trucks of each type in need of winter tires.

a) Using *x* as the number of six-wheelers and *y* as the number of ten-wheelers, state the function rule.

b) Graph the inequalities that represent the constraints.

c) Find the coordinates of each vertex.

d) Ignoring the situation, find the vertex whose coordinates maximize the function rule.

e) Considering the situation, could these coordinates be a solution? Explain.

f) Using a scanning line, find the solution for this optimization problem.

24 BLOCKING UVA AND UVB RAYS

The sun's rays can damage skin. We must protect ourselves especially against type A (UVA) and Type B (UVB) ultraviolet rays. A pharmaceutical company asks a biochemist to invent a compound for a lotion to filter out these two types of rays. To meet the company's requirements, the biochemist must produce at least 150 mL of a compound containing at least twice as much sun-block against UVAs as against UVBs. In addition, the compound must contain a minimum of 30 mL of UVB sun-block. The biochemist must produce this compound at the lowest possible price. One millilitre of UVA blocking agent costs 2¢ to produce, while one millilitre of UVB blocking agent costs 4¢.

a) If *x* represents the number of millilitres of UVA blocking agent and *y* the number of millilitres of UVB blocking agent contained in the compound, state the function rule.

b) How many millilitres of UVA blocking agent and UVB blocking agent should be used to produce a sun lotion at the lowest cost?

We should not expose ourselves to direct sunlight without the protection of an appropriate sun-block. We should especially avoid sunburns.

25 PROTECTING COMPUTER FILES

Computer files can be write-protected or read-protected. Carol has access to an application that contains at least 4 read-protected files. When we group half of the write-protected files and all read-protected files, we have no more than 6 files. At most there are 3 more read-protected files than write-protected files. Carol wants to know the contents of each file. It takes 30 s to open a write-protected file and 120 s to open a read-protected file. How many files of each type must the application contain to minimize the time it will take Carol to open them?

The concept of optimization is recent. In fact, it is only since 1947 that we have developed the methods for solving this type of problem. Computers are currently used to solve optimization problems consisting of a large number of inequalities and variables.

26 AYE, AYE, CAPTAIN!

Isabel is an apprentice ship's pilot and hopes one day to become a captain. During a one-month on-the-job training session, she must work on a catamaran and a sailboat. The number of hours she works per month on the catamaran exceeds the number of hours she works on the sailboat by at most 40 h.

Isabel has to work between 20 h and 40 h a month on the sailboat. The training lasts for a total of 60 to 100 h. On the catamaran, Isabel is paid $4/h and on the sailboat she earns $7/h. How must Isabel divide her time if she wishes to maximize her earnings during her training?

Docked catamaran

27 THE POWER OF SUGGESTION

A group of at least 40 people volunteered to be hypnotized. It is believed that suggestible people are easier to hypnotize than those who are strong-willed. In this group, the number of skeptical people combined with twice the number of suggestible people does not exceed 120. Although there are at least as many suggestible people as there are skeptical people, there are no more than 50 suggestible individuals. If a suggestible person has a 70% chance of being hypnotized and a skeptical person only a 35% chance, how many people of each type are required to hypnotize the maximum number of people?

28 FILLED TO CAPACITY

A rock concert is organized in a stadium that can hold 10 000 people. The tickets were sold in advance via ticket outlets, and at the stadium door on the day of the concert. At least 4000 tickets are sold in advance and a maximum of 3000 tickets can be sold at the stadium door. The number of tickets sold at the door is greater than one quarter of the tickets sold in advance. An advance ticket costs $18, while a ticket sold at the door costs $20.

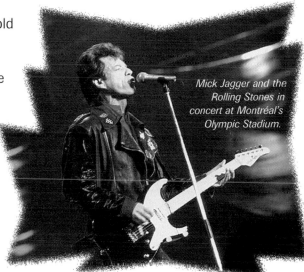

Mick Jagger and the Rolling Stones in concert at Montréal's Olympic Stadium.

a) What is the maximum profit that this concert can yield?

b) In this situation, how many tickets were sold in advance via ticket outlets?

29 THE Y2K BUG

In the late 1990s, companies around the world became concerned that their computers were not able to deal with dates in the year 2000. They began hiring consultants to make their computers "Y2K compatible." A company affected by this problem spends at most $100 000 over a six-month period to hire computer programmers and technicians. The services of a programmer cost $20 000 for six months and those of a technician, $10 000. There must be at least 2 programmers to begin the work and each should be assisted by least 2 technicians. If, in six months, a programmer can do 15% of the work and a technician can do 10%, how many programmers and technicians must the company hire to do as much of the work as possible in 6 months?

The world's first computer, the ENIAC, was invented in 1946 by two U.S. scientists. It was used to calculate rocket trajectories.

30 THE MAN FROM HAUSLABJOCH

In September 1991, after lying for dozens of centuries locked in a glacier, the Hauslabjoch Man was found in the Ötzal Alps. At the institution where the body is preserved, scientists attempted to determine the man's age using carbon dating and scanner dating techniques. The carbon dating test revealed that the body was not more than 8000 years old, while according to the scanner test, it was between 3000 and 5000 years old. For greater accuracy, they also carried out a combination of tests which revealed that the average of the ages obtained by each method was between 4000 and 6000 years.

Carbon is an element that occurs widely in nature and is a fundamental component of all living matter. The age of a fossil or skeleton can be estimated by the amount of carbon-14, or radioactive carbon, it contains.

a) Let x represent the man's age obtained by carbon dating and y the age obtained using scanner dating. Represent each of the results as an inequality.

b) Graph the polygon of constraints for the set of possible results.

c) If the specialists calculated the age of the Hauslabjoch Man using the rule $A = 0.6x + 0.4y$, what is his:

1) Maximum age?　　　2) Minimum age?

31 MOLECULES OF UNKNOWN ORIGIN

A research centre wants to test the interaction between oxygen atoms and molecules of unknown origin that came from a meteorite. After several laboratory experiments were conducted, a reaction occurred between the two when all the following conditions were met:

- The sum of the number of molecules of unknown origin and twice the number of oxygen atoms is equal to or greater than 8.

- The number of molecules of unknown origin does not exceed 12.

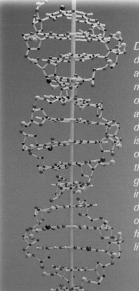

- The sum of the number of oxygen atoms and the number of molecules of unknown origin is not greater than 16.

If the molecule of unknown origin has 5 atoms, what is the maximum number of atoms involved in the reaction?

DNA, or deoxyribonucleic acid, is a very long molecule consisting of two spirals arranged in a double helix. DNA is the basic material of chromosomes, the carriers of genes. Thus, DNA indirectly determines the organization and functioning of all living matter.

32 MAKE YOUR MONEY WORK FOR YOU

Alan, a fanatic roulette player at the casino, developed a betting technique he thinks is infallible. He places one chip per slot on a certain number of black and red squares. The difference between the number of red slots chosen and half the number of black slots chosen must not exceed 4, while the difference between the number of black slots and one sixth of the number of red slots must not exceed 3. If the total number of slots chosen is greater than 1 and he bets $10 per black slot and $5 per red slot, what is Alan's maximum bet?

Calculating probabilities shows that a roulette player will lose, if not the first time, certainly in the long run. The casino reimburses up to 35 times the bet, but the ball can actually end up in 38 different slots (the first 36 numbers plus the 0 and the 00). Therefore, over a large number of plays, the casino has a theoretically unbeatable advantage of around 5.5%.

33 THE MOST FOR THE LEAST

A contractor wants to build a house with walls that look like a checkerboard. At least 2 t of white bricks and 2 t of black bricks are needed to build the house. The brick supplier, however, only has 4 t of white brick in stock. The difference between the number of tonnes of black bricks and the number of tonnes of white bricks does not exceed 3, while their sum does not exceed 9.

a) Find the coordinates of each of the vertices of the polygon of constraints in this example.

b) Explain the meaning of each of the coordinates of this vertex.

c) If 1 t of white bricks costs $400 and 1 t of black bricks costs $300, what is the minimum amount that the contractor needs to purchase the brick?

Photograph of a checkerboard from the Middle Ages. The game of checkers was invented around the year 1000, most likely in the south of France. The medieval version, called "fierges" used a chessboard and 12 pieces for each player. The pieces were moved along a diagonal in any direction. The black-and-white checkerboard dates back to the 16th century.

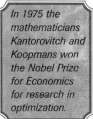

In 1975 the mathematicians Kantorovitch and Koopmans won the Nobel Prize for Economics for research in optimization.

POP·QUIZ

3

1. Let $A(7, 10)$, $B(10, 6)$, $C(20, 4)$ and $D(15, 12)$ be the vertices of a polygon of constraints. Of the points forming this polygon, which has coordinates that generate:

   a) A maximum if the function rule is $M = 40x + 10y$?

   b) A minimum if the function rule is $M = 2x + 3y$?

2. **A PREFABRICATED HOUSE**

   A factory that makes prefabricated houses has two models: one with a garage and one without. The factory can deliver a maximum of 22 houses per month and must deliver at least 18. To reduce inventory, it is decided that at least 6 houses without a garage will be built during the month. To fill the orders, they must deliver at least 2 more houses without a garage than houses with a garage. It costs $38 000 to build the model without a garage and $35 000 for the model with a garage. How many houses of each model must the factory build to minimize its production costs and fulfill its orders?

3. **WINNING ISN'T EVERYTHING . . .**

   An artist must make trophies and plaques for a school's sports awards ceremony. The winners receive a trophy and finalists get a plaque. A minimum of 8 winners and a maximum of 56 finalists must be selected. At least twice as many plaques as trophies are to be awarded. A trophy takes 8 g of bronze to make and a plaque needs 4 g. The artist has at most 320 g of bronze. A trophy costs the school $30 and a plaque costs $12. How many winners and finalists should the selection committee choose to minimize costs for the award ceremony.

4. **SHAMPOO YOU COULD DRINK**

   In order to stand out from its competitors, a company decides to create a bubble-gum flavoured shampoo. The shampoo comes in 200 mL and 600 mL bottles. The company wants to bottle at least 60 L of shampoo per day. However, it can fill no more than 120 bottles per day. The smaller format is expected to sell at least 4 times better than the larger format. Under these conditions, what will be the company's maximum daily profit if the profit is 32¢ per 100 mL?

Interview with...

Mary Fairfax Somerville
(1780-1872)

Mrs. Somerville, is it true that you only went to school for one year?

Yes! My father was an Admiral in the British Navy and I was raised near the sea. The beach was my backyard. But when I was 9, and my father returned after a long absence, he said I was becoming "uncivilized." He then sent me to a boarding school for young girls.

But why only for a year?

I was unhappy there: we were made to memorize entire pages out of the dictionary! We were also forced to wear an iron corset to keep our backs straight. I cried so much during that year that my parents pulled me out.

Where did your interest in mathematics come from?

As a child, stars and constellations always fascinated me. In a book on navigation, I read that one had to be well grounded in mathematics in order to learn astronomy. This led me to study mathematics.

How did you manage it without going to school?

Alone! My brother's private tutor helped me, though: he agreed to buy math textbooks on my behalf in secret. Women were not allowed to buy such books, and my parents were against me studying such a topic.

So you studied secretly?

I studied at night, while my family was sleeping. One day the servants complained to my parents of candles mysteriously disappearing. My father discovered why and confiscated the candles.

Mary Fairfax Somerville wrote three other science books that further solidified her reputation. She was one of the first two women to be elected to the British Royal Astronomical Society. The explorer Parry named an island in the Arctic "Somerville" in her honour, and one of the first colleges for women at Oxford is called "Somerville College."

Mary Somerville spent much of her childhood waiting for her father to return from his long sea voyages.

a) If Mary measured 1.4 m, find the maximum distance she could see to the horizon.

b) Find the maximum distance a person measuring 1.7 m could see standing on a cliff 30 m high.

MY PROJECTS

PROJECT 1   The ABCs of school administration

For this project, pretend you are the principal of a secondary school. Not an easy job! Among other tasks, you must account for various elements in the school budget, such as the number of students attending the school and the number of teachers required for the school to function properly. Some of these elements are given below:

• Minimum number of students and teachers required to keep the school open.

• The student-to-teacher ratio to ensure teaching quality.

• Maximum capacity of the school in relation to the space available.

• Average cost of educating a student.

The project is to set up a certain number of constraints, find a function rule that represents your school's administration, and then solve the resulting optimization problem and interpret the results.

PROJECT 2   A well-planned diet

Have you ever been on some kind of diet (physical fitness diet, no salt diet, weight-loss diet, etc.)? If so, this project will surely interest you. If not, you should know that, according to statistics, chances are you will be on a diet at some point in your life.

A good weight-loss diet consists of two indispensable elements: balanced meals and exercise.

This project involves conducting realistic research that takes into account the time constraints related to preparing balanced meals and being physically active. The following are several examples:

• Calculating your appropriate body weight.

• Number of kilojoules allowed daily.

• Average cost of physical activities and the diet plan.

• Weight loss resulting from exercise and one day of dieting.

Once you have determined the number of constraints and a rule to represent the objective, you must solve the optimization problem and provide an accurate interpretation of the results. Also, explain the limits of the study in the real world.

I KNOW THE MEANING OF THE FOLLOWING EXPRESSIONS:

Boundary: A line marking the limit of a half-plane.

Constraint: Condition that is described in words and that can be represented algebraically as an inequality.

First-degree inequality in two variables: Algebraic statement that can be written in the form $y \gtrless ax + b$ and whose graph is a half-plane delimited by a boundary line.

Function rule: Algebraic rule or equation that represents the objective.

Half-plane: Graph of the solution set of a first-degree inequality in two variables.

Closed half-plane: A half-plane whose coordinates for the boundary belong to the solution set of the inequality. The boundary is drawn as a solid line.

Open half-plane: A half-plane whose coordinates for the boundary are not part of the solution set of the inequality. The boundary is drawn as a dotted line.

Inequality: An algebraic statement consisting of one or more variables and an inequality symbol.

Maximum: The greatest value of the objective.

Minimum: The smallest value of the objective.

Optimization: Process that determines the maximum or minimum while taking into account certain constraints.

Objective function: The function to be optimized.

Polygon of constraints: Figure on a Cartesian plane that corresponds to the solution set of a system of inequalities representing constraints.

Scanning line: Line that represents the function rule and that is shifted through successive translations to find the minimum or maximum of the objective.

Solution of an inequality: Value that satisfies an inequality. The set of these values is called the solution set of the inequality.

Solution of an inequality in two variables: Any ordered pair whose coordinates satisfy the inequality. The solution set is formed by all these pairs.

System of inequalities: Two or more inequalities derived from a single situation and that use the same variables.

METRIC RELATIONSHIPS

MAIN IDEAS

- ▶ Constructing a deductive system in geometry.
- ▶ The logic of a proof.
- ▶ Similarity and metric relationships in the right triangle.
- ▶ Metric relationships in the circle.

TERMINAL OBJECTIVE

- ▶ To solve geometry problems.

INTERMEDIATE OBJECTIVES

- ▶ To **understand** geometric proofs.
- ▶ To **prove** propositions related to circles and right triangles.
- ▶ To **find** measurements in circles and right triangles.

| ELEMENTS OF A DEDUCTIVE SYSTEM |
| PROOF |
| STEPS IN A PROOF |

ELEMENTS OF A DEDUCTIVE SYSTEM

Seeking a foundation

Several hundred years before the Christian Era, the first Greek mathematicians, including Thales and Pythagoras, put forward many geometric propositions and results that all seemed equally credible. But the plethora of statements and the lack of foundation for them created confusion. Euclid thus took on the enormous task of tidying up the mess.

Thales of Alexandria, perhaps the first Greek to take an interest in geometry, was inspired to do so during a visit to Egypt.

The year is 290 BC; the place, Alexandria, Egypt. King Ptolemy I shows Euclid around the Academy founded by Plato, where he has just appointed the mathematician as a professor.

Until the 19th century, mathematicians were known as geometers.

So, Euclid, you have decided to organize geometry! How do you plan to go about it?

I've been thinking about it for a long time! But where do I begin? I have to start somewhere! I've found an intriguing approach. . .

Euclid used the following principle to organize geometry: a mathematical statement is true only if it can be deduced from statements that have already been proved. Euclid therefore had to identify fundamental statements that could be used to prove other statements. However, these fundamental statements had to be proved as well. Since the process could be endless, Euclid had to accept a number of statements without proving them. To avoid controversy, he used the most obvious statements. These basic statements are called **axioms** (or postulates); the conjectures to be proved are called **theorems.**

The rigour demanded in mathematics requires that words be carefully chosen, and **carefully defined.** Euclid had the same difficulties with the definitions that he experienced with theorems. To define one term, he had to use others. To avoid circular definitions, he was forced to use certain terms without defining them. These words are called **basic terms.**

Basic terms and axioms are like the atoms of geometry.

The main elements in a deductive system are basic terms, definitions, axioms and theorems.

Like Euclid, we will construct a **system** of definitions, axioms and theorems for geometry.

First, the basic terms must be identified:

a) Choose a few geometry words that could be considered basic terms. For example, start with a word such as "triangle" and formulate a definition for it. Then define each of the geometric terms used in the first definition. Continue until all the basic terms have been found.

There are several geometries, each organized according to its own system of axioms.

Another way to find basic terms is to ask what geometry is.

In your opinion, what exactly is geometry?

Geometry is the science of space. Think of space as a pile of planes that contain line segments, which themselves are made up of points.

The concept of space can be a starting point. We have an intuitive knowledge of space—at least the space in which we exist and that we perceive with our senses. We appear to live in a **three-dimensional space** in which objects are placed relative to each other in terms of height, width and depth.

b) We usually say that space is made up of points, line segments and planes. Can these terms be defined?

What exactly is a point?

A point is something that has no size.

Space can be divided into parts, and the point is the smallest possible part. A point has no length, no height and no width. Space is often said to be a set of points distributed in three dimensions. A plane can thus be defined as a set of points distributed in two dimensions, and a line segment can be defined as a set of points distributed in one dimension. But how can "dimension" be defined?

When we speak of a dimension, such as height, width or depth, the concept of the line is implicit. But if we use "line" to define "dimension," and then use "dimension" to define "line," we create a vicious circle.

To complicate things further, the usual concept of a line refers to a set of points such that there is always another point between any two points on the line; a line can therefore be subdivided endlessly. However, this runs counter to the idea that there is a limit to the subdivision of space, that limit being the point. It is a paradox!

Mathematicians and philosophers debated these issues for a long time. Today, mathematicians get around the difficulty by treating **point, line** and **plane** as basic terms.

This means we can stop trying to define these terms. However, we carefully describe the properties of these elements in our arguments using axioms. This is known as the **axiomatic approach.**

It is difficult to imagine an infinite line and an infinite number of points between two points.

Of course it is! We use limited representations when, in fact, geometric figures exist only in our imaginations.

Axioms about points, lines and planes

- Any line is a set of at least two points.
- Through any two distinct points, there is exactly one line.
- Every plane contains at least three points that are not all on the same line.

Since the axiom states that a line is a set of points, we can state that a point **belongs** or does not belong to a given line, or that a line **passes through** or does not pass through a given point. The word "collinear" can thus be defined without creating a vicious circle.

Points are **collinear** when they belong to the same line.

c) What axiom can we use to state that two points are always collinear?

d) Using words that have already been defined, or the three basic terms introduced so far, define:

1) Intersecting lines. 2) Parallel lines.

So it is possible to base deductions on a few axioms and definitions.

You've got it! But the statements that we can deduce, called **theorems,** must be proved or demonstrated.

These definitions and axioms allow us to deduce an initial theorem.

Intersecting Line Theorem

Two distinct lines have at most one point in common.

Problem

Hypothesis: *AB* and *CD* are two distinct lines.

Conclusion: *AB* and *CD* have at most one point in common.

Proof

1. Imagine that lines *AB* and *CD* have two different points in common, *M* and *N*.

2. In this case, two different lines would pass through these two different points, contradicting the axiom that states that exactly one line passes through two points.

3. Therefore, two distinct lines have, at most, one point in common.

On the other hand, the concept of **parallelism** leads to an axiom that seems self-evident.

Parallel Axiom (also called the Parallel Postulate)

> Through a point not on a given line, there can be drawn one and only one line parallel to the given line.

Of course, not all of geometry can be based upon axioms involving points and lines. For example, they cannot help us define these two expressions: "a point between two other points" and "two points on the same side of a line." Two additional axioms are needed.

Ray Axiom

> Any point *P* belonging to a line *l* determines two subsets of this line, called **rays,** such that:
>
> • *l* is the union of the two subsets;
>
> • the intersection of the two subsets contains only *P*, which is the **origin** or endpoint;
>
> • each subset contains at least one point other than *P*.

The ray with endpoint *P* that contains another point *A* is usually called "ray *PA*."

The Ray Axiom leads to these two definitions:

> Two rays are **opposite** when they:
>
> • have the same origin;
>
> • have only the origin in common;
>
> • are on the same line.
>
> Point *P* is said to be between points *A* and *B* when rays *PA* and *PB* are opposite.

e) Define "line segment" and "triangle" using only terms introduced thus far.

A line segment with endpoints A and B is written $\overline{AB}$; the triangle defined by points A, B and C is written $\triangle ABC$.

The idea that a point divides a line into two subsets can also be used in the case of a line relative to a plane.

Half-Planes Axiom

Any line l in a given plane determines two subsets of points, **called half-planes,** such that:

- the plane is the union of the two subsets;
- line l is the intersection of the two subsets;
- if the half-plane contains points A and B, it also contains line segment AB;
- if the half-plane contains point A and the other contains point B, then line l contains at least one point on line segment AB.

f) Make sketches to illustrate the different possibilities for this axiom, depending on whether points A and B are on line l or not (there are 4 cases).

g) Using basic terms and words that have already been defined, write an appropriate definition for each of these expressions:

1) Two points "on the same side" of a line.

2) Two points "on opposite sides" of a line.

You are interested in all kinds of figures. Surely you are also interested in the measurement of these figures.

True! The word geometry means "measurement of the earth," so the idea of measurement cannot be ignored.

According to Proclus, the Egyptians invented geometry for the purposes of surveying land that was frequently flooded by the Nile.

Historically, geometry developed out of all kinds of measurement problems, particularly those related to line segments and angles.

Measurement consists of assigning numbers to certain magnitudes. Thus, the concept of measurement introduces numbers into geometry. To introduce the measurement of a line segment, however, the concept of **distance** must come into play.

Distance axioms

- A function d associates a positive real number and a unit called distance to each pair of points A, B; the function is written $d(A, B)$.
- The distance between points A and B is zero if and only if $A = B$.
- The distance between two points is not related to their order ($d(A, B) = d(B, A)$).

It is this distance between two points A and B that is used to define the **length** of line segment AB. The distance is usually accompanied by a unit.

These axioms ensure that whenever two distinct points exist, there is a positive number corresponding to the distance between these two points, or to the length of the line segment that connects them. These axioms alone are not enough to define all the characteristics of the concept of distance, however.

h) For three points A, B and C, how many pairs of points, and how many distances can there be?

i) Can any three positive real numbers correspond to the distances between three points?

j) For each of the cases shown, what can be said about $d(A, C)$ relative to $d(A, B)$ and $d(B, C)$?

These considerations justify a fourth axiom involving distance.

Three-Point Axiom

Given three points, and three distances between these points considered pairwise:

- each distance is smaller than or equal to the sum of the other two distances;
- the three points are collinear if and only if one of the three distances is equal to the sum of the other two distances;
- a point is between two other points if and only if the sum of the distances from this point to each of the other two points is equal to the distance between these other two points.

k) The Three-Point Axiom leads to the following theorem. Complete the statement.

Triangle Inequality Theorem

In a triangle, the length of any side is smaller than ▆▆▆▆.

l) Is it possible to construct a triangle with sides 2 cm, 3 cm and 7 cm?

m) Determine the possible interval for the length of the third side of a triangle if the other two sides measure 6 cm and 9 cm.

n) Complete the statement.

"A point is located on a side of a triangle if and only if ███████."

Another fundamental measurement in geometry is that of the angle. Before introducing this measurement, though, the concept of angle must be defined.

The angle is a complex concept. How would you define it?

An angle is a broken line. This is why it always measures less than 180°.

o) Define the concept of angle using basic terms or words that have already been defined.

p) Do rays *AB* and *AC* form one angle or two angles?

If an angle is defined as a figure formed by two rays with the same origin, it can be assigned a measure by adding this new axiom:

Angle Measure Axiom

The function m that associates a real number and a unit with any angle *BAC* is called the measure of the angle; this function is written m ∠ *BAC*.
If the degree is the unit of measure, then 0° ≤ m ∠ *BAC* ≤ 180°.

  m ∠*BAC* = 0° if and only if rays *AB* and *AC* are coincident.

  m ∠*BAC* = 180° if and only if rays *AB* and *AC* are opposite.

If an angle is defined as that part of a plane bounded by two rays having the same origin, then both non-reflex angles and reflex angles can be determined.

The reflex angle is designated by an arc. If the measure is expressed in degrees, then $0° \leq m \angle BAC \leq 360°$.

Non-reflex angle   Reflex angle

1. The concept of angle measure allows the following terms to be introduced. Define them.

   a) Zero angle   **b)** Acute angle   **c)** Right angle

   d) Obtuse angle   **e)** Straight angle

2. What is meant by supplementary or complementary angles?

3. Several other definitions are associated with angles. Use the sketches shown below to write a definition of adjacent angles.

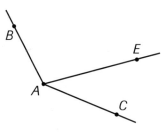 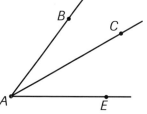 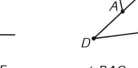

$\angle BAC$ and $\angle CAE$ $\angle BAC$ and $\angle CAE$ $\angle BAC$ and $\angle CDE$
  are not adjacent.   are adjacent.   are not adjacent.

4. What is meant by aligned adjacent angles?

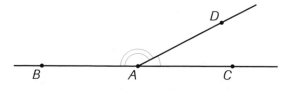

5. What statement can be formulated about two aligned adjacent angles?

6. Write a definition of "vertically opposite angles" based on the ray concept used to define angles.

7. Use a drawing to show what is meant by:

a) Alternate interior angles. **b)** Alternate exterior angles. **c)** Corresponding angles.

8. Naming lines and points, and using the concepts of "same side," "opposite sides" and "between," write definitions of:

a) Alternate interior angles. **b)** Alternate exterior angles. **c)** Corresponding angles.

9. Define:

a) The bisector of an angle. **b)** Perpendicular lines.

c) The perpendicular bisector of a line segment.

10. Points *A, B, C, D* and *E* are on a plane such that no line passes through three of the points. How many lines can be drawn that pass through two of them? (Use a sketch to illustrate your answer.)

11. Justify the following statement using the definitions and axioms that have already been introduced.

"If rays *AB* and *AC* are opposite, and if rays *AC* and *AD* are opposite, then rays *AB* and *AD* are coincident."

12. Provide a definition of "congruent line segments."

13. Provide a definition of the following types of triangle:

a) Isosceles. **b)** Equilateral. **c)** Right.

14. Provide a definition of the following:

a) Parallelogram. **b)** Rectangle. **c)** Rhombus. **d)** Square.

15. Given a plane containing line *l* and three points *A, B* and *C* not belonging to *l*, the following possibilities exist:

    1) *A* and *B* are on the same side of *l*, and *B* and *C* are on the same side of *l*.

    2) *A* and *B* are on the same side of *l*, and *B* and *C* are on opposite sides of *l*.

    3) *A* and *B* are on opposite sides of *l*, and *B* and *C* are on opposite sides of *l*.

a) For each case, state the relationship between *A* and *C* with respect to line *l*.

b) Justify each of your answers using axioms that have already been introduced.

a) Given three points *M, N* and *O* where $d(M, N) < d(M, O) + d(N, O)$. Do the three points form a triangle? Justify your answer.

b) Prove that the length of each side of a triangle *ABC* is greater than the difference between the lengths of the two other sides.

PROOF

Description game

Here is the description of a plane figure:

"Equilateral triangle *CDE* is constructed on side *CD* of square *ABCD* such that point *E* is on the same side of line *CD* as points *A* and *B*."

a) In which of these drawings does the position of point *E* correspond to the description?

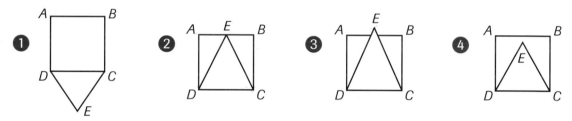

b) State why you excluded the other drawings.

Adding elements to the figure often makes justification easier.

In a proof, justifications can be:

- a starting hypothesis;
- a definition;
- an axiom;
- a theorem.

c) Line segments *AE* and *EB* are added to the initial description to obtain the figure shown here. Find the measure of each of the figure's 12 interior angles. Give reasons for each of your answers.

Deductive reasoning

Although this is not always immediately apparent, the axioms and theorems used to prove other theorems are, from a logical point of view, conditional or biconditional statements.

This is a **conditional** statement:

> **If** "HYPOTHESIS," **then** "CONCLUSION."
>
> "HYPOTHESIS," → "CONCLUSION."

Thus, the theorem:

"Two aligned adjacent angles are supplementary"

corresponds, in logical terms, to:

"**If** two adjacent angles are aligned, **then** they are supplementary."

A **biconditional** statement is as follows:

> "STATEMENT 1" **if and only if** "STATEMENT 2."
>
> "STATEMENT 1" ↔ "STATEMENT 2"

For example, the following is a biconditional statement: "Alternate interior angles are congruent **if and only if** the two lines intersected by a transversal are parallel."

Given the conditional statement:

> If "STATEMENT 1," then "STATEMENT 2,"

the following conditional statement is its **converse**:

> If "STATEMENT 2," then "STATEMENT 1."

a) State the converse for each of the following.

1) "If two adjacent angles are aligned, then they are supplementary."

2) "Vertically opposite angles are congruent."

b) If a conditional statement is true, is its converse necessarily true?

In fact, a biconditional statement is simply a convenient way to simultaneously state both a conditional statement and its converse.

Thus, the conditional statements:

"**If** alternate interior angles are congruent, **then** the two lines intersected by a transversal are parallel"

and

"**If** two lines intersected by a transversal are parallel, **then** the alternate interior angles are congruent"

become:

"Alternate interior angles . . . if and only if . . ."

c) Rewrite each statement as a conditional statement.

1) Vertically opposite angles are equal in measure.

2) The sum of the measures of the interior angles of a triangle is 180°.

3) A convex quadrilateral is a parallelogram if and only if its opposite sides are congruent.

4) Two triangles with a congruent angle between two congruent corresponding sides are isometric (congruent).

5) A triangle is a right triangle if and only if the square of the length of one of its sides is equal to the sum of the squares of the lengths of the other two sides.

6) The diagonals of a rhombus are perpendicular.

I would think that the order of the elements in a conditional statement can be reversed only in the case of a biconditional statement.

To construct a proof, we must use deductive reasoning to create a series of statements. Each step in the reasoning process leads to a new statement in the proof. This reasoning process is based on a logical principle called *modus ponens.*

Exactly! This is very important in stating a theorem or a problem: it is essential to know how to identify the "hypothesis" and the "conclusion."

Modus ponens

Each time two statements of the following type are accepted:

  Statement ①: Hypothesis *X* implies conclusion *Y.*

  Statement ②: The current situation demonstrates hypothesis *X.*

A third statement must also be accepted:

  Statement ③: Conclusion *Y* is also true in the current situation.

For example:

① If a quadrilateral contains four right angles, it is a rectangle.

② A square has four right angles.

③ Therefore a square is a rectangle.

The following proof of a theorem uses the principle of *modus ponens*:

Vertically Opposite Angles Theorem

Vertically opposite angles are congruent.

Problem

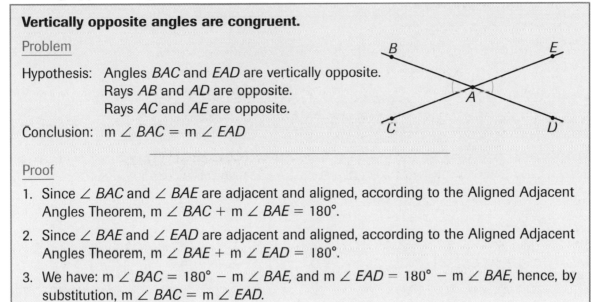

Hypothesis: Angles *BAC* and *EAD* are vertically opposite.
Rays *AB* and *AD* are opposite.
Rays *AC* and *AE* are opposite.

Conclusion: m ∠ *BAC* = m ∠ *EAD*

Proof

1. Since ∠ *BAC* and ∠ *BAE* are adjacent and aligned, according to the Aligned Adjacent Angles Theorem, m ∠ *BAC* + m ∠ *BAE* = 180°.

2. Since ∠ *BAE* and ∠ *EAD* are adjacent and aligned, according to the Aligned Adjacent Angles Theorem, m ∠ *BAE* + m ∠ *EAD* = 180°.

3. We have: m ∠ *BAC* = 180° − m ∠ *BAE*, and m ∠ *EAD* = 180° − m ∠ *BAE*, hence, by substitution, m ∠ *BAC* = m ∠ *EAD*.

This proof includes **three steps in reasoning.** Each one involves the application of *modus ponens*. The first two steps use the Aligned Adjacent Angles Theorem; the last uses the Substitution Axiom for equality. Here is how it works.

The first step corresponds to this reasoning:

Since these statements are accepted:
• if two adjacent angles are aligned, then they are supplementary,
• ∠ *BAC* and ∠ *BAE* are adjacent and aligned,
we must also accept the statement:
• m ∠ *BAC* + m ∠ *BAE* = 180° or m ∠ *BAC* = 180° − m ∠ *BAE*.

The second step is similar to the first:

Since these statements are accepted:
• if two adjacent angles are aligned, then they are supplementary,
• ∠ *BAE* and ∠ *EAD* are adjacent and aligned,
we must also accept the statement:
• m ∠ *BAE* + m ∠ *EAD* = 180° or m ∠ *EAD* = 180° − m ∠ *BAE*.

The third step uses this reasoning:

Since these statements are accepted:
• if two numbers are both equal to a third number, then they are equal to each other,
• m ∠ *BAC* = 180° − m ∠ *BAE* and m ∠ *EAD* = 180° − m ∠ *BAE*,
we must also accept the statement:
• m ∠ *BAC* = m ∠ *EAD*.

Proofs are an essential part of geometry. Without them, geometry would be nothing more than a science of observation.

A statement can usually be proven in several different ways. In the case of conditional statements, either a **direct** or an **indirect** proof can be given.

The proof of the Vertically Opposite Angles Theorem is a direct proof.

We begin with the statement to be proved.

"If two angles are vertically opposite angles, then they are congruent."

The "hypothesis" of the statement to be proved is accepted at the start:

Given two vertically opposite angles ∠ *BAC* and ∠ *EAD*.

After three steps in reasoning, the "conclusion" of the statement to be proved is reached:

m ∠ *BAC* = m ∠ *EAD*

A **direct proof** consists of:

1. Initially accepting the "hypothesis" of the statement to be proved.

2. Reaching the "conclusion" of the statement to be proved after a number of steps in reasoning.

An **indirect proof** or **proof by contradiction** consists of:

1. Initially accepting the "hypothesis" of the statement to be proved.

2. Initially accepting the negation of the "conclusion" of the statement to be proved.

3. After a number of steps in reasoning, contradicting an already proved statement such as an hypothesis, a definition, an axiom or a theorem.

The proof of the Intersecting Line Theorem seen earlier is a proof by contradiction. Here is why:

The hypothesis of the statement to be proved is accepted:

"Given two lines *AB* and *CD*."

The negation of the conclusion is accepted:

"The intersection of two lines *AB* and *CD* **does not contain** at most one point." It thus contains at least two points, for example *M* and *N*.

This statement contradicts an axiom.

It implies that "two distinct lines can pass through two points," which contradicts the axiom that states that "one and only one line passes through two points."

We must therefore accept the following statement:

"The intersection of two lines contains at most one point."

STEPS IN A PROOF

Approach

People who write proofs must be few and far between! Do your students enjoy drawing up proofs?

Not always! Recently one of my students asked me what he would gain from demonstrating proofs. I had my servant give him 3 oboli, since he was putting a price on learning! As you know, the advancement of knowledge is priceless.

The obol was an ancient Greek coin made of silver.

Drawing up a proof requires a specific procedure that, when followed, increases one's ability to prove propositions.

There are three main stages in demonstrating a proof:

– **state the problem;**

– **find the approach;**

– **construct the proof.**

① It is important to start by **clearly stating** the problem. To do this, you must:

> • identify the "hypothesis" and the "conclusion";
> • construct the figure that illustrates the statement, and label each part of the figure;
> • write out the hypothesis and the conclusion based on the constructed figure.

② Once the problem has been stated accurately, you **formulate an approach** to reflect the **general idea** of the proof. To do this, you must:

> • identify the relevant axioms and theorems, and formulate the main steps leading to the conclusion.

Such work demands thought. A good way to formulate the general idea of the proof is to imagine you are telling it to someone else.

③ The final step is to **construct the proof.** To do this, you must:

> • clearly show each step in reasoning, accompanied by the appropriate justifications.

A proof can be laid out in two columns (one for the statements and the other for the justifications), or in paragraphs, where each paragraph corresponds to a step in reasoning and includes the relevant justifications.

Learning to write proofs is a long-term process that requires a lot of practice.

The rethinking of the fundamentals of geometry focused attention on spaces rather than on figures. Figures became sets of points governed by what is called transformational geometry.

Isometric (congruent) triangles provide a good opportunity to develop proof-writing skills. Remember that:

> Figures are congruent if and only if they are related by an isometry.

a) Describe what is meant by an isometry.

The following theorem can be easily demonstrated using the properties of isometries:

Isometric (Congruent) Figures Theorem

> **The corresponding elements of two isometric figures are always congruent.**

It is not always necessary to refer to isometries, however, to show that two triangles are isometric. It is enough that certain **minimal conditions** be met.

b) Isometries can be used to prove three cases in which the congruence of a few elements guarantees that the two triangles are isometric (congruent), and therefore that the other elements are also congruent. State the three examples.

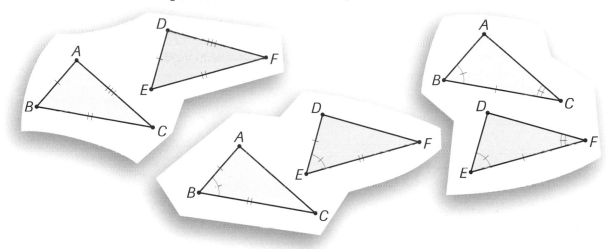

To determine the corresponding elements, think of an isometry that establishes correspondence between the vertices. This determines the corresponding angles and sides; that is, the angles and sides that are in relation.

c) If an isometry establishes this correspondence of the vertices in two triangles *ABC* and *DEF*, find the pairs of:

1) Corresponding angles.   2) Corresponding sides.

$A \mapsto D$
$B \mapsto E$
$C \mapsto F$

The notation
$\triangle ABC \cong \triangle DEF$ shows that there is correspondence between vertices A and D, B and E, C and F.

d) In general, if △ *ABC* ≅ △ *DEF*, can we conclude that:

1) △ *ABC* ≅ △ *DFE*?   2) △ *CBA* ≅ △ *FED*?

e) If △ *ABC* ≅ △ *ACB*, what can be concluded about this triangle?

The following proofs use isometric triangles.

Isosceles Triangle Theorem

> **In an isosceles triangle, the angles opposite the congruent sides are congruent.**

Problem

Hypothesis: Given △ *ABC* with $\overline{AB} \cong \overline{AC}$.

Conclusion: Prove that ∠ *B* ≅ ∠ *C*.

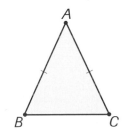

Approach

Adding point M in the middle of $\overline{BC}$, we can use one of the cases of isometric triangles to arrive at the conclusion.

In a sense, proofs are the visible part of geometry.

Construction of the proof

Demonstrate each step in reasoning using one of the two styles of proof.

Here are the two proofs created. Notice that each has the same problem, hypothesis and conclusion.

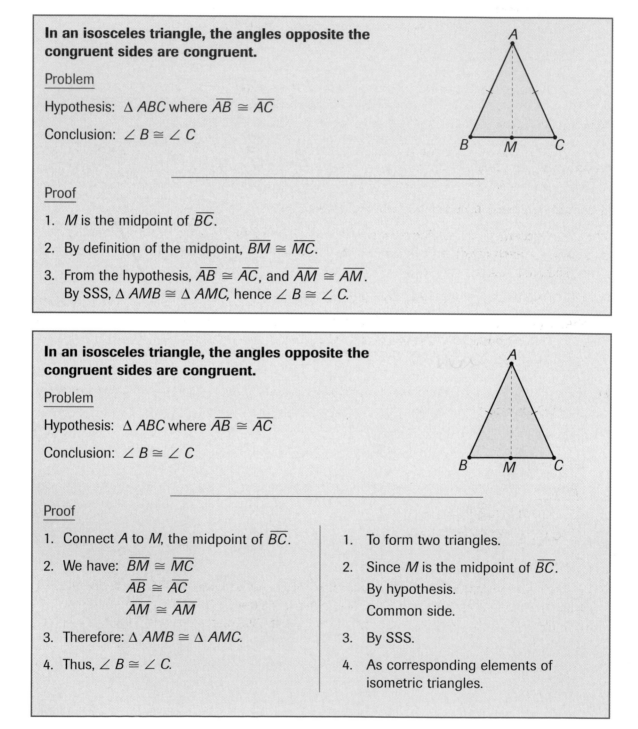

In an isosceles triangle, the angles opposite the congruent sides are congruent.

Problem

Hypothesis: $\triangle ABC$ where $\overline{AB} \cong \overline{AC}$

Conclusion: $\angle B \cong \angle C$

Proof

1. M is the midpoint of $\overline{BC}$.

2. By definition of the midpoint, $\overline{BM} \cong \overline{MC}$.

3. From the hypothesis, $\overline{AB} \cong \overline{AC}$, and $\overline{AM} \cong \overline{AM}$.
   By SSS, $\triangle AMB \cong \triangle AMC$, hence $\angle B \cong \angle C$.

In an isosceles triangle, the angles opposite the congruent sides are congruent.

Problem

Hypothesis: $\triangle ABC$ where $\overline{AB} \cong \overline{AC}$

Conclusion: $\angle B \cong \angle C$

Proof

1. Connect A to M, the midpoint of $\overline{BC}$.

2. We have: $\overline{BM} \cong \overline{MC}$
   $\overline{AB} \cong \overline{AC}$
   $\overline{AM} \cong \overline{AM}$

3. Therefore: $\triangle AMB \cong \triangle AMC$.

4. Thus, $\angle B \cong \angle C$.

1. To form two triangles.

2. Since M is the midpoint of $\overline{BC}$.
   By hypothesis.
   Common side.

3. By SSS.

4. As corresponding elements of isometric triangles.

f) Complete the procedure for proving the converse of the Isosceles Triangle Theorem.

1. Write the statement: ▇▇▇▇▇▇.

2. Problem:
   Hypothesis: △ *ABC* where ∠ *B* ≅ ∠ *C*
   Conclusion: $\overline{AB}$ ≅ $\overline{AC}$

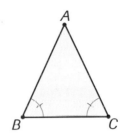

3. Formulate an approach: map the triangle onto itself using transformation *A* ↦ *A*, *B* ↦ *C* and *C* ↦ *B*, then show the isometry of the triangles.

4. Construct the proof: ▇▇▇▇▇▇.

g) Here is a theorem concerning the perpendicular bisector of a segment:

Perpendicular Bisector Theorem

> **A point is on the perpendicular bisector of a segment if and only if it is equidistant from the endpoints of the segment.**

Here, the statement to be proved is biconditional.

The usual procedure for proving a biconditional statement is to divide the proof into two parts, one for each conditional statement. Theoretically we can start with either one, but we may sometimes wish to use the first statement to prove the second.

1) Given the first statement, write the second statement.

   PART 1 (→): If a point is on the perpendicular bisector of a segment, then it is equidistant from the endpoints of the segment.

   PART 2 (←): ▇▇▇▇▇

2) To prove each part, we must state the problem, formulate an approach and construct the proof. Complete the following.

   PART 1

   Statement: ▇▇▇▇▇

   Problem

   Hypothesis: ▇▇▇▇▇.
   Conclusion: ▇▇▇▇▇.

   Approach

   By joining any point on the perpendicular bisector to the endpoints of the segment, two triangles are formed; they can be shown to be isometric by SAS. The case where the point is on both the segment and the perpendicular bisector must also be taken into account.

   Construction of the proof

   ▇▇▇▇

PART 2

Statement: ▆▆▆▆▆▆▆

Problem

    Hypothesis: ▆▆▆▆▆▆ .

    Conclusion: ▆▆▆▆▆▆ .

Approach

By joining the point to the endpoints and to the midpoint of the segment, two triangles are formed; they can be shown to be isometric by SSS. It can then be shown that the segment joining the point to the midpoint is a perpendicular, using the Aligned Adjacent Angles Theorem. The possibility that the point is on both the segment and the right bisector must also be taken into account.

Construction of the proof

▆▆▆▆▆▆▆

h) The following theorems will be important in the study of metric relationships in the circle. Complete and illustrate each one.

1) **Perpendicular Theorem**

> **Through a given point, exactly one perpendicular can be drawn to a given line.**

2) **Theorems on parallel and perpendicular lines**

> - **Two lines that are parallel to a third line are** ~~parallel~~ **to each other.**
> - **Two lines that are perpendicular to a third line are** ~~parallel~~ **.**
> - **Given two parallel lines, any line perpendicular to one is** ~~perpendicular~~ **to the other.**

3) **Alternate Interior Angle Theorem**

> **If a transversal cuts two lines at two distinct points, the** ~~alternate interior angles~~ **are congruent if and only if the two lines are** ~~parallel~~ **.**

4) **Corresponding Angle Theorem**

> **If a transversal cuts two lines at two distinct points, the** ~~corresponding angles~~ **are congruent if and only if the two lines are** ~~parallel~~ **.**

5) **Right Triangle Isometry Theorems**

> - **Two right triangles in which one pair of corresponding sides and one pair of corresponding acute angles are** ~~congruent~~ **must be** ~~congruent~~ **.**
> - **Two right triangles in which two pairs of corresponding sides are** ~~congruent~~ **must be** ~~congruent~~ **.**

6) **Exterior Angle Theorem**

> **The measure of an exterior angle of a triangle is equal to the sum of the measures of the** ~~angles~~ **.**

Euclid, isn't there a quicker way to study geometry than by using all these proofs?

Unfortunately, Your Majesty, there is no royal road to geometry.

Euclid (c. 300 BC),
Archimedes
(287–212 BC) and
Apollonius (c. 225
BC) were the three
leading geometers
of ancient times.
Without a doubt,
Archimedes was
the most important.

1. Two line segments AC and BD intersect at point O. If $\angle ACB \cong \angle DBC$ and $\angle ABC \cong \angle DCB$, prove $\triangle ABC \cong \triangle DCB$.

2. In $\triangle BAC$, $\overline{AB} \cong \overline{AC}$ and M is the midpoint of $\overline{BC}$. Prove that ray AM divides $\angle BAC$ into two congruent angles.

3. Given $\angle BAC$ and a point M such that $\overline{MB} \perp AB$ and $\overline{MC} \perp AC$ where $\overline{MB} \cong \overline{MC}$, prove that AM is the bisector of $\angle BAC$.

4. If points P and P' are on opposite sides of line AB, $\angle PAB \cong \angle P'AB$ and $\overline{AP} \cong \overline{AP'}$, prove $PP' \perp AB$.

5. In $\triangle ABC$, $\angle B \cong \angle C$. Point P is on line BC such that $AP \perp BC$. Prove that P is the midpoint of $\overline{BC}$.

6. Line l is a transversal of parallel lines l_1 and l_2 at points P and Q respectively. Point A is on l_1 and point B is on l_2 such that they lie on opposite sides of l. Prove that alternate interior angles APQ and PQB are congruent.
(Suggestion: Add midpoint M to $\overline{PQ}$ and draw a line perpendicular to l_1 through M.)

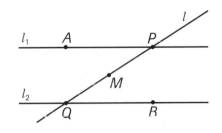

7. Use the Alternate Interior Angle Theorem to prove the Corresponding Angles Theorem.

8. Use the figure shown on the right, where $CD \parallel AB$, to prove the Triangle Angle Sum Theorem.

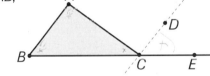

9. Prove the Exterior Angle Theorem.

10. Prove this theorem about parallelograms: "In a parallelogram, opposite sides and opposite angles are congruent."

The death of
Apollonius signalled
the end of the
golden age of
geometry.
Subsequent
geometers were of
lesser importance:
Hero (c. 75),
Menelaus (c. 100),
Claudius Ptolemy
(85–165) and
Pappus (320).

Theorems on parallel and perpendicular lines can be proved by contradiction. The first two are fairly straightforward. Try to do the proofs.

1) Lines l_1, l_2 and l_3 are such that $l_1 \parallel l_3$ and $l_2 \parallel l_3$. We must prove that l_1 is parallel to l_2. Assume that l_1 and l_2 are not parallel, and thus they must meet at a point P. Show that this contradicts an axiom, and the parallelism must therefore be accepted.

2) Use the same method to show that two lines perpendicular to a third line are parallel to each other.

SIMILARITY

FROM EUCLID TO CABRI

Software

Today graphics software is used more and more often in the study of geometry. This type of software allows us to construct and study all kinds of geometric configurations. The problems in this section refer to a specific software application, called *Cabri*.

In the *Cabri* workspace, various basic geometric objects, such as points, segments, lines, rays, circles and triangles can be drawn just as they would be on paper using a ruler and compasses. *Cabri* is faster, though, and we can ask it to:

If only I'd had software!

- perform geometric constructions such as perpendiculars, bisectors, right bisectors, and parallel lines;

- copy lengths or angles;

- display angle measures, lengths, perimeters, areas, etc., and the results of calculations that use these measurements;

- modify the basic objects while preserving the properties of the constructed objects;

- verify certain properties, etc.

Here is an example of how *Cabri* works.

$\triangle ABC$ and a ray with endpoint E are drawn.

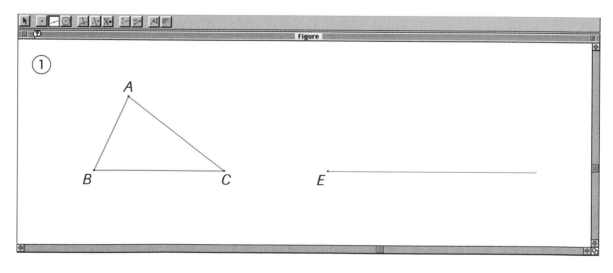

The length of $\overline{BC}$ is copied onto the ray, such that $\overline{EF} \cong \overline{BC}$.

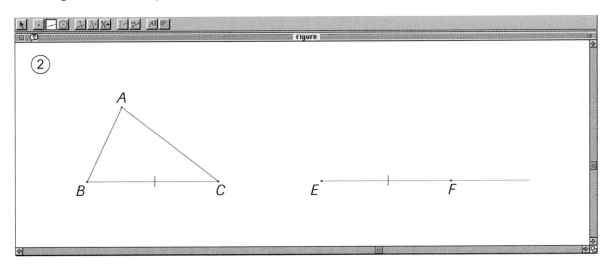

Angle B is copied to point E, and angle C is copied to point F, forming two rays that intersect at D.

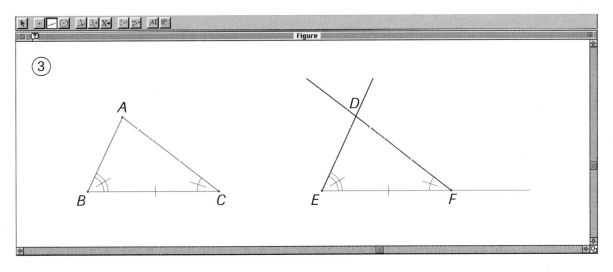

We ask the software to display the lengths of $\overline{AB}$, $\overline{AC}$, $\overline{DE}$, $\overline{DF}$, $\angle A$ and $\angle D$.

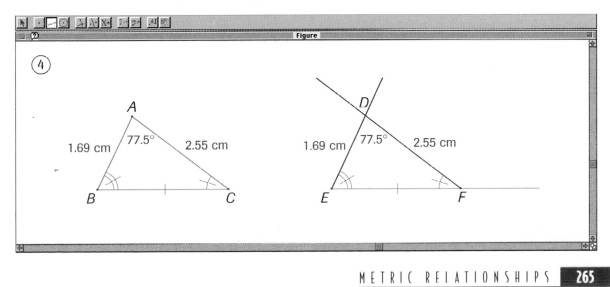

We can move point *A* by clicking and dragging it with the mouse. Notice that everything connected with this point also moves, and the two triangles retain their properties relative to one another.

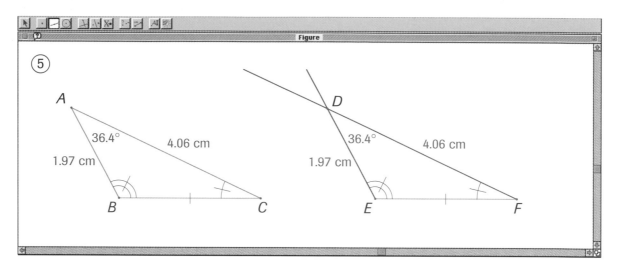

a) How do we know that △ *ABC* ≅ △ *DEF*?

b) Can we conclude that the two figures are isometric simply by measuring them with a ruler or asking the software to measure them?

Software applications are tools we can use to explore and verify properties or conjectures. We cannot rely on them for formal proof, however: we must still prove our propositions using logical reasoning.

SIMILAR TRIANGLES

A matter of shape

The following is constructed: point *O* and three lines passing through it and through the vertices of △ *ABC*.

A dilatation with centre *O* is defined that maps point *A* onto point *D* on ray *OA*. A line parallel to side *AB* is drawn through *D*.

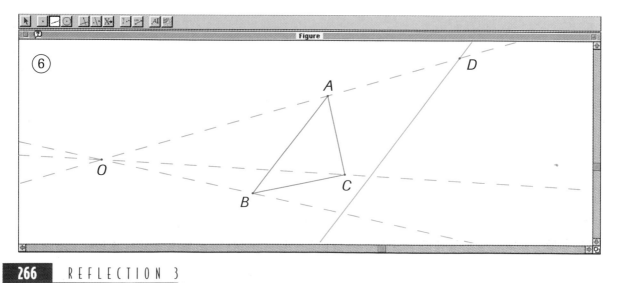

A line parallel to *AC* is then drawn through *D*. From *E* (intersection of *OB* and the first parallel line), a line parallel to *BC* is drawn, giving △ *DEF*.

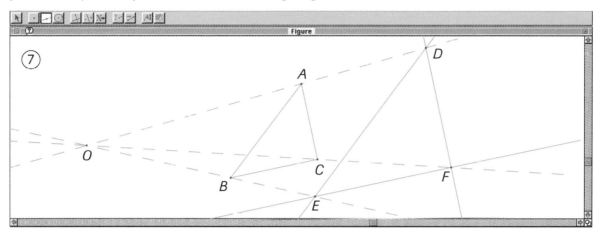

a) What characteristic do these triangles share? Justify your answer.

The computer is asked to display the angle measures for the triangles.

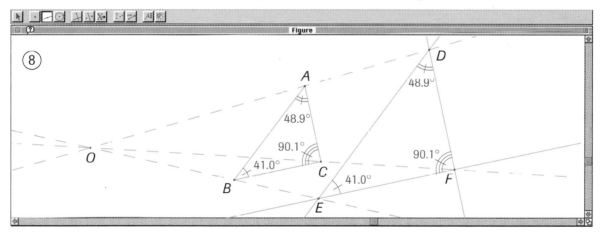

b) What characteristic do the corresponding angles of the triangles share?

Next, the computer is asked to give the lengths of the sides of these triangles, and the lengths of $\overline{OA}$ and $\overline{AD}$.

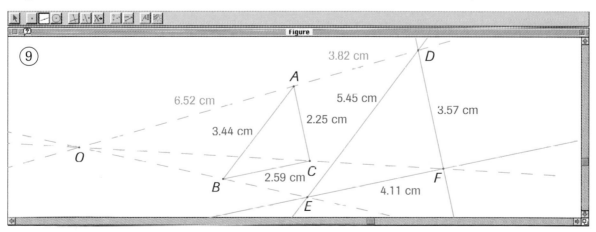

c) What do you notice about the lengths of the corresponding sides of the two triangles?

Dilatations and compositions of isometries and dilatations form the larger family of similarity transformations. These allow similar figures to be defined.

Two figures are **similar** if and only if they are associated by a similarity transformation.

The following theorem is easily demonstrated using the properties of similarity transformations.

Similar Figures Theorem

Two figures are similar if and only if their corresponding angles are congruent and the lengths of their corresponding sides are proportional.

To show that two polygons are similar based on this theorem, we need only show that their corresponding angles are congruent and the lengths of their corresponding sides are proportional. Not all these conditions need be met, however, to demonstrate that two triangles are similar.

d) There are three cases in which a certain number of conditions must be met to prove that two triangles are similar. Write out the three theorems that correspond to each of these cases.

Here is a final construction done with *Cabri.*

△ *ABC* and a line segment *EF* of any given length are drawn.

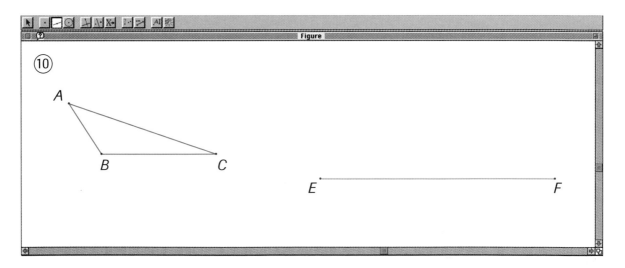

Angle *B* is copied to point *E* and angle *C* is copied to point *F*, forming two rays that intersect at *D*.

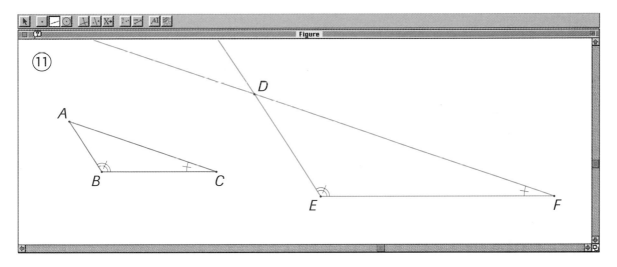

e) What statement can be used to affirm that triangles *ABC* and *DEF* are similar?

The computer is asked to display the side lengths of triangles *ABC* and *DEF*, and the measures of angles *A* and *D*.

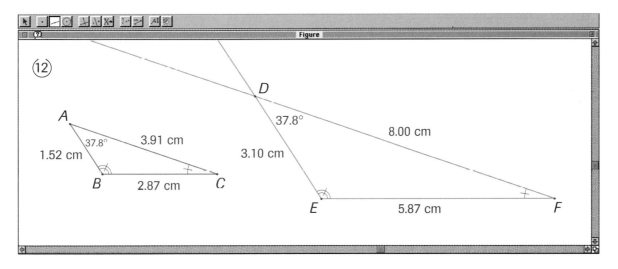

f) Did *Cabri* represent these figures as expected?

g) What are the ratios of the three pairs of corresponding sides?

h) What can account for these differences?

i) Point A is moved, changing all the values except those of $\overline{BC}$ and $\overline{EF}$. What is the similarity ratio?

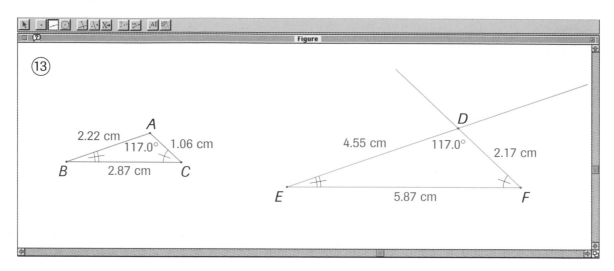

j) This time, point *F* is moved. What is the similarity ratio?

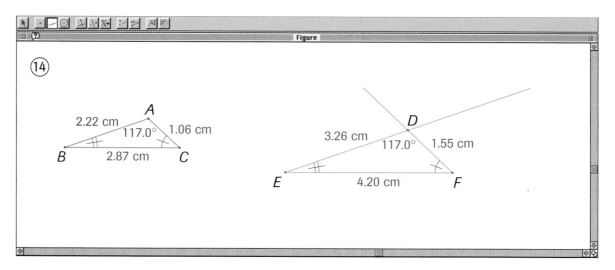

k) Why does the ratio change when *F* is moved, but not when *A* is moved?

Interactive geometry software helps us quickly explore and verify various geometric properties. They must still be proved, however.

I) The concept of dilatation can be used to prove the AA theorem of similar triangles.

Problem

Hypothesis: $\triangle ABC$ and $\triangle DEF$ with $\angle B \cong \angle E$ and $\angle C \cong \angle F$
Conclusion: $\triangle ABC \sim \triangle DEF$

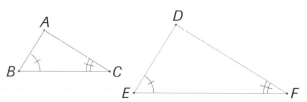

Approach

There are two cases:

1. If line segments *BC* and *EF* are congruent, then triangles *ABC* and *DEF* are isometric by ASA; thus the ratios of corresponding sides are all 1, and the triangles are similar.

2. If sides *BC* and *EF* are different lengths, a dilatation *h* with centre *D* and ratio $\dfrac{\text{m } \overline{BC}}{\text{m } \overline{EF}}$, can be applied; the image of $\triangle DEF$ under *h* is $\triangle DE'F'$. Triangles $\triangle DEF$ and $DE'F'$ are similar under the dilatation.

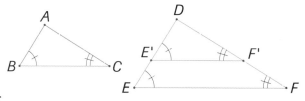

   Now it is sufficient to show that $\triangle ABC$ and $\triangle DE'F'$ are isometric.

   There is a similarity (an isometry followed by a dilatation) that maps $\triangle ABC$ onto $\triangle DEF$ The triangles are therefore similar.

Write out the proof for this.

An analogous method can be used for the other two cases of similarity (SSS and SAS).

An ingenious proof

Sometimes proving a theorem requires a construction that may not be apparent at first, like this example taken from Euclid's *Elements*.

$\triangle ABC$ and the bisector of $\angle A$, which intersects $\overline{BC}$ at *A'*, are drawn in *Cabri*. Then we label $a_1 = \text{m } \overline{CA'}$, $a_2 = \text{m } \overline{A'B}$, $b = \text{m } \overline{AC}$ and $c = \text{m } \overline{AB}$. Finally, we ask the computer to display these values.

Proclus, a 5th century Greek philosopher, wrote a commentary on Euclid's Elements.

Here are the values obtained for four possible positions of point A.

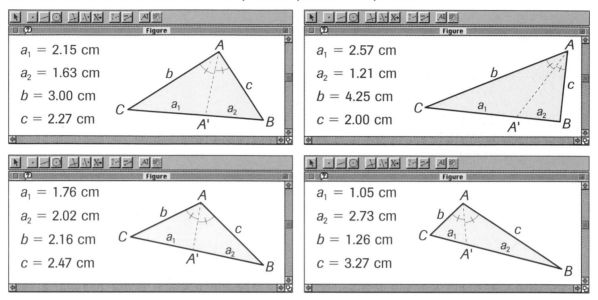

$a_1 = 2.15$ cm
$a_2 = 1.63$ cm
$b = 3.00$ cm
$c = 2.27$ cm

$a_1 = 2.57$ cm
$a_2 = 1.21$ cm
$b = 4.25$ cm
$c = 2.00$ cm

$a_1 = 1.76$ cm
$a_2 = 2.02$ cm
$b = 2.16$ cm
$c = 2.47$ cm

$a_1 = 1.05$ cm
$a_2 = 2.73$ cm
$b = 1.26$ cm
$c = 3.27$ cm

a) Find the relationship that exists between these values, and write a statement that could resemble a theorem.

Now look at the approach Euclid took to prove this theorem in his *Elements*.

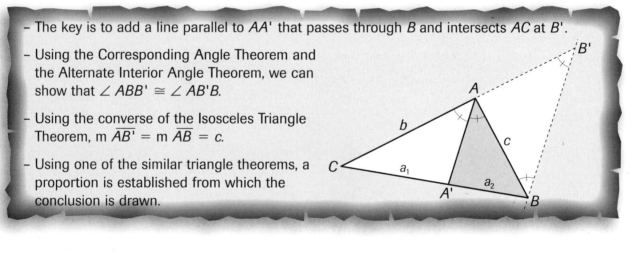

- The key is to add a line parallel to AA' that passes through B and intersects AC at B'.

- Using the Corresponding Angle Theorem and the Alternate Interior Angle Theorem, we can show that $\angle ABB' \cong \angle AB'B$.

- Using the converse of the Isosceles Triangle Theorem, m $\overline{AB'}$ = m $\overline{AB}$ = c.

- Using one of the similar triangle theorems, a proportion is established from which the conclusion is drawn.

1. In this figure, it is claimed that triangles ACB and EDB are similar. Describe a similarity transformation that maps one onto the other, and determine the line segment that corresponds to $\overline{EB}$.

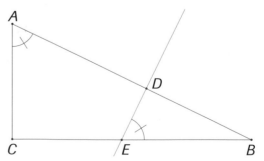

2. Consider this figure.

a) It is claimed that triangles *ABC* and *ADB* are similar. Describe a similarity transformation that maps one onto the other, and determine the line segment that corresponds to $\overline{BD}$.

b) It is also claimed that triangles *BCD* and *ABD* are similar. Describe a similarity transformation that maps one onto the other, and determine the line segment that corresponds to $\overline{BD}$.

c) Finally, it is claimed that triangles *ABC* and *BDC* are similar. Describe a similarity transformation that maps one onto the other, and determine the line segment that corresponds to $\overline{BD}$.

3. In this figure, midpoints *M* and *P* have been joined. Show that triangles *AMP* and *ABC* are similar figures.

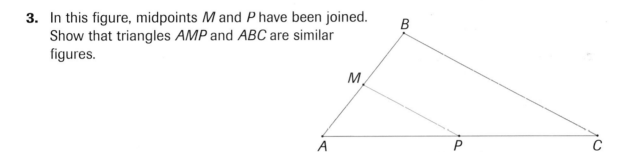

4. In $\triangle ABC$, $CD \parallel AB$ is drawn from vertex *C*. Another line parallel to *BC* is drawn from point *D*, then $\overline{AC}$ is extended until it intersects the second parallel line at *E*.

Show that $\dfrac{m\ \overline{AC}}{m\ \overline{CE}} = \dfrac{m\ \overline{AB}}{m\ \overline{CD}}$.

5. In each case, find the value of *x* and state the relationship you use to calculate it.

a)

b)

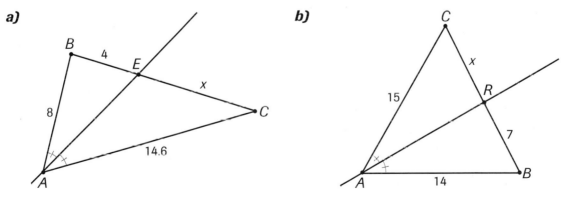

6. It is immediately obvious that two right triangles with proportional sides are similar. Why?

7. Prove that two right triangles with one pair of congruent acute angles are similar.

8. What is the minimum condition for two triangles to be similar if they are:

    a) Right?   **b)** Isosceles?   **c)** Equilateral?

9. Two triangles are similar if their corresponding angles are congruent. Is this statement true for figures with more than 3 sides? Illustrate your answer.

10. Given an isosceles triangle with apex A and B' on $\overline{AC}$ such that $\overline{BB'}$ is the bisector of $\angle B$; m $\overline{BC}$ = 30 cm and m $\overline{B'C}$ = 12 cm. What is m $\overline{AB}$?

11. Triangle ABC and triangle DEF are similar. Use the information given to calculate the missing lengths.

    a) m $\overline{AB}$ = 5, m $\overline{AC}$ = 8, m $\overline{BC}$ = 11, $\dfrac{\text{m } \overline{DE}}{\text{m } \overline{AB}}$ = 2

    b) m $\overline{AB}$ = 3, m $\overline{AC}$ = 7, m $\overline{EF}$ = 14, $\dfrac{\text{m } \overline{DF}}{\text{m } \overline{AC}}$ = 4

    c) $\dfrac{\text{m } \overline{BC}}{\text{m } \overline{AC}}$ = 3, $\dfrac{\text{m } \overline{AB}}{\text{m } \overline{DE}}$ = $\dfrac{2}{3}$, m $\overline{DF}$ = 12, m $\overline{DE}$ = 27

12. In this figure, parallel line segments AB, CD and EF connect points on two lines that meet at O.

    a) State an appropriate theorem for this situation.

    b) Find a ratio that forms a proportion with $\dfrac{\text{m } \overline{AB}}{\text{m } \overline{CD}}$.

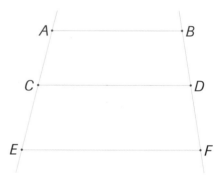

13. If a : b as b : d, then b is the "geometric mean" (or the "proportional mean") between a and d. Given this information, determine a geometric mean between:

    a) 8 and 12   **b)** $2\sqrt{2}$ and 9   **c)** m and n   **d)** 2a and 8a

14. A surveyor must measure the distance between landmarks P and Q, located on opposite sides of a river. Luckily, he can use a nearby bridge. He established the distances shown in the figure by choosing points A and B located on a line that passes through the middle of the bridge. This in turn formed two congruent angles, $\angle QAP$ and $\angle PAB$. Using this method, the surveyor was able to calculate d(P, Q). Explain his reasoning and calculate the distance.

THINK TANK

a) Give the minimum conditions for similarity between:

1) Two squares.

2) Two rhombuses.

3) Two rectangles.

4) Two parallelograms.

b) Under what condition are two spears similar?

RIGHT TRIANGLES

METRIC RELATIONSHIPS

Right triangles have always been of great interest in geometry, since they allow us to establish many different relationships. Most of these can be proved using triangle similarity theorems. The most famous relationship in the right triangle is the Pythagorean Theorem.

Pythagorean Theorem

a) Read the following proof carefully, then explain it to another student.

Pythagorean Theorem

In a right triangle, the square on the hypotenuse is equal to the sum of the squares on the other two sides.

Problem

Hypothesis: Given $\triangle ABC$ with a right angle at C.
Given $a = m\ \overline{BC}$, $b = m\ \overline{AC}$
and $c = m\ \overline{AB}$.

Conclusion: $a^2 + b^2 = c^2$

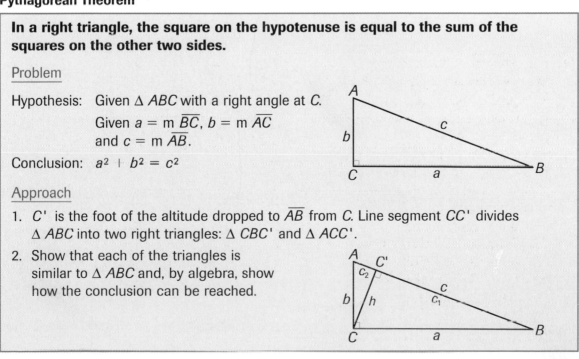

Approach

1. C' is the foot of the altitude dropped to $\overline{AB}$ from C. Line segment CC' divides $\triangle ABC$ into two right triangles: $\triangle CBC'$ and $\triangle ACC'$.

2. Show that each of the triangles is similar to $\triangle ABC$ and, by algebra, show how the conclusion can be reached.

The proof is as follows:

Proof

1. Let C' be the foot of the altitude dropped to $\overline{AB}$ from C, with $c_1 = $ m $\overline{BC'}$, $c_2 = $ m $\overline{AC'}$ and $h = $ m $\overline{CC'}$.

2. Since $\angle B$ is a common angle and $\angle C'$ and $\angle C$ are right angles, $\triangle CBC' \sim \triangle ABC$ by AA similarity case.

   Thus $\dfrac{a}{c} = \dfrac{c_1}{a} = \dfrac{h}{b}$, and $a^2 = cc_1$.

3. Since $\angle A$ is a common angle, and $\angle C'$ and $\angle C$ are right angles, $\triangle ACC' \sim \triangle ABC$ by AA.

   Therefore, $\dfrac{b}{c} = \dfrac{h}{a} = \dfrac{c_2}{b}$, and $b^2 = cc_2$.

4. Finally, $a^2 + b^2 = c(c_1 + c_2) = c^2$.

b) Read the following proof carefully, then explain it to another student.

Converse of the Pythagorean Theorem

If the square of the length of the longest side of a triangle is equal to the sum of the squares of the lengths of the other two sides, it is a right triangle.

Problem

Hypothesis: Given $\triangle ABC$.
 Given $a = $ m $\overline{BC}$, $b = $ m $\overline{AC}$ and $c = $ m $\overline{AB}$.
 $a^2 + b^2 = c^2$.

Conclusion: $\triangle ABC$ is a right triangle.

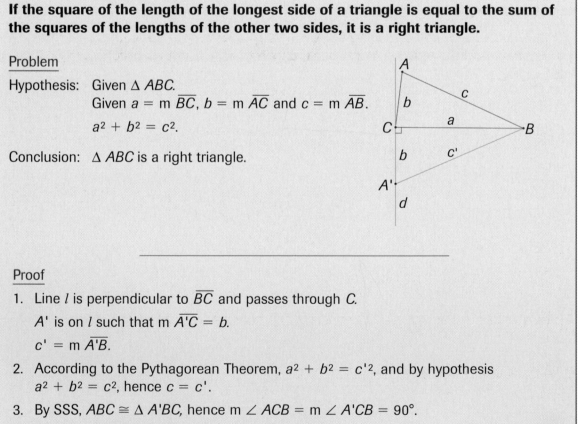

Proof

1. Line l is perpendicular to $\overline{BC}$ and passes through C.
   A' is on l such that m $\overline{A'C} = b$.
   $c' = $ m $\overline{A'B}$.

2. According to the Pythagorean Theorem, $a^2 + b^2 = c'^2$, and by hypothesis $a^2 + b^2 = c^2$, hence $c = c'$.

3. By SSS, $ABC \cong \triangle A'BC$, hence m $\angle ACB = $ m $\angle A'CB = 90°$.

4. $\triangle ABC$ is a right triangle.

The Pythagorean Theorem focuses directly on the lengths of the sides of a right triangle. Other relationships emerge when the altitude dropped from the right angle is considered.

c) How many pairs of similar triangles are generated by the altitude to the hypotenuse?

d) Justify the similarity of each pair of triangles.

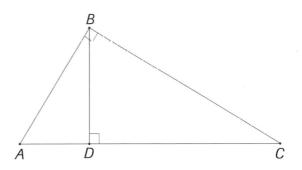

The proportions generated by these similarities are the basis for important relationships in right triangles.

Two of these relationships involve the altitude and the hypotenuse.

e) Complete the proof of the first theorem.

Altitude to the Hypotenuse Theorem

> **The length of the altitude to the hypotenuse of a right triangle is the geometric mean between the lengths of the segments into which the altitude divides the hypotenuse.**
>
> Problem
>
> Hypothesis: ▄▄▄▄
>
> Conclusion: $\dfrac{m\ \overline{AD}}{m\ \overline{BD}} = \dfrac{m\ \overline{BD}}{m\ \overline{DC}}$
>
>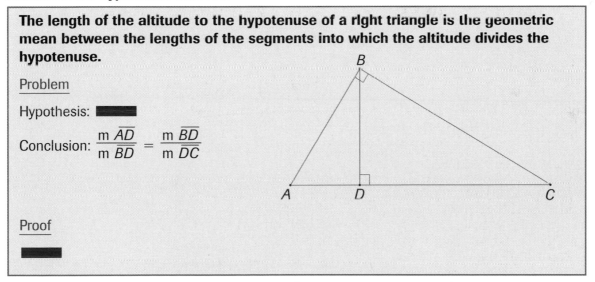
>
> Proof
>
> ▄▄▄▄

The lengths of sides and of various segments in a right triangle can be calculated using this theorem.

f) Calculate the missing lengths in these right triangles.

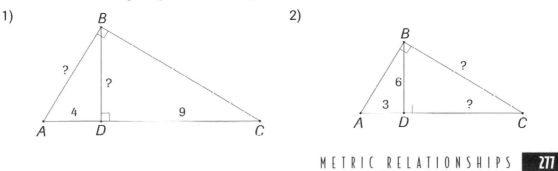

1)

2)

g) Complete the proof for the second theorem.

Product of the Sides Theorem

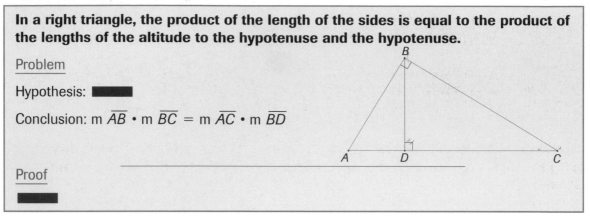

In a right triangle, the product of the length of the sides is equal to the product of the lengths of the altitude to the hypotenuse and the hypotenuse.

Problem

Hypothesis: ▇▇▇▇▇

Conclusion: m $\overline{AB}$ • m $\overline{BC}$ = m $\overline{AC}$ • m $\overline{BD}$

Proof

▇▇▇▇▇

This theorem establishes the relationship between the length of the sides and the altitude to the hypotenuse in a right triangle.

h) Calculate the missing lengths.

1)

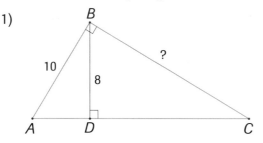

2)

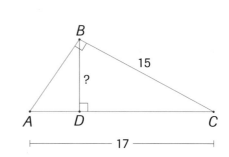

Orthogonal projection

In this plane, a geometric mapping has been applied with the following rule:

"Any point *P* is mapped onto *P'*, which is the foot of the perpendicular dropped from *P* to a given line *l* that passes through *P'*."

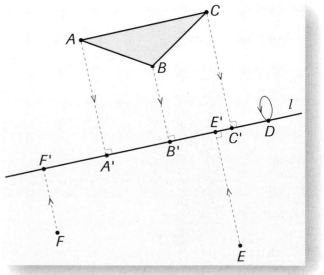

a) Show how each figure below is transformed by this mapping:

1) A point.   2) A line segment.

3) A triangle.   4) A line.

5) The plane.

b) What is the image of any point on line *l*?

c) What is the fundamental difference between an orthogonal projection and a reflection?

Given a line l, an **orthogonal projection** is the mapping of every point P' in the plane containing l onto point P', which is the foot of a line perpendicular to l and passing through P.

P' is the **projection** of P on l.

Since projection preserves the order of the points, the projection of line segment PQ on line l is the segment defined by projections P' and Q' of points P and Q respectively. If $\overline{PQ} \perp l$, the projection of PQ is the projection of P.

Applying the concept of projection to right triangles leads to certain observations. The altitude to the hypotenuse plays an important role in the projection of the sides on the hypotenuse.

d) On hypotenuse AB, what is the projection of:

1) $\overline{AC}$?

2) $\overline{BC}$?

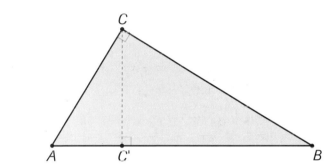

The concept of projection highlights another metric relationship in the right triangle.

e) Complete the proof.

Proportional Mean Theorem

> **In a right triangle, each side is the geometric mean between the hypotenuse and that side's projection on the hypotenuse.**
>
> Problem
>
> Hypothesis: △ ABC is right-angled at C.
> C' is the projection of C on $\overline{AB}$.
>
> $\overline{BC'}$ is the projection of $\overline{BC}$ on $\overline{AB}$ and $\overline{AC'}$ is the projection of $\overline{AC}$ on $\overline{AB}$.
>
>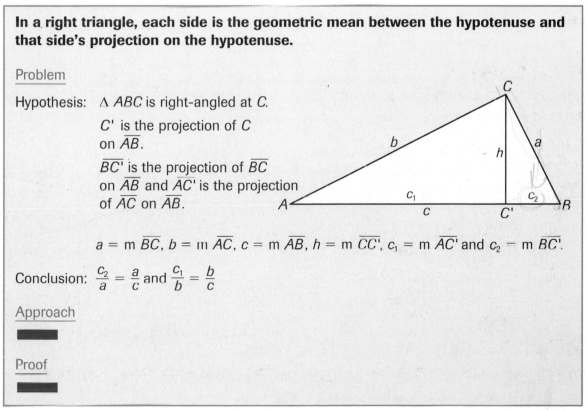
>
> $a = m\ \overline{BC},\ b = m\ \overline{AC},\ c = m\ \overline{AB},\ h = m\ \overline{CC'},\ c_1 = m\ \overline{AC'}$ and $c_2 = m\ \overline{BC'}$.
>
> Conclusion: $\dfrac{c_2}{a} = \dfrac{a}{c}$ and $\dfrac{c_1}{b} = \dfrac{b}{c}$
>
> Approach
>
> ▬▬
>
> Proof
>
> ▬▬

f) Use this theorem to find the missing lengths in the triangles shown below.

1)

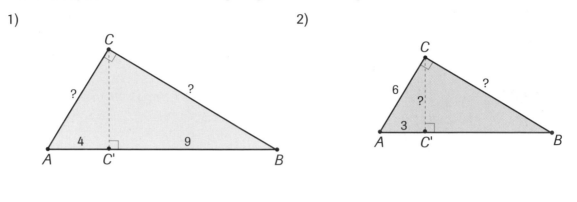

2)

INVESTMENT 4

1. Determine an appropriate approach and write out the proof for each theorem.

a) **Acute Angle Theorem**

The acute angles of a right triangle are complementary.

Problem

Hypothesis: △ *ABC* is right-angled at *C.*

Conclusion: m ∠ *A* + m ∠ *B* = 90°

Proof

▬▬▬

b) **30° Angle Theorem**

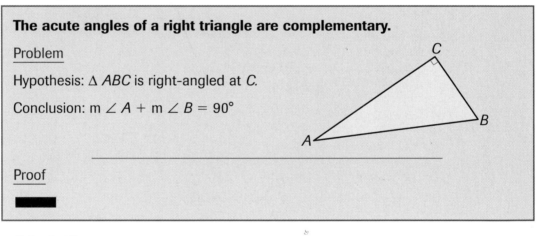

If a right triangle contains a 30° angle, the side opposite the 30° angle is one-half the length of the hypotenuse.

Problem

Hypothesis: △ *ABC* is right-angled at *B*; angle *A* measures 30°.

Conclusion: m $\overline{BC}$ = $\frac{1}{2}$ m $\overline{AC}$

Proof

▬▬▬

2. Here is another way of proving the **Pythagorean Theorem.** Complete it by filling in the missing information.

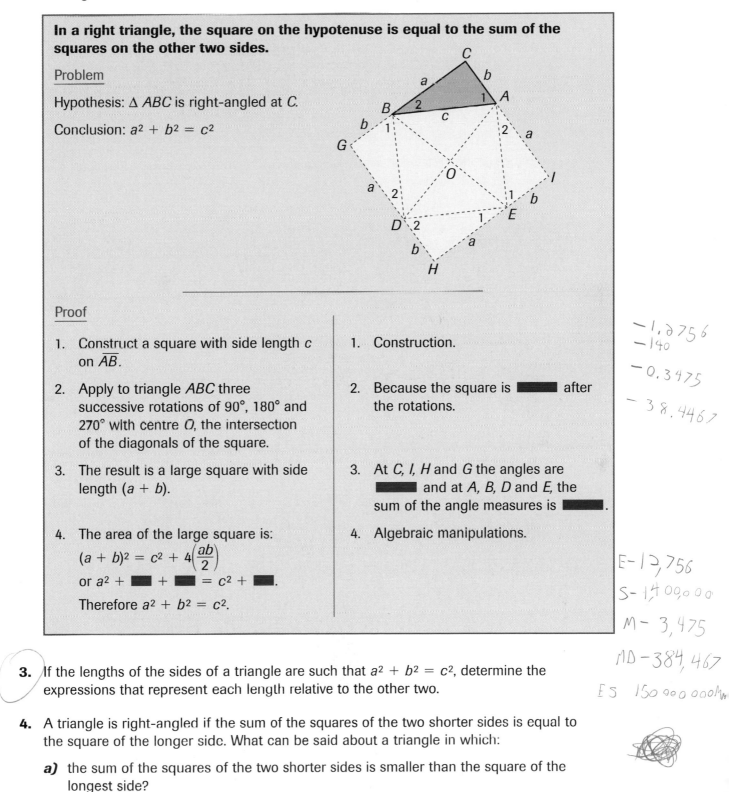

In a right triangle, the square on the hypotenuse is equal to the sum of the squares on the other two sides.

Problem

Hypothesis: $\triangle ABC$ is right-angled at C.

Conclusion: $a^2 + b^2 = c^2$

Proof

1. Construct a square with side length c on $\overline{AB}$.

   1. Construction.

2. Apply to triangle ABC three successive rotations of 90°, 180° and 270° with centre O, the intersection of the diagonals of the square.

   2. Because the square is ▬▬▬ after the rotations.

3. The result is a large square with side length $(a + b)$.

   3. At C, I, H and G the angles are ▬▬▬ and at A, B, D and E, the sum of the angle measures is ▬▬▬.

4. The area of the large square is:
   $$(a + b)^2 = c^2 + 4\left(\frac{ab}{2}\right)$$
   or $a^2 +$ ▬▬ $+$ ▬▬ $= c^2 +$ ▬▬.
   Therefore $a^2 + b^2 = c^2$.

   4. Algebraic manipulations.

3. If the lengths of the sides of a triangle are such that $a^2 + b^2 = c^2$, determine the expressions that represent each length relative to the other two.

4. A triangle is right-angled if the sum of the squares of the two shorter sides is equal to the square of the longer side. What can be said about a triangle in which:

  a) the sum of the squares of the two shorter sides is smaller than the square of the longest side?

  b) the sum of the squares of the two shorter sides is greater than the square of the longest side?

5. A spiral is constructed starting with an isosceles right triangle with side 1 cm.

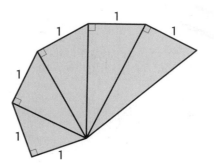

a) Find the lengths of the series of hypotenuses.

b) Using the appropriate trigonometric ratio, find the series of angle measures formed at the centre of the spiral.

6. Prove this statement: "Given a square with side a, the length of the diagonal is $a\sqrt{2}$."

7. These two right triangles are similar. Find the lengths of *a*, *b* and *e*.

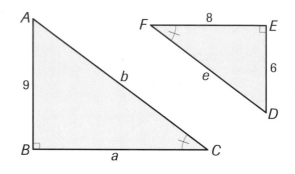

8. Find each missing length and write a statement that justifies your calculation.

a)

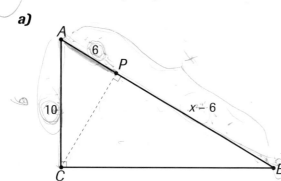

b)

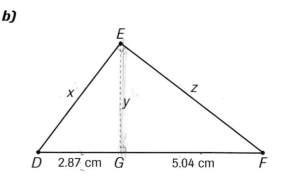

c)

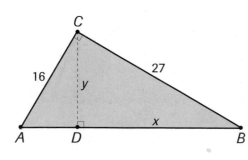

d)

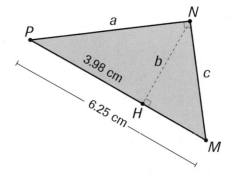

e)

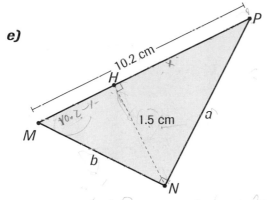

f)

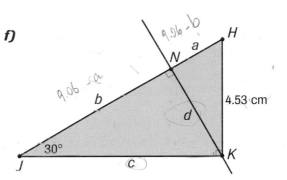

9. The three right triangles in this figure are similar. Angle *A* measures 30°, and line segment *BF* measures 4 cm. Given that $\overline{CG}$ measures 12 cm and that *D* is a midpoint, find:

a) The length of $\overline{EG}$;

b) The perimeter of △ *FED*.

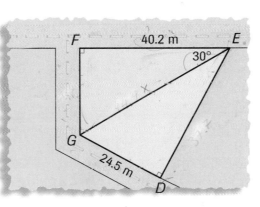

10. Two lots have the given shapes and dimensions. Find the area of lot *EFGD*. Justify each step.

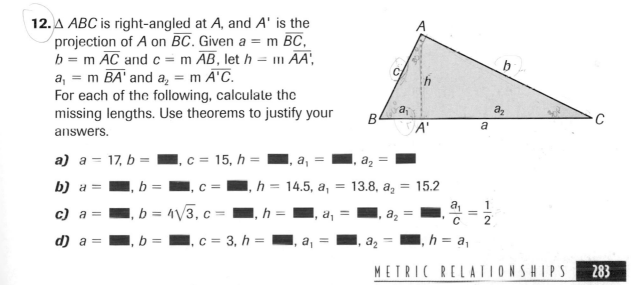

11. What metric relationship in the right triangle is directly connected to the calculation of a triangle's area? Explain this connection.

12. △ *ABC* is right-angled at *A*, and *A'* is the projection of *A* on $\overline{BC}$. Given $a = m\ \overline{BC}$, $b = m\ \overline{AC}$ and $c = m\ \overline{AB}$, let $h = m\ \overline{AA'}$, $a_1 = m\ \overline{BA'}$ and $a_2 = m\ \overline{A'C}$. For each of the following, calculate the missing lengths. Use theorems to justify your answers.

a) $a = 17$, $b = \blacksquare$, $c = 15$, $h = \blacksquare$, $a_1 = \blacksquare$, $a_2 = \blacksquare$

b) $a = \blacksquare$, $b = \blacksquare$, $c = \blacksquare$, $h = 14.5$, $a_1 = 13.8$, $a_2 = 15.2$

c) $a = \blacksquare$, $b = 4\sqrt{3}$, $c = \blacksquare$, $h = \blacksquare$, $a_1 = \blacksquare$, $a_2 = \blacksquare$, $\frac{a_1}{c} = \frac{1}{2}$

d) $a = \blacksquare$, $b = \blacksquare$, $c = 3$, $h = \blacksquare$, $a_1 = \blacksquare$, $a_2 = \blacksquare$, $h = a_1$

13. In $\triangle ABC$, A' is the projection of A on $\overline{BC}$. Given $a = m\,\overline{BC}$; $b = m\,\overline{AC}$, $c = m\,\overline{AB}$, $h = m\,\overline{AA'}$, $a_1 = m\,\overline{BA'}$ and $a_2 = m\,\overline{A'C}$.

For each example, determine whether $\triangle ABC$ is a right triangle. If it is, give the location of the right angle. Lengths are in centimetres.

a) $a = 24$, $b = 25$, $c = 7$ **b)** $a = 16$, $b = 8$, $c = 15$

c) $b = 16$, $c = 12$, $h = 9.6$ **d)** $b = 84$, $c = 13$, $a_2 = \dfrac{7056}{85}$

14. $\triangle ABC$ is right-angled at A and M is the midpoint of $\overline{AC}$.
A' and M' are projections of A and M respectively on $\overline{BC}$.
Find the value of $m\,\overline{MM'}$ in terms of the lengths of the triangle's sides if $a = m\,\overline{BC}$,
$b = m\,\overline{AC}$ and $c = m\,\overline{AB}$.

15. $\triangle ABC$ is right-angled at A, and A' is the projection of A on $\overline{BC}$ and A'' is the projection of A' on $\overline{AC}$. Prove that:

a) $\overline{AA'}$ and $\overline{A'A''}$ divide $\triangle ABC$ into three similar triangles.

b) The length of $\overline{AA'}$ is the geometric mean between $m\,\overline{AB}$ and $m\,\overline{A'A''}$.

16. The ratio of the area of triangle DEB to that of quadrilateral $ADEC$ is $1:3$. Find the lengths of the sides of triangle ABC using the given measurements.

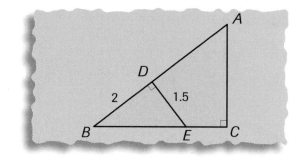

17. The following relationship exists in right triangles. Complete the proof.

In a right triangle, the length of the median to the hypotenuse is equal to one-half the length of the hypotenuse.

Problem

Hypothesis: $\triangle ABC$ is right-angled at
C, and $\overline{CE}$ is the median
to hypotenuse AB.

Conclusion: ▬▬▬

Approach

From E, the midpoint of $\overline{AB}$, draw EF parallel to $\overline{BC}$.

18. Triangle *ABC* is right-angled at *B*, and *M* is the midpoint of $\overline{AC}$.

   a) State a theorem that relates the midpoint *M* to the three vertices of triangle *ABC*.

   b) Use the given lengths to find m $\overline{BC}$.

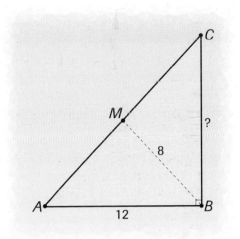

19. Triangle *ABC* is right-angled at *C*. Medians *BN* and *CM* are drawn, intersecting and forming right angles at *P*. Side *BC* measures 18 units and ∠ *A* measures 30°.

   Find the length of median *BN*.

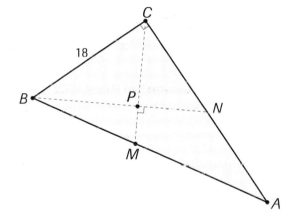

20. A machinist has a long sheet of metal that is 6 cm wide. She must cut out a piece shaped like the figure on the right. To make her cut, she draws $\overline{CE} \perp \overline{BA}$.

   Find m $\overline{BE}$.

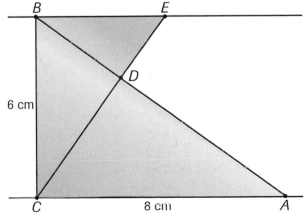

21. Given that *a* and *b* are the sides of a right triangle and *h* is the altitude from the right angle, prove that $\dfrac{1}{a^2} + \dfrac{1}{b^2} = \dfrac{1}{h^2}$.

22. Prove: "In a right triangle, the squares of the lengths of the sides are proportional to the lengths of their respective projections on the hypotenuse."

These two problems can be solved on paper, but are also ideal for solving by teams of students using geometry software.

a) Given rectangle *ABCD* and a variable point *P* on $\overline{AB}$, under what conditions will triangle *CPD* be right-angled at *P*?

$a = \text{m } \overline{AD} = \text{m } \overline{BC}$, $b = \text{m } \overline{AB} = \text{m } \overline{CD}$, $b_1 = \text{m } \overline{AP}$ and $b_2 = \text{m } \overline{PB}$.

1) Construct a rectangle such that its length and width can be modified. Label the vertices *A*, *B*, *C* and *D*. Add point *P* to line segment *AB*.

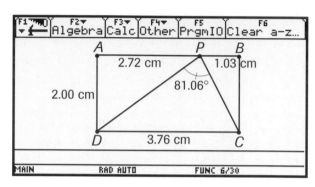

2) Can *P* be placed so that ∠ *CPD* is a right angle? Is this always possible no matter what the rectangle's dimensions?

To view the various possibilities, ask the software to display the measure of ∠ *CPD* and the lengths of the line segments.

3) Formulate and demonstrate a theorem of this type:

"Triangle *CPD* is right-angled at *P* if and only if ▬▬," where the statement shows the relationship that exists between the lengths of segments *AD*, *AP* and *PB*.

b) Given a rectangle *ABCD* with a variable point *P* in the same plane, where $a = d(A, P)$, $b = d(B, P)$, $c = d(C, P)$ and $d = d(D, P)$, what is the relationship between these four distances?

1) Construct rectangle *ABCD* and point *P*, and display the values of *a*, *b*, *c* and *d*. Change the position of *P* and try to discover a relationship between the four values.

(Hint: Look for certain positions of *P* that might make it easier to find the relationship, and determine whether *P* can be moved without affecting the four distances.)

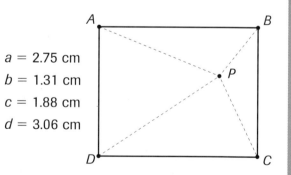

$a = 2.75$ cm
$b = 1.31$ cm
$c = 1.88$ cm
$d = 3.06$ cm

2) Show that the relationship found in 1) is necessarily true for all possible positions of *P*.

(Hint: For each vertex, there is both a horizontal and a vertical component for the distance from *P* to the vertex.)

3) Is this relationship valid for all possible positions of *P* in space?

CIRCLES

LINES AND SEGMENTS IN THE CIRCLE

Two circles that barely touch

In a way, the circle can be considered the perfect geometric figure. It is everywhere around us. The circle is the basis for one of the greatest inventions in human history: the wheel.

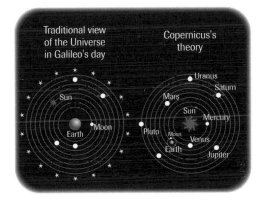

Long ago the circle was seen as the perfect figure, central to the workings of the heavens. The Universe was thought to be an immense spherical canopy with unmoving stars. Inside the canopy, the planets and the Sun revolved around the Earth in circular orbits. The Earth was the fixed and immobile centre of all the circles: the centre of the Universe. This idea was so crucial to the religious beliefs at the time that the first learned men who questioned it, such as Copernicus, Kepler and Galileo, caused enormous controversy, later suffering censure and even personal attacks.

a) Give a definition of a circle.

The circle is a deceptively simple figure, with surprising properties. These properties have been discovered gradually by successive generations of mathematicians.

b) Using a ruler and compasses, draw two circles that touch at only one point, then answer the following questions.

   1) Write a precise description of the procedure for drawing two circles that touch at only one point.

   2) Why are you asked to use a ruler as well as compasses?

   3) What property do two tangent circles have?

   4) Describe a foolproof method for drawing two tangent circles.

The **distance** between each point on the circle and the centre is called the **radius.** Any segment that joins a point on the circle to the centre is also called a radius.

This definition leads to the following conclusion, among others:

> **All radii of a given circle are congruent.**

c) How can the **interior** and **exterior** of a circle be defined relative to the radius?

d) What is meant by **concentric** circles?

e) Under what condition are two circles **isometric**?

f) What is the difference between a circle and a **disk**?

A line and a circle, or two circles, are **tangent** if they are coplanar and have exactly one point in common, called the **point of tangency**.

When a line and a circle are tangent, the line is said to be **tangent** to the circle. When a line and a circle have two points in common, the line is said to be **secant** to the circle. A line and a circle with no points in common are called **disjoint.**

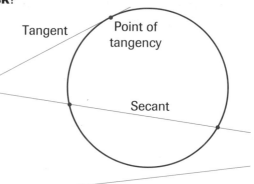

g) The relative positions of a line and a circle can be expressed in terms of the radius. Complete the following statements, which will be accepted without proof here.

Theorem of the position of a line relative to a circle.

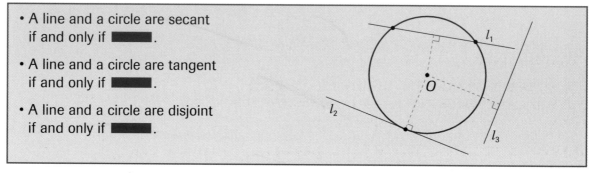

- A line and a circle are secant if and only if ■■■.

- A line and a circle are tangent if and only if ■■■.

- A line and a circle are disjoint if and only if ■■■.

h) These statements lead to the following theorem. Read the proof and extract the general idea.

Tangent to the Radius Theorem

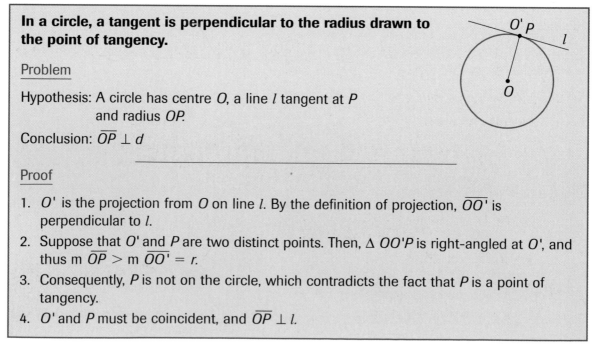

In a circle, a tangent is perpendicular to the radius drawn to the point of tangency.

Problem

Hypothesis: A circle has centre O, a line l tangent at P and radius OP.

Conclusion: $\overline{OP} \perp d$

Proof

1. O' is the projection from O on line l. By the definition of projection, $\overline{OO'}$ is perpendicular to l.

2. Suppose that O' and P are two distinct points. Then, $\triangle OO'P$ is right-angled at O', and thus m $\overline{OP}$ > m $\overline{OO'}$ = r.

3. Consequently, P is not on the circle, which contradicts the fact that P is a point of tangency.

4. O' and P must be coincident, and $\overline{OP} \perp l$.

i) Imagine two circles that are initially apart but move toward each other. Study the six possible configurations shown here.

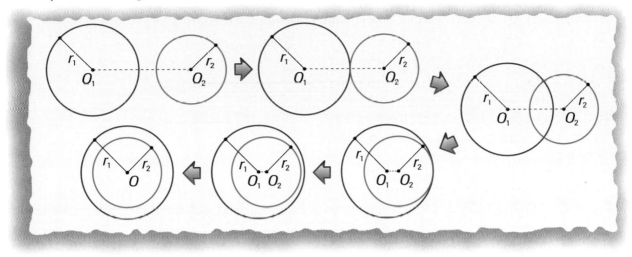

For each case, state the relationship between d(O_1, O_2), r_1 and r_2.

Chords in a circle

A **chord** is determined by joining two points on a circle by a line segment. If the chord passes through the centre of the circle, it is called a **diameter.**

The diameter also refers to the **length** of any chord that passes through the centre.

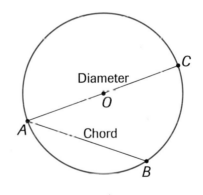

a) What is the relationship between the diameter and the radius of a circle?

Several statements about the concept of diameter can be made and proved.

b) An initial statement can be formulated by comparing the diameter to other chords in the circle. Follow the four steps of this procedure.

1) Complete the statement.

   Diameter Theorem

   The diameter is ███.

2) <u>Problem</u>

   Hypothesis: A circle with centre O has diameter AB and chord PQ.

   Conclusion : m $\overline{AB}$ ⩾ m $\overline{PQ}$

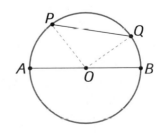

3) <u>Approach</u>

   Use the Three-Point Axiom.

4) Construct the proof.

An interesting phenomenon is observed if a triangle is formed from the diameter and another point on the circle, as shown here.

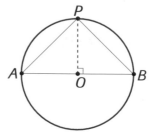

c) Find the measure of angle *APB*. Justify your answer.

d) It can be shown that the measure of angle *APB* remains constant when the position of *P* on the circle is changed.

1) Write a clear statement of this theorem.

Right Angle Theorem

Joining any point *P* on a circle to the endpoints of the diameter forms a ▰▰▰.

2) State the problem.

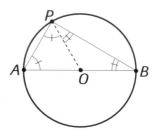

3) Determine an approach to the proof using the figure shown here.

4) Construct the proof.

A circle has centre *O* and a diameter *AB* that intercepts chord *PQ* at *M*.

e) Write conjectures depending on whether:

1) $\overline{AB}$ is or is not perpendicular to $\overline{PQ}$;

2) *M* is or is not the midpoint of $\overline{PQ}$.

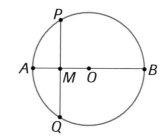

f) Two converse statements can be made.

1) Complete the first statement.

Perpendicular Diameter Theorem

In a circle, any diameter perpendicular to a chord other than the diameter divides ▰▰▰.

2) Problem

Hypothesis: A circle with centre *O* has a diameter *AB* perpendicular to chord *PQ* at point *M* ≠ *O*.

Conclusion: $\overline{PM} \cong \overline{MQ}$

3) Approach

Two right triangles are formed when the endpoints of the chord are joined to the centre of the circle. Show that these triangles are isometric to arrive at the conclusion.

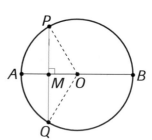

4) Construct the proof.

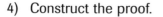

5) Complete the second statement, which is the converse of the first.

> **In a circle, a diameter that divides a chord other than a diameter into two congruent parts ▬▬.**

6) Problem

Hypothesis: A circle with centre O has a diameter AB that cuts chord PQ at $M \neq O$ such that $\overline{PM} \cong \overline{MQ}$.

Conclusion: $\overline{AB} \perp \overline{PQ}$

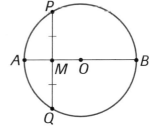

7) Determine the approach.

8) Construct the proof.

g) Look at the figure and complete the following statement.

Congruent Chords Theorem

> **In a circle, two chords are congruent if and only if ▬▬.**

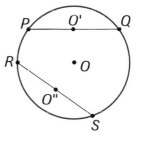

h) The last statement is biconditional.

1) Complete the statement of the first condition.

> **In a circle, two congruent chords are ▬▬.**

2) Problem

Hypothesis: A circle with centre O has two congruent chords PQ and RS.

Conclusion: $d(O, \overline{PQ}) = d(O, \overline{RS})$

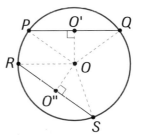

3) Determine the approach.

4) Construct the proof.

5) Complete the statement of the second condition.

> **In a circle, two chords that are equidistant from the centre are ▬▬.**

6) State the problem:

Hypothesis: A circle with centre O has ▬▬.

Conclusion: ▬▬

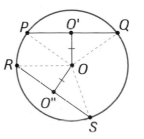

7) Determine the approach.

8) Construct the proof.

So far, we have demonstrated the following statements about circles:

- **The radii of a circle are congruent.**

- **The diameter is the longest chord in a circle.**

- **A right angle is formed by joining point P on a circle to the endpoints of a diameter.**

- **In a circle, a diameter is perpendicular to a chord (other than a diameter) if and only if it divides that chord into two congruent parts.**

- **In a circle (or in two isometric circles), two chords are congruent if and only if they are equidistant from the centre of the circle (or from the centres of their respective circles).**

1. What is the relationship between a radius and a diameter in the same circle?

2. What can be said about two circles that have the same radius?

3. Is it true that all circles are similar? If so, give their similarity ratio.

4. Two circles have radii 10 cm and 18 cm respectively. Over what interval is the distance between their centres if the circles are:

    a) Internally tangent?

    b) Secant?

    c) Internally disjoint?

5. An athlete uses a sling to throw a projectile at a target 15 m away. He spins the sling in a circle above his head, then releases the projectile. If the sling is 1 m long, at what distance from the target must the athlete release the projectile so that it will hit the target?

6. Use sketches to show that two circles can have between 0 and 4 common tangents, depending on the relative positions of the circles.

7. A cellular telephone company wants to install two-way antennas in an urban area, using a grid pattern. Each antenna has a range of 10 km. What is the maximum distance between two antennas that will allow a cell phone to work anywhere in the grid area?

8. A sailboat crosses the Atlantic, heading for Newfoundland. With this trajectory, the sailor's first sight of land will be a 30 m high lighthouse. Find the sailor's distance from the lighthouse at the instant he sights the top of the lighthouse, given the following assumptions:

– the earth is perfectly round;

– the sea is calm and visibility is excellent;

– the earth's radius is approximately 6500 km.

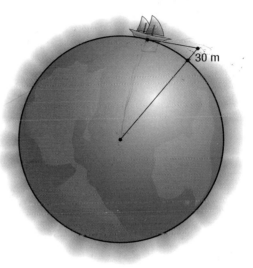

9. Three circles with the same radius are tangent in pairs. Show that the three centres and the three points of tangency both form two equilateral triangles.

10. Two circles have centres O and O' and tangents AB and CD in common. The following lengths are given:

$d(O, A) = 3$ cm

$d(O', B) = 2$ cm

$d(O, O') = 8$ cm

a) Use these lengths to calculate:

1) $d(A, B)$

2) $d(C, D)$

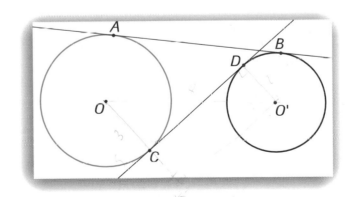

b) Given two externally disjoint circles with radii r_1 and r_2 and distance s between the centres, determine a general formula for the distance between the points of tangency of:

1) The external common tangent (AB).

2) The internal common tangent (CD).

11. Display two externally tangent circles on a graphing calculator.

12. Write a calculator program that will display two tangent circles based on information entered. The circles can be externally or internally tangent, depending on the numbers entered.

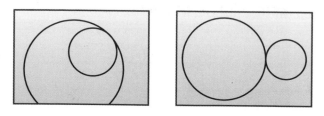

13. A 28 cm chord is 3 cm from the centre of a circle. Find the radius of the circle.

14. Isosceles triangle *ABC* is inscribed in a circle with radius 5 cm. Base *BC* measures 8 cm. Find the length of the other two sides of the triangle.

15. For each example, find the length of chord KE using the given lengths and information.

a)   *b)*

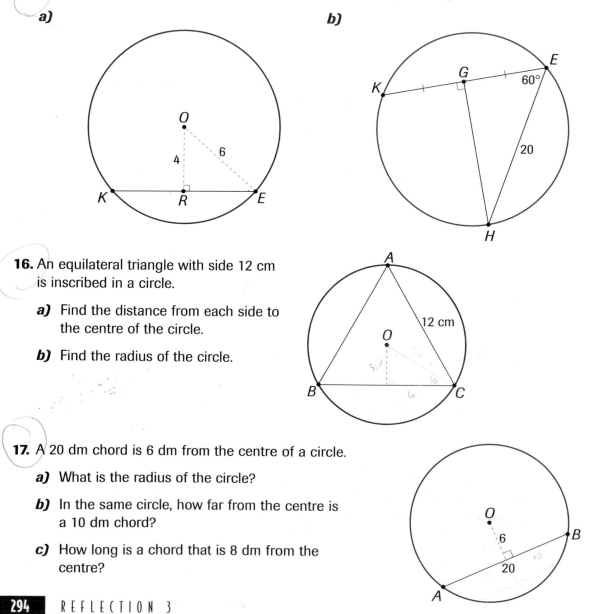

16. An equilateral triangle with side 12 cm is inscribed in a circle.

    a) Find the distance from each side to the centre of the circle.

    b) Find the radius of the circle.

17. A 20 dm chord is 6 dm from the centre of a circle.

    a) What is the radius of the circle?

    b) In the same circle, how far from the centre is a 10 dm chord?

    c) How long is a chord that is 8 dm from the centre?

18. In a circle, two chords measuring 8 cm and 10 cm have an endpoint in common and are perpendicular. What is the diameter of the circle?

19. Two concentric circles have radii of 8 cm and 10 cm respectively. What is the length of any chord in the large circle that is tangent to the small circle?

20. Point *M* is 12 cm from the centre of a circle with radius 8 cm. A line segment that is tangent to the circle is drawn from point *M* to *P*, the point of tangency. What is the length of the tangent segment?

21. A 12 cm chord is drawn in a circle with radius 8 cm. A parallel chord is drawn 10 cm away. What is the length of the second chord?

22. An explorer discovers the remains of an ancient city whose plaza appears to be a perfect disk. To measure the disk's area, he must find its centre. How should he proceed?

City in ancient Greece

THINK TANK

An ingenious use of the Right-Angle Theorem allows for the creation of a tangent to a circle that passes through a given point.

a) Given a circle with centre *O* and point *P* outside the circle, how can you find point *T* on the circle such that *PT* is tangent to the circle?

b) Given a circle with centre *O* and point *P* outside the circle, write a set of instructions to be entered into a geometry software program to display a geometric construction of a tangent to the circle that passes through point *P*.

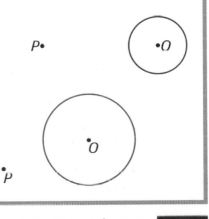

ARCS OF CIRCLES

Famous figures

Greek mathematicians such as Archimedes were very interested in figures formed by the **arcs** of circles. Here are some of the more famous figures.

a) Examine these figures and explain how they are constructed.

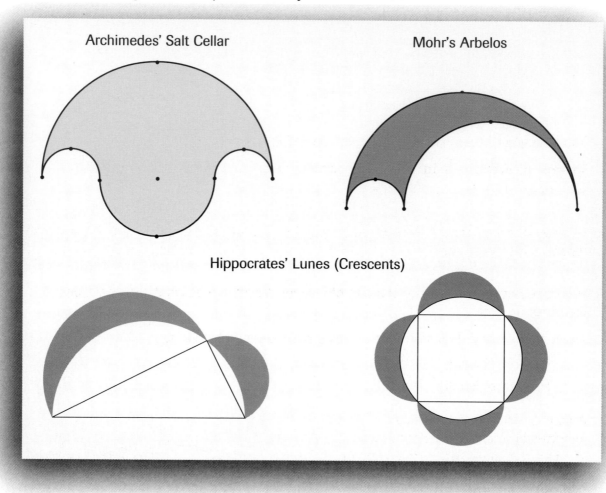

Archimedes' Salt Cellar

Mohr's Arbelos

Hippocrates' Lunes (Crescents)

Trying to formulate a rigorous definition of an **arc of a circle** leads to the same difficulties encountered when defining an angle. An arc is a portion of a circle that is defined by two points on the circle.

Two points on a circle determine two arcs, however. How can we differentiate between them?

One solution is to create three categories of arc: semicircle, minor arc and major arc.

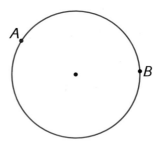

Two points *A* and *B* are on a circle with centre *O*.

1. If $\overline{AB}$ is a diameter, the set containing *A*, *B* and the points on one side of *AB* is called a **semicircle.**

2. If $\overline{AB}$ is not a diameter, the set containing A, B and the points located within $\angle$ *AOB*, is called a **minor arc,** and the set containing A, B and the points located outside $\angle$ *AOB* is called a **major arc.**

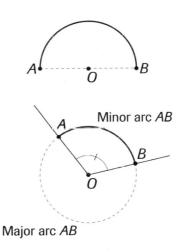

Minor arc *AB*

Major arc *AB*

The endpoints of the minor arc are used to label it; it is written $\overset{\frown}{AB}$.

To avoid confusion, a third letter corresponding to a point between the endpoints is sometimes used; for example, $\overset{\frown}{ACB}$.

Any semicircle, minor arc or major arc is called an **arc.** An arc is **subtended** by the chord that connects its endpoints.

An arc is therefore a fundamental part of a circle. It can be measured, just as we can measure the circle.

There are two ways to define the measurement of an arc of a circle:

– in terms of angle measure;

– in terms of length.

A complete circle has 360 small congruent parts that each correspond to 1°. Thus, the arc measures the **fraction of 360** that corresponds to its part of the circle.

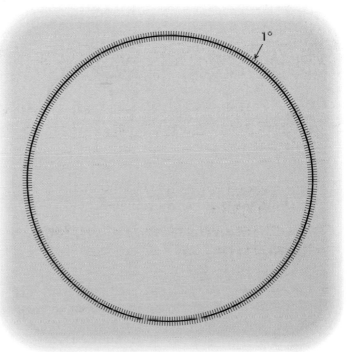

b) What is the degree measure of an arc representing:

1) A semicircle?

2) A quarter-circle?

3) An eighth of a circle?

4) $\frac{2}{5}$ of a circle?

5) $\frac{37}{360}$ of a circle?

6) $\frac{a}{b}$ of a circle.

Every arc has a corresponding **central angle.**

> The **arc measure** is the **same** as that of the **central angle,** which is the angle whose vertex is the **centre of the circle** and whose sides pass through the **endpoints of the arc.**

c) What is the measure of the three arcs shown here?

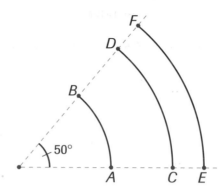

The second way of measuring the arc uses the radius of the circle. In this case, we refer to a **length measurement** instead of a degree measure.

An arc can be said to measure 1 radius, 2 radii, or *x* radii of its circle.

Since the perimeter of a circle is $2\pi r$, the measurement of an arc corresponds to the portion of $2\pi r$ intercepted by its endpoints.

For an arc of *n*°, its length measurement is:

$$\mathbf{m\ \widehat{AB}\ =\ \frac{n}{360}\ \times\ 2\pi r}$$

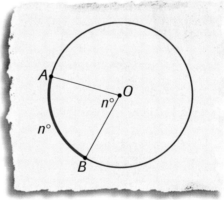

d) Study the figure on the right and determine, in terms of length:

1) m $\widehat{AB}$

2) m $\widehat{ACB}$

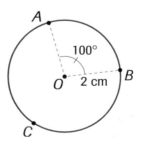

e) In this figure, $\overline{AC}$ is a diameter and m $\angle$ *BOC* = 50°. Chord *AB* measures 19.3 cm and chord $\overline{BC}$ measures 9 cm. Find the arc measurements in this figure:

1) in degrees;   2) in centimetres.

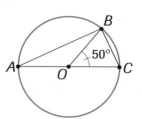

When comparing arcs on the same circle (or on circles with the same radius), the angle measure of the arc is sufficient. When arcs on circles with different radii are being compared, or when length measurements are required, units of length are used.

Several statements about arcs can be made and proved. They form the basis of many relationships, especially those involving angle measures in a circle.

An initial statement about arcs is introduced below.

f) Complete the proof.

Congruent Arcs and Chords Theorem

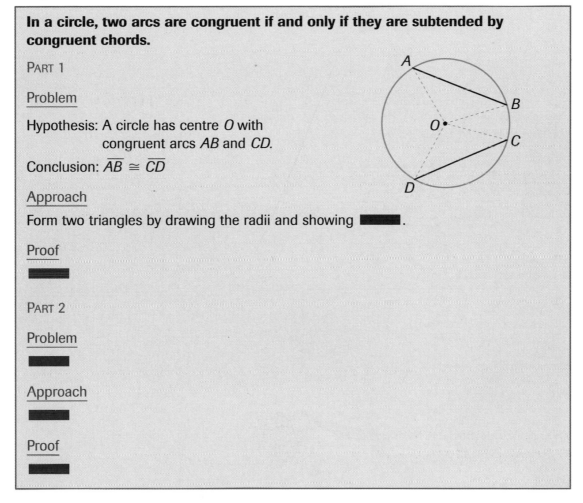

In a circle, two arcs are congruent if and only if they are subtended by congruent chords.

PART 1

Problem

Hypothesis: A circle has centre *O* with congruent arcs *AB* and *CD*.

Conclusion: $\overline{AB} \cong \overline{CD}$

Approach

Form two triangles by drawing the radii and showing ▬▬▬.

Proof

▬▬▬

PART 2

Problem

▬▬▬

Approach

▬▬▬

Proof

▬▬▬

Here is a second statement about arcs:

Arcs Between Parallel Lines Theorem

Two parallel lines that are secant or tangent to a circle intercept congruent arcs on the circle.

There are three cases to consider.

g) For the first two cases, study the proofs and determine the approach.

Two parallel lines that are tangent to a circle intercept congruent arcs.

Problem

Hypothesis: A circle has centre O and two parallel lines l and l' that are tangent at points T and T'.

Conclusion: It must be shown that T and T' determine two congruent semicircles.

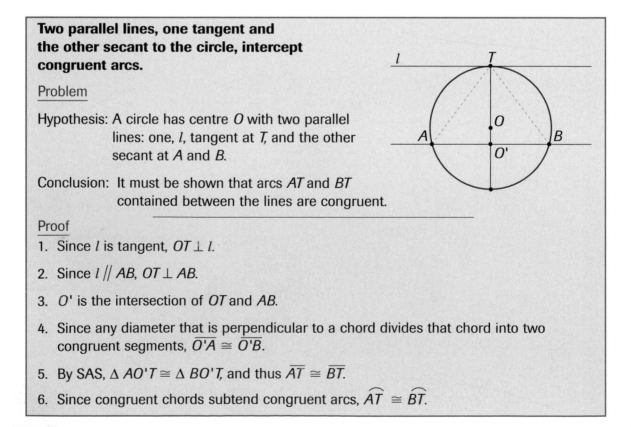

Proof

1. Since any radius that terminates at a point of tangency is perpendicular to the tangent, $\overline{OT} \perp l$ and $\overline{OT'} \perp l'$.

2. Since any line that is perpendicular to another line is also perpendicular to a line parallel to that line, $OT' \perp l$.

3. Since only one line perpendicular to l can pass through point O, lines OT and OT' are coincident.

4. Therefore $\overline{TT'}$ is a diameter and points T and T' determine two semicircles on the same circle, which are necessarily congruent.

Two parallel lines, one tangent and the other secant to the circle, intercept congruent arcs.

Problem

Hypothesis: A circle has centre O with two parallel lines: one, l, tangent at T, and the other secant at A and B.

Conclusion: It must be shown that arcs AT and BT contained between the lines are congruent.

Proof

1. Since l is tangent, $OT \perp l$.

2. Since $l \parallel AB$, $OT \perp AB$.

3. O' is the intersection of OT and AB.

4. Since any diameter that is perpendicular to a chord divides that chord into two congruent segments, $\overline{O'A} \cong \overline{O'B}$.

5. By SAS, $\triangle AO'T \cong \triangle BO'T$, and thus $\overline{AT} \cong \overline{BT}$.

6. Since congruent chords subtend congruent arcs, $\overset{\frown}{AT} \cong \overset{\frown}{BT}$.

h) Complete the proof.

Two parallel lines secant to a circle intercept congruent arcs.

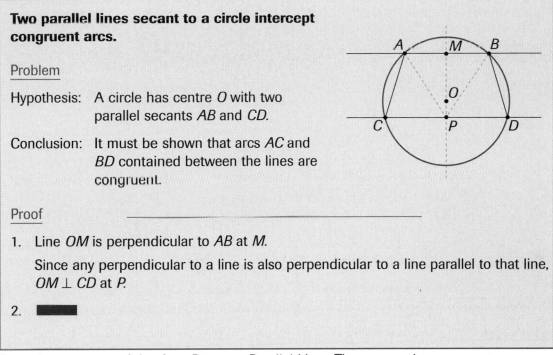

Problem

Hypothesis: A circle has centre *O* with two
parallel secants *AB* and *CD*.

Conclusion: It must be shown that arcs *AC* and
BD contained between the lines are
congruent.

Proof _____

1. Line *OM* is perpendicular to *AB* at *M*.

    Since any perpendicular to a line is also perpendicular to a line parallel to that line,
    OM ⊥ *CD* at *P.*

2. ▮▮▮▮

---

i) State the converse of the Arcs Between Parallel Lines Theorem and use a counter-
example to show that this converse is false.

1. Find the degree measure of the following arcs.

a) m $\widehat{AD}$

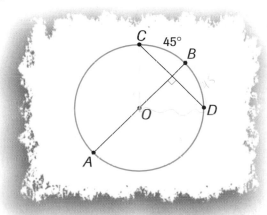

b) m $\widehat{BC}$

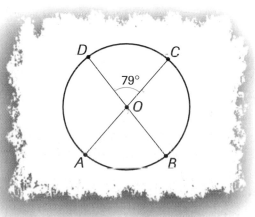

2. Find the length of each arc. The radius is 10 cm. Justify each step of your approach.

a) m $\overset{\frown}{BC}$

b) m $\overset{\frown}{BA}$

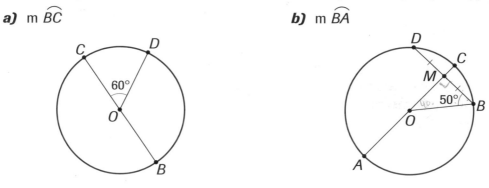

3. Find the length of the radius of each circle. Given lengths are in centimetres. Justify each step of your approach.

a)

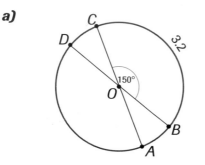

b)

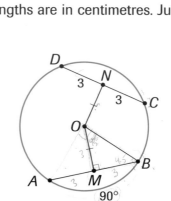

4. In this figure, $\overline{AB}$ is a diameter and arc *BC* measures 90°. If side *BC* measures 4 units, what is the length, in units, of the diameter? Justify your approach.

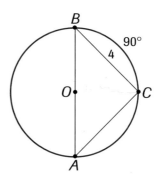

5. In this figure, $DC \parallel AB$ and line *MN* passes through the centre of the circle and intersects chords *DC* and *AB* at their midpoints. Using the given lengths, calculate the perimeter of trapezoid *ABCD*. Justify each step of your approach.

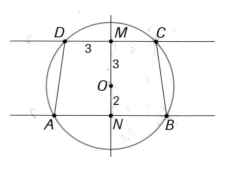

6. Given a circle with centre *O* and two diameters *AB* and *CD*, prove that minor arcs *BD* and *AC* are congruent.

7. A circle has centre O, radius r and diameter AB. Point M is on diameter AB and is the midpoint of $\overline{AO}$. Chord UV is perpendicular to $\overline{AB}$ and passes through point M. Prove that m $\overline{MU} = \dfrac{\sqrt{3}}{2}r$.

8. How can a geometric construction be created in which two arcs are joined with no break at the meeting point? Try to do so using a ruler and compasses.

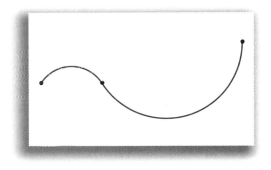

9. Use diameter AB to calculate the area of Archimedes' Salt Cellar and Mohr's Arbelos, each bounded by the semicircles shown.

a) m $\overline{AB}$ = 12 cm

b) m $\overline{AB}$ = 20 cm

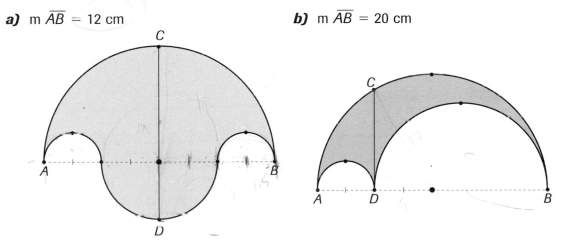

10. For each of the figures above, calculate the length of $\overline{CD}$ and then the area of the interior of the circle with diameter $\overline{CD}$. What do you notice?

The Rhind papyrus states that the area of the interior of a circle is approximately equal to the area of a square with side measuring 8/9 of the diameter of the circle.

11. Calculate the area of each of Hippocrates' Lunes using the given measurements.

a) $\overparen{ACB}$ is a semicircle.

b) $ABCD$ is a square inscribed in a circle.

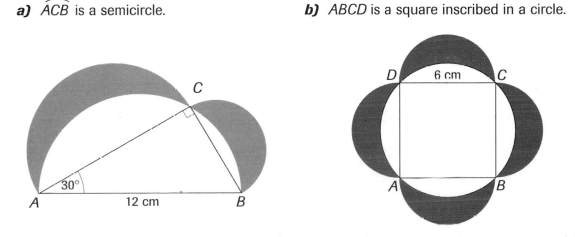

12. For each of the figures in question 11, calculate the area of the right triangle and the area of the square. Compare these areas to the areas of the Lunes.

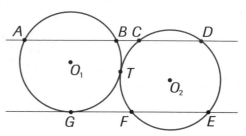

a) These two isometric circles are tangent at point T. Lines *AD* and *GE* are parallel, and either secant or tangent to the two circles. Are the four arcs between the parallels congruent? If they are, justify your answer. If not, state the conditions under which they would be congruent.

b) Explain the relationship that exists between the degree measure of each arc subtended by a side of a regular polygon inscribed in a circle and the number of sides in the polygon.

ANGLES IN THE CIRCLE

Surprising relationships between a point and a circle

With geometry software, some amazing relationships between a point and a circle can be uncovered and explored.

a) The work below was carried out using a geometry software application. Study it, or try to carry out the same task.

1. A circle with centre *O* and a point *P* are drawn. The point can be moved so that it is either inside the circle, on the circle or outside the circle.

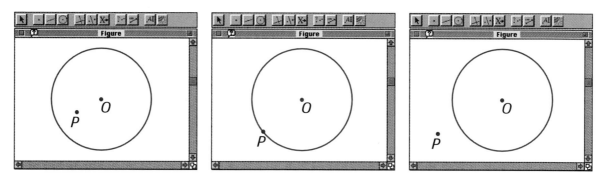

2. Points *A* and *B* are added on the circle, followed by lines *PA* and *PB*, which intercept the circle at *A'* and *B'* respectively. When *P* is inside the circle, each of the lines is secant to the circle. When *P* is on the circle, but not on *A* or *B*, it is coincident with points *A'* et *B'*. When *P* is outside the circle, *PA* and *PB* are secant or tangent.

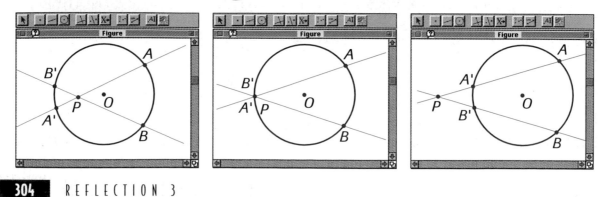

We're looking for the measure of angle APB.

3. If we ask the software to display this angle measure, we can observe how the value changes depending on the position of point P.

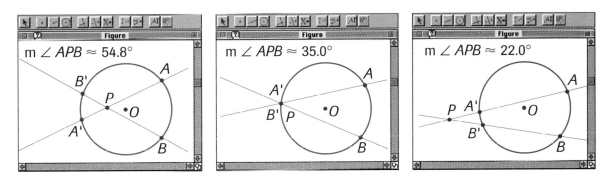

m ∠ APB ≈ 54.8°

m ∠ APB ≈ 35.0°

m ∠ APB ≈ 22.0°

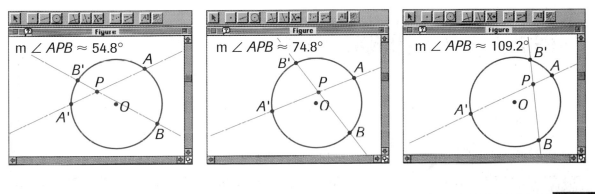

Let's look at the possible values for m ∠ APB when P is inside the circle.

b) To understand what is happening, we must make a distinction between what changes along with P and what remains constant. Which elements change with P, and which ones are invariant when P moves around inside the circle?

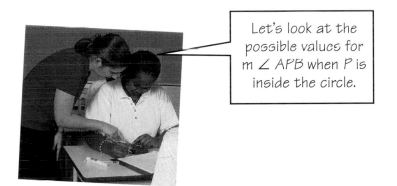

m ∠ APB ≈ 54.8°

m ∠ APB ≈ 74.8°

m ∠ APB ≈ 109.2°

We can observe what happens when the position of P shifts toward centre O, or when it shifts toward the circle. Study the different values for m ∠ APB as P moves from P_1 to P_{18}.

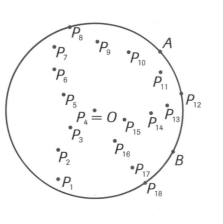

P	m ∠ APB	P	m ∠ APB
1	38.5°	10	67.5°
2	45.0°	11	165.9°
3	53.5°	12	145.0°
4	70.0°	13	179.4°
5	52.0°	14	141.0°
6	44.9°	15	95.2°
7	39.0°	16	70.6°
8	35.0°	17	56.3°
9	47.1°	18	35.0°

Let's see what happens when P stays on the circle.

If point P is on the circle, m ∠ APB is invariant as long as P remains within the same arc. If P changes arc, its old and new measures are supplementary.

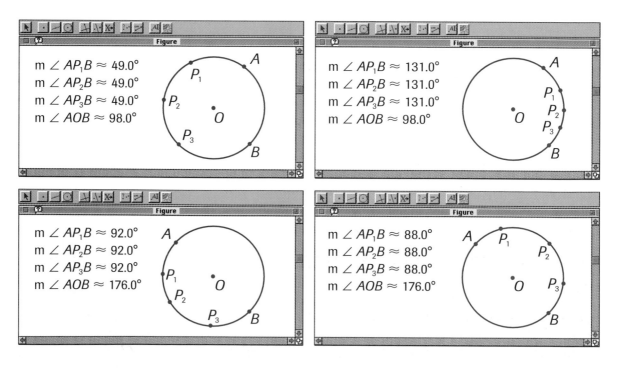

m ∠ AP₁B ≈ 49.0°
m ∠ AP₂B ≈ 49.0°
m ∠ AP₃B ≈ 49.0°
m ∠ AOB ≈ 98.0°

m ∠ AP₁B ≈ 131.0°
m ∠ AP₂B ≈ 131.0°
m ∠ AP₃B ≈ 131.0°
m ∠ AOB ≈ 98.0°

m ∠ AP₁B ≈ 92.0°
m ∠ AP₂B ≈ 92.0°
m ∠ AP₃B ≈ 92.0°
m ∠ AOB ≈ 176.0°

m ∠ AP₁B ≈ 88.0°
m ∠ AP₂B ≈ 88.0°
m ∠ AP₃B ≈ 88.0°
m ∠ AOB ≈ 176.0°

c) Provide a simple way of expressing m ∠ APB relative to the measure of the arc contained within its sides.

This phenomenon leads to a very useful definition and theorem.

> An **inscribed angle** is an angle whose vertex is on a circle and whose two sides are secant or tangent to the circle.

d) Complete the statement of this theorem.

Inscribed Angle Theorem

> **The measure of an inscribed angle ▬▬.**

To prove this statement, we will consider two cases.

FIRST CASE The two sides of the angle are secant.

There are three situations, depending on whether:
- one side of the angle is a diameter;
- the two sides of the angle are on opposite sides of the centre;
- the two sides of the angle are on the same side of the centre.

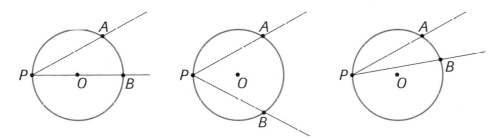

Let's look at the first situation.

Problem

Hypothesis: A circle has centre O and points P, A and B, with diameter $\overline{PB}$.
$\overset{\frown}{AB}$ is the arc between the sides of $\angle APB$.

Conclusion: $m \angle APB = \dfrac{m \overset{\frown}{AB}}{2}$

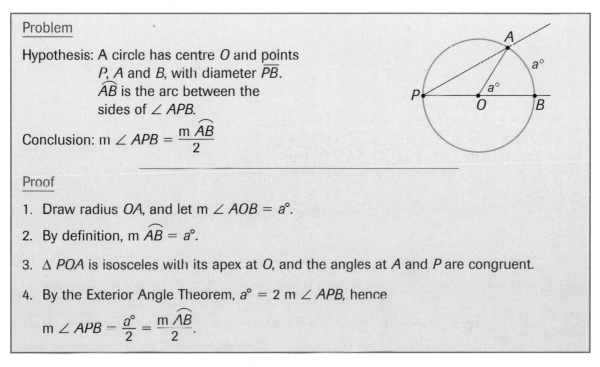

Proof

1. Draw radius OA, and let $m \angle AOB = a°$.

2. By definition, $m \overset{\frown}{AB} = a°$.

3. $\triangle POA$ is isosceles with its apex at O, and the angles at A and P are congruent.

4. By the Exterior Angle Theorem, $a° = 2\, m \angle APB$, hence

$$m \angle APB = \frac{a°}{2} = \frac{m \overset{\frown}{AB}}{2}.$$

e) How would you approach the proof if the two sides of the inscribed angle were on opposite sides of the centre?

f) How would you approach the proof if the two sides of the inscribed angle were on the same side of the centre?

SECOND CASE One or both sides of the angle are tangent.

If both sides of the angle are tangent to the circle, there are two possibilities.

1) If the two sides are coincident, the measure of the angle is 0° and the arc between the two sides is null. Since 0°/2 = 0°, the theorem is proved.

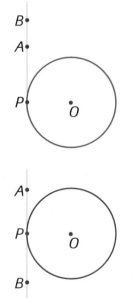

2) If the two sides are opposite, then it can be said that the entire circle is contained between the sides.
Therefore m ∠ APB = 180° = 360°/2.

g) How would you approach the proof if one of the sides was tangent and the other was secant?

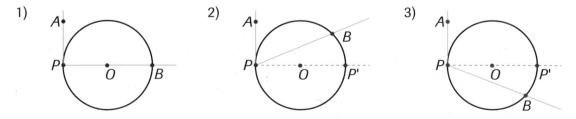

Note that **the measure of any inscribed angle is always one-half the measure of the intercepted arc.**

We have discovered the connection between the measure of the inscribed angle and the measure of the intercepted arc. It seems logical to ask what happens when *P* is inside the circle.

h) Study these examples generated by a software application that moves *P* to various points inside the circle, in order to discover the relationship between the arc measures.

P	m ∠ APB	m ∠ AOB	m ∠ A'OB'
1	53.0°	60.0°	46.0°
2	35.0°	60.0°	10.0°
3	116.0°	60.0°	172.0°
4	112.0°	104.0°	120.0°
5	73.0°	104.0°	42.0°
6	97.4°	144.8°	50.0°
7	129.5°	173.0°	86.0°

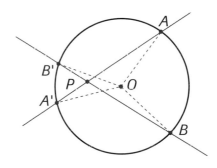

i) Complete the proof of the theorem for this relationship.

Interior Point Theorem

An angle whose vertex is inside a circle measures ▬▬.

Problem

Hypothesis: Points *A* and *B* are on a circle with centre *O*. Point *P* is inside the circle, and lines *AP* and *BP* intercept the circle at *A*' and *B*' respectively.

Conclusion: $m \angle APB = \dfrac{m\ \overset{\frown}{AB}\ +\ m\ \overset{\frown}{A'B'}}{2}$

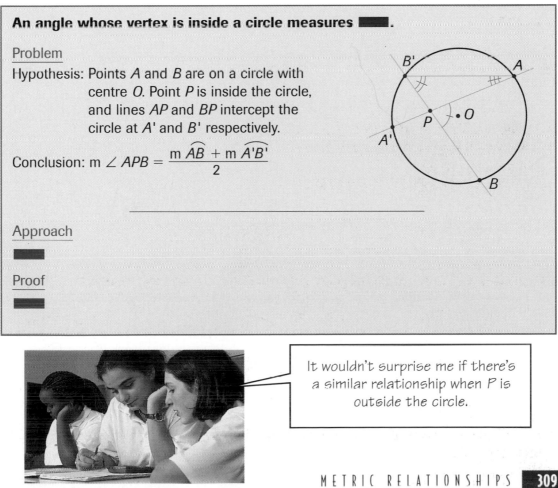

Approach

▬▬

Proof

▬▬

j) Study these examples generated by a software application that moves *P* to various points outside the circle, in order to discover the relationship between the arc measures.

P	m ∠ APB	m ∠ AOB	m ∠ A'OB'
1	17.0°	60.0°	26.0°
2	25.0°	60.0°	10.0°
3	56.0°	172.0°	60.0°
4	8.0°	120.0°	104.0°
5	31.0°	104.0°	42.0°
6	55.0°	160.0°	50.0°
7	78.5°	173.0°	16.0°

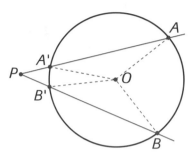

k) Complete the proof of the theorem for this relationship.

Exterior Point Theorem

An angle whose vertex is outside the circle measures ███.

Problem

Hypothesis: Points *A* and *B* are on a circle with centre *O*. Point *P* is outside the circle and lines *AP* and *BP* intercept the circle at *A'* and *B'* respectively.

Conclusion: m ∠ APB = $\dfrac{\text{m } \widehat{AB} - \text{m } \widehat{A'B'}}{2}$

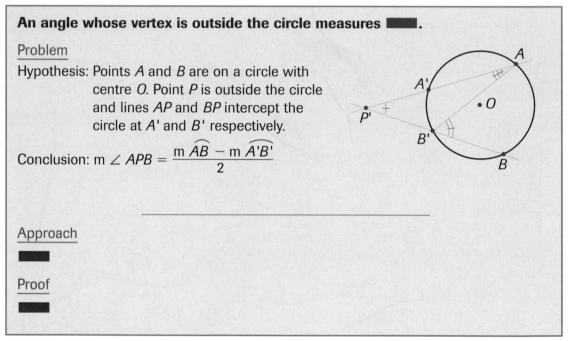

Approach

███

Proof

███

The following statements can be made about angles in a circle.

In a circle, the measure of a central angle is equal to the measure of its intercepted arc.

An inscribed angle measures one-half its intercepted arc.

An angle whose vertex is between the circle and its centre measures one-half the sum of its intercepted arcs.

An angle whose vertex is outside the circle measures one-half the difference of its intercepted arcs.

We can use these relationships to prove other statements and solve problems.

1. Calculate the measure of angle *E* in each case.

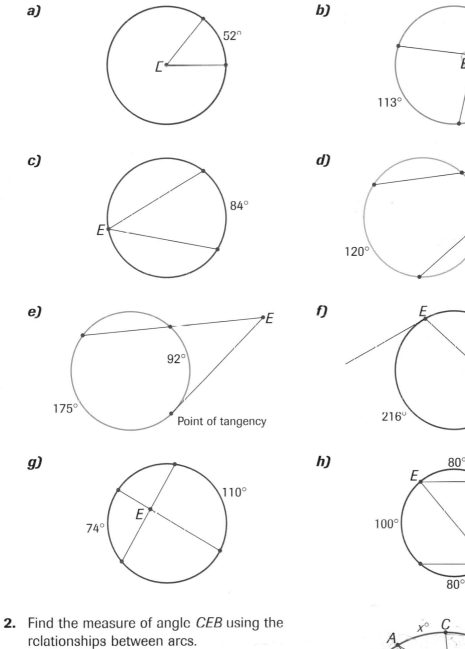

a)

52°

C

b)

56°

E

113°

c)

84°

E

d)

52°

E

120°

e)

92°

E

175°

Point of tangency

f)

E

216°

Extensive knowledge of geometry was needed to construct the pyramid at Gizeh, c. 2900 BC.

g)

110°

E

74°

h)

80°

E

100°

80°

2. Find the measure of angle *CEB* using the relationships between arcs.

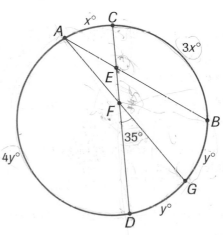

x° C

A

3x°

E

F

B

35°

4y°

y°

G

y°

D

3. Find the degree measure of arc *AB*.

a)

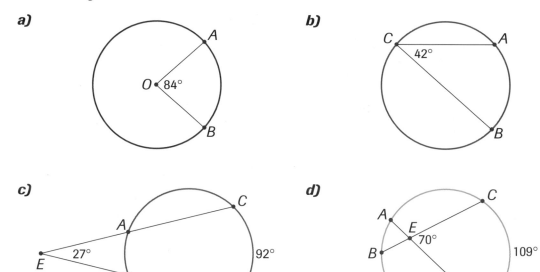

b)

c)

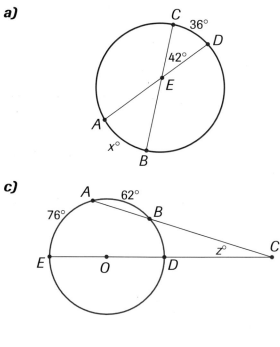

d)

4. Find the measure of the angle or the arc identified.

a)

b)

c)

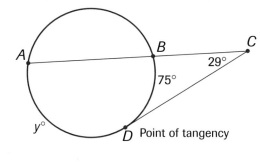

d)

e)

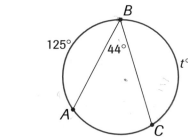

f)

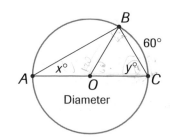

5. Find the missing value and state the relationship that allows it to be determined.

a)

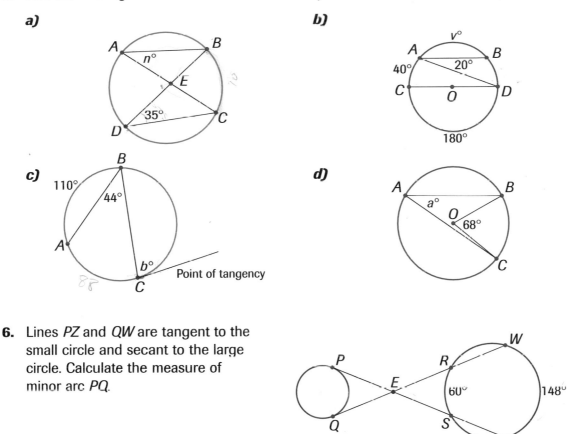

b)

c)

d)

6. Lines *PZ* and *QW* are tangent to the small circle and secant to the large circle. Calculate the measure of minor arc *PQ*.

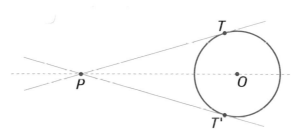

7. Points *A*, *B* and *C* are on a circle with centre *O*. Prove that if *BO* is the bisector of ∠ *ABC*, then minor arcs *AB* and *BC* are congruent.

8. In a circle with centre *O*, diameter *AB* divides minor arc *CD* into two congruent parts. Prove that this diameter is perpendicular to chord *CD*.

9. In a circle with centre *O*, diameter *AB* measures 8 cm. Arc *CD* measures 120°. *AB* divides arc *CD* into two congruent parts. What is the length of chord *AC*?

10. A circle has centre *O* and point *P* is outside the circle. Prove that *OP* is a bisector of the angle formed by the two tangents to the circle that pass through *P*.

11. The Right Angle Theorem states that any point *P* on the circle connected to the endpoints of a diameter forms a right angle.

a) State the converse of this theorem.   **b)** Prove the converse.

12. A circle has diameter *DA*. From point *C*, outside the circle, secants *CBA* and *CDE* are drawn such that *CDE* is parallel to diameter *BG*.

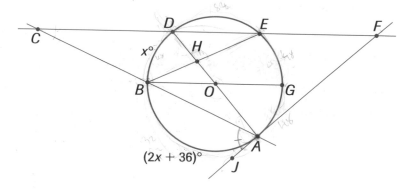

Tangent *AJ* is drawn from point *A* and intersects the extension of the other secant at *F*. Arc *BA* measures 36° more than twice the measure of arc *BD*.

a) Find the degree measure of angle *BAJ*.

b) Find the measure of angle *DHE*.

c) Show that triangle *CDA* is isosceles.

THINK TANK

a) Two tangents are drawn from point *P* to a circle with centre *O*. Discuss the required conditions for *P* to be a right angle.

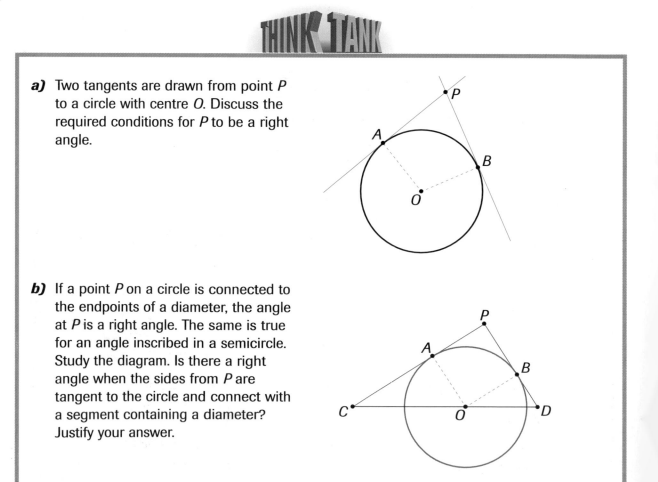

b) If a point *P* on a circle is connected to the endpoints of a diameter, the angle at *P* is a right angle. The same is true for an angle inscribed in a semicircle. Study the diagram. Is there a right angle when the sides from *P* are tangent to the circle and connect with a segment containing a diameter? Justify your answer.

DISTANCES IN A CIRCLE

Relationships between distances

Let's keep looking at the configuration created by a point joined to a circle by two lines. This time, let's think about **distance** instead of angle.

Points A and B are on circles with centre O. Point P is moved first inside and then outside the circle. Points A' and B' are the respective points of intersection of PA and PB with the circle.

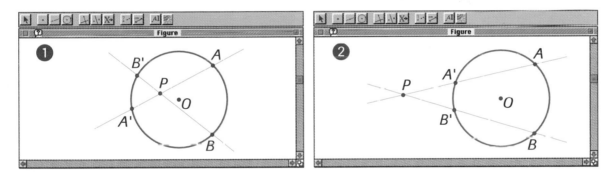

Various relationships exist for the distances between P and the other points.

To find them, two specific cases are fed into the software. In each case, the distance between P and the various points on the circle is calculated.

a) Find a relationship between these distances.

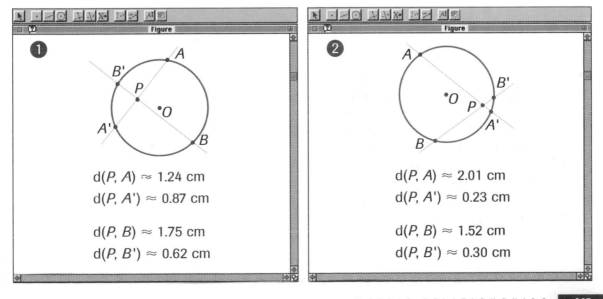

① d(P, A) ≈ 1.24 cm
d(P, A') ≈ 0.87 cm

d(P, B) ≈ 1.75 cm
d(P, B') ≈ 0.62 cm

② d(P, A) ≈ 2.01 cm
d(P, A') ≈ 0.23 cm

d(P, B) ≈ 1.52 cm
d(P, B') ≈ 0.30 cm

b) Does this relationship hold true for all chords passing through *P*?

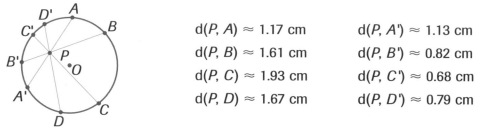

d(*P*, *A*) ≈ 1.17 cm	d(*P*, *A'*) ≈ 1.13 cm
d(*P*, *B*) ≈ 1.61 cm	d(*P*, *B'*) ≈ 0.82 cm
d(*P*, *C*) ≈ 1.93 cm	d(*P*, *C'*) ≈ 0.68 cm
d(*P*, *D*) ≈ 1.67 cm	d(*P*, *D'*) ≈ 0.79 cm

c) Complete the proof of the theorem involving this relationship.

Secant Chord Theorem

If two chords intersect in a circle, ▮▮▮▮.

Problem

Hypothesis: Points *A* and *B* are on
a circle with centre *O*.

Point *P* is inside the circle, and lines *AP*
and *BP* intercept the circle at *A'* and *B'* respectively.

Conclusion: ▮▮▮▮

_____

Approach

▮▮▮▮

Proof

▮▮▮▮

> And now the question we have all been waiting
> for: What happens when P is outside the circle?

d) Check if this relationship applies to instances where P is outside the circle.

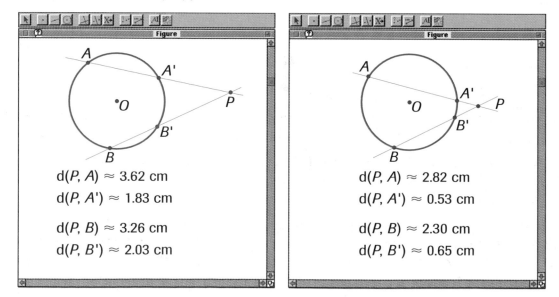

d(*P*, *A*) ≈ 3.62 cm	d(*P*, *A*) ≈ 2.82 cm
d(*P*, *A'*) ≈ 1.83 cm	d(*P*, *A'*) ≈ 0.53 cm
d(*P*, *B*) ≈ 3.26 cm	d(*P*, *B*) ≈ 2.30 cm
d(*P*, *B'*) ≈ 2.03 cm	d(*P*, *B'*) ≈ 0.65 cm

e) Does this relationship hold true for any secant to the circle?

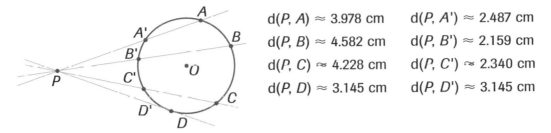

d(P, A) ≈ 3.978 cm	d(P, A') ≈ 2.487 cm
d(P, B) ≈ 4.582 cm	d(P, B') ≈ 2.159 cm
d(P, C) ≈ 4.228 cm	d(P, C') ≈ 2.340 cm
d(P, D) ≈ 3.145 cm	d(P, D') ≈ 3.145 cm

We can thus state that, given a point *P* and a secant:

Constant Product Theorem

> **The product of the distance from P to each point of intersection with the circle is invariant.**

f) State this relationship in terms of the lengths of two secant segments drawn to the circle from a point outside the circle.

g) Determine the approach.

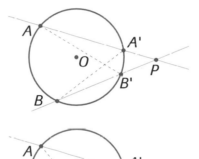

h) Show that this relationship holds true even if one of the secants becomes a tangent.

The following statements about **distances from a point inside or outside a circle** can be made.

• Given a circle and a line secant to the circle that passes through any point *P*, **the product of the distances from *P* to each point of intersection with the circle is invariant.**

This statement leads to the next three statements:

• **If two chords intersect in a circle, the product of the lengths of the segments of one chord is equal to the product of the lengths of the segments of the other chord.**

• **If two secants are drawn from a point *P* outside the circle, the product of the lengths of the secant segments of one is equal to the product of the lengths of the secant segments of the other.**

• **If a secant segment and a tangent segment are drawn from a point *P* outside the circle, the length of the tangent segment is the geometric mean between the lengths of the secant segments.**

1. Find the length of $\overline{EB}$ in units.

a)

b)

c)

d)

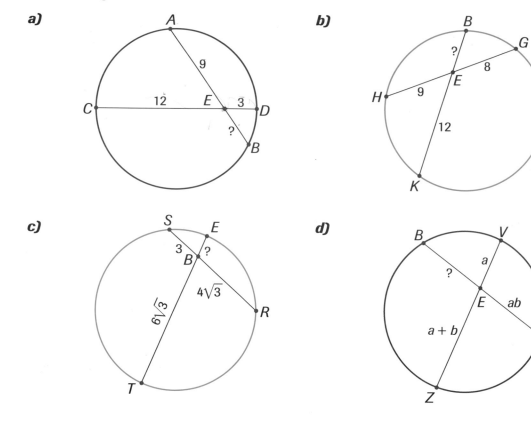

2. Find the missing length. All lengths are in centimetres.

a)

b)

c)

d)

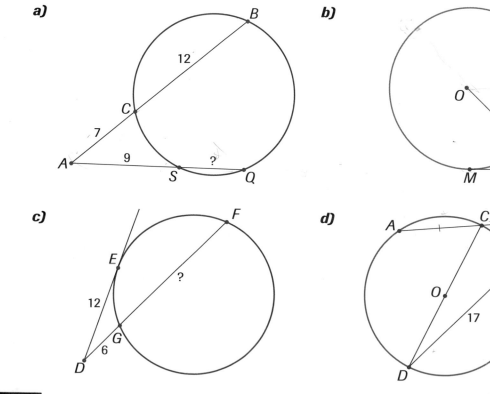

3. Show that: "If two tangents are drawn to a circle from a point outside the circle, the distances to the points of tangency are equal."

4. Show that: "If two tangent segments are drawn to a circle from point P outside the circle, the segment that joins P to the centre of the circle is a bisector of angle P."

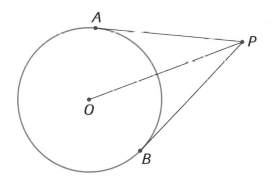

5. Two tangent segments PN and PM are drawn to a circle with radius 10 cm from point P outside the circle. If the segments measure 15 cm, find the distance between point P and the centre.

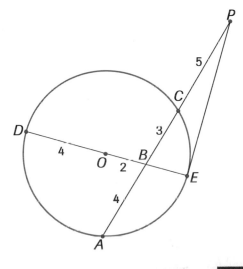

6. Point M is located 15 cm from centre O of a circle with radius 9 cm. A tangent segment is drawn from point M to the circle at A. Find the length of the tangent segment.

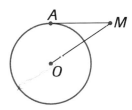

7. In this figure, $\overline{DE}$ is a diameter and PE is a tangent. In each example, calculate the length from the given values, using two different methods each time.

a) m $\overline{PE}$ b) m $\overline{DE}$

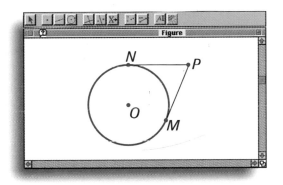

8. The endpoints of chords *AC* and *BD* are joined by diagonals. Segment *AB* is drawn to complete triangle *ADB*. Lengths are given for some segments. Use them to determine m $\overline{BD}$, justifying each step of your approach.

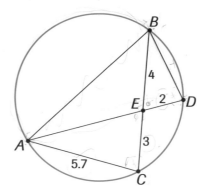

9.

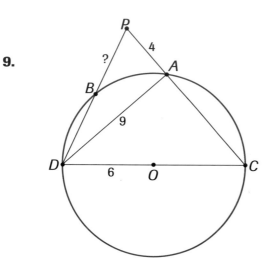

Point *P* outside a circle is connected to the endpoints of a diameter. One of these endpoints is connected to one of its points of intersection with the circle. Find the length of $\overline{PB}$ using the information provided.

10. In this figure, *ABCD* is an isosceles trapezoid. One of its non-parallel sides is extended until it intersects the line containing the diameter at *P*. This diameter is perpendicular to the shorter base. Using the information provided and justifying your approach, find:

a) The value of *b*

b) m $\overline{EP}$

c) The value of *a*

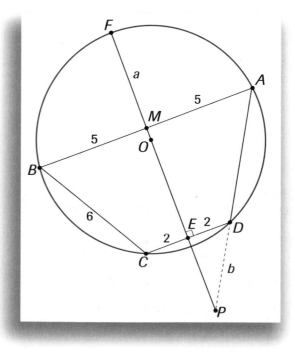

11. The bisector of angle *B* is drawn in triangle *ABC*. Using the given lengths, find the length of side *BC*. Justify each step of your approach.

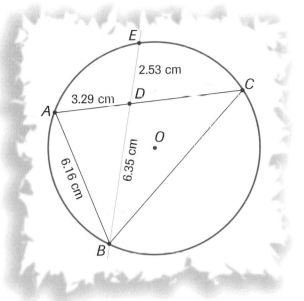

12. Medians *BE* and *AG* of triangle *ABC* are extended to the edges of the circle. Find the length of $\overline{DE}$ and $\overline{EC}$. Justify each step of your approach.

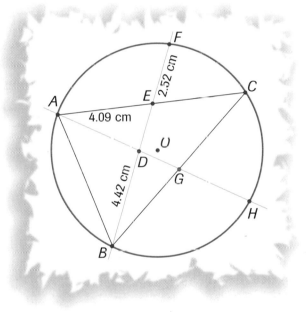

THINK TANK

The **product** of the distances from point *P* to each point of intersection of a secant through that point and a circle is called the **power of the point *P*** relative to the circle.

This number can be calculated using two distances: the distance *x* between *P* and the centre of the circle, and the radius *r* of the circle.

1) Show that the power of a point *P* is $r^2 - x^2$ if *P* is inside the circle.

2) Show that the power of a point *P* is $x^2 - r^2$ if *P* is outside the circle.

Math Express 4

Here is a list of the important propositions that have been added to those seen in previous years.

Angle Bisector Theorem

In any triangle, the bisector of an angle divides the opposite side into two segments whose lengths are proportional to those of the adjacent sides.

Altitude to the Hypotenuse Theorem

The length of the altitude to the hypotenuse of a right triangle is the geometric mean between the lengths of the segments into which the altitude divides the hypotenuse.

Product of the Sides Theorem

In a right triangle, the length of the hypotenuse multiplied by the length of the altitude to the hypotenuse is equal to the product of the lengths of the sides of the right angle.

Projection on the Hypotenuse Theorem

The square of the length of either side of a right triangle is equal to the product of the length of the hypotenuse and the projection of that side on the hypotenuse.

Diameter Theorem

The diameter is the longest chord of a circle.

Right Angle Theorem

A right angle is formed when any point *P* on a circle is joined to the endpoints of the diameter. Any angle inscribed in a semicircle is a right angle.

Diameter Chord Theorem

Any diameter perpendicular to a chord divides that chord into two congruent parts.

Congruent Chord Theorem

Two chords in a circle are congruent if and only if they are equidistant from the centre.

Tangent to the Radius Theorem

In a circle, a tangent is perpendicular to the radius drawn to the point of tangency.

Congruent Arc Theorem

Arcs in a circle are congruent if and only if they are subtended by congruent chords.

Arcs Between Parallel Lines Theorem

Two parallel lines, whether secant or tangent, intercept congruent arcs of a circle.

Inscribed Angle Theorem

The measure of an inscribed angle is one-half the measure of its intercepted arc.

Interior Point Theorem

The measure of an angle formed by two chords that intersect inside a circle is one-half the sum of the measures of the arcs intercepted by the angle and its vertically opposite angle.

Exterior Angle Theorem

The measure of an angle whose vertex is located outside a circle is half the difference between the measures of the intercepted arcs.

Constant Product Theorem

Given a circle and a secant to the circle passing through any point *P*, the product of the distances from *P* to each of the points of intersection in the circle is constant.

If two chords intersect inside a circle, the product of the lengths of the segments of one chord is equal to the product of the lengths of the segments of the other chord.

If two secants are drawn to a circle from an external point, the product of the lengths of one secant and its external part is equal to the product of the lengths of the other secant and its external part.

If a tangent and a secant of a circle contain the same external point *P*, the length of the tangent segment is the geometric mean between the length of the secant segment and its external part.

WORKOUT 4

1 Find two ways to write 30 as the sum of two or more consecutive whole numbers.

2 Explain how to calculate the following expression using mental arithmetic.

$$3(1 + 3 + 5 + 7 + 9 + ... + 49) - 1101$$

3 Minh spends a third of his money, then spends 2/3 of what he has left. He is left with 12¢. How much money did he have to start with?

4 How far can you calculate the expression $(((2^2)^2)^2)^2...$ using mental arithmetic? (Use a calculator to check.)

5 Use mental arithmetic to determine which of these numbers are not perfect squares.

| 329 476 | 389 452 | 389 565 | 234 568 | 399 424 |

6 Use mental arithmetic to complete the table below. Extend the sequence as far as possible.

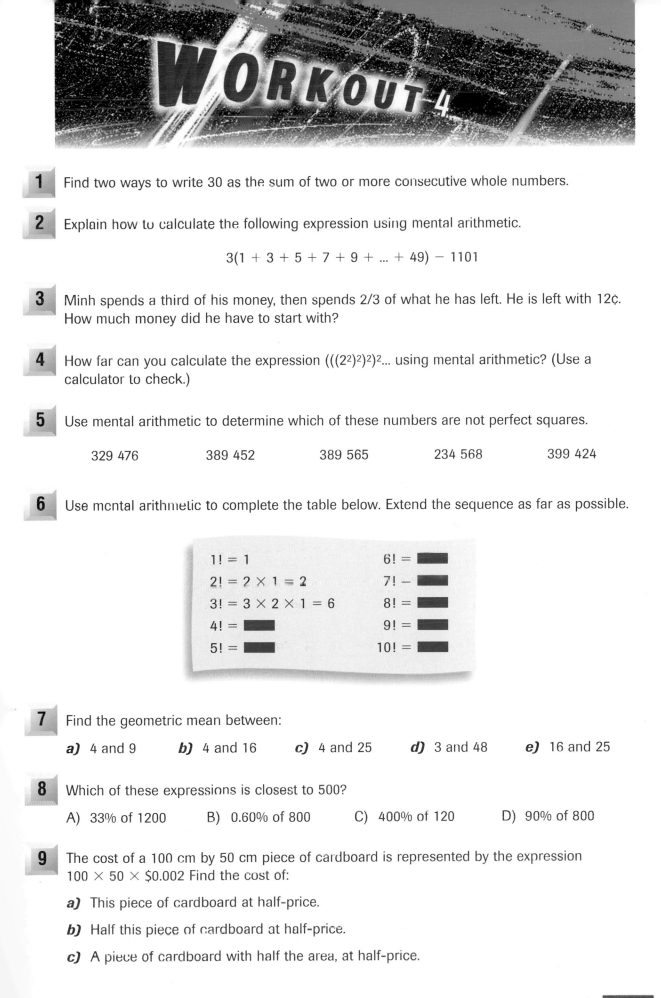

$1! = 1$	$6! = $ ▬
$2! = 2 \times 1 = 2$	$7! - $ ▬
$3! = 3 \times 2 \times 1 = 6$	$8! = $ ▬
$4! = $ ▬	$9! = $ ▬
$5! = $ ▬	$10! = $ ▬

7 Find the geometric mean between:

a) 4 and 9   **b)** 4 and 16   **c)** 4 and 25   **d)** 3 and 48   **e)** 16 and 25

8 Which of these expressions is closest to 500?

A) 33% of 1200   B) 0.60% of 800   C) 400% of 120   D) 90% of 800

9 The cost of a 100 cm by 50 cm piece of cardboard is represented by the expression $100 \times 50 \times \$0.002$ Find the cost of:

a) This piece of cardboard at half-price.

b) Half this piece of cardboard at half-price.

c) A piece of cardboard with half the area, at half-price.

10 If x is negative, which of these expressions has the greatest value?

A) $-2(x + 3)$ B) $-2x - 3$ C) $-2x - 6$ D) $-2x + 6$

11 Give a geometric representation of:

a) a^2 **b)** ab **c)** $a(a + 2)$ **d)** $a(a + b)$ **e)** $(a + 2)(a + 3)$

12 Use mental arithmetic to find the angle measures in these isosceles triangles.

a)

b)

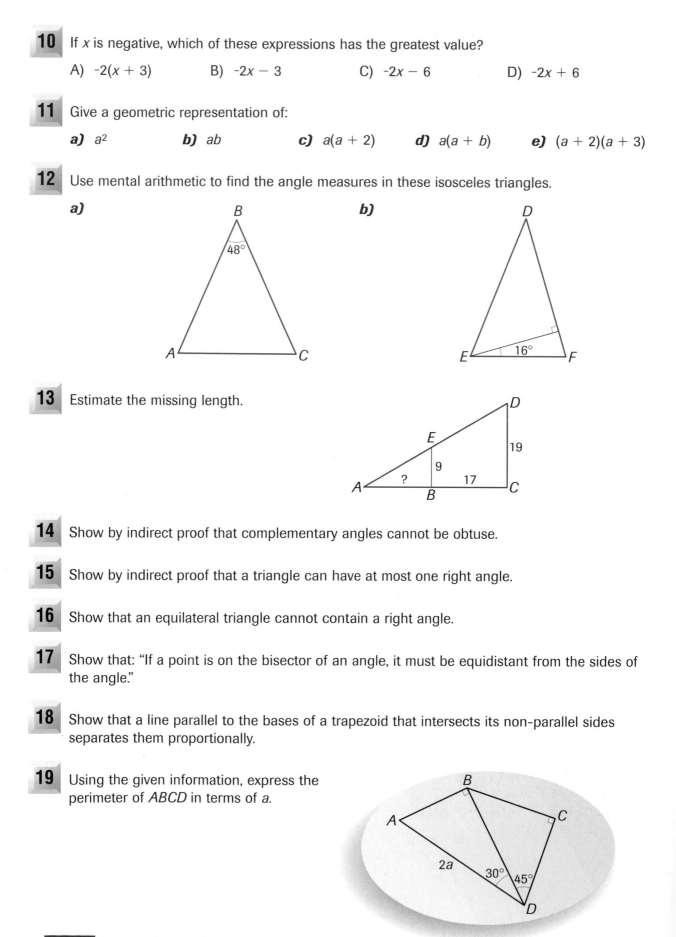

13 Estimate the missing length.

14 Show by indirect proof that complementary angles cannot be obtuse.

15 Show by indirect proof that a triangle can have at most one right angle.

16 Show that an equilateral triangle cannot contain a right angle.

17 Show that: "If a point is on the bisector of an angle, it must be equidistant from the sides of the angle."

18 Show that a line parallel to the bases of a trapezoid that intersects its non-parallel sides separates them proportionally.

19 Using the given information, express the perimeter of *ABCD* in terms of a.

20 Triangle *ABC* is right-angled at *C*. Point *E* is located 2 cm from *C*. Segment *EF* is drawn perpendicular to side *AB*. Triangle *EBF* has sides measuring 6, 8 and 10 cm. Find the side lengths of triangle *ABC*.

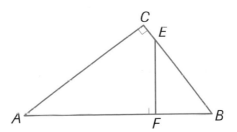

21 Using the given information, find all the angle measures and side lengths of triangles *FBC* and *ABD*.

22 Find the values of *x* and *y* in these figures, given that ∠ *B* is a right angle and $\overline{BD}$ is an altitude.

a)

b)

23 Determine whether triangle *QDV* is an isosceles right triangle.

24 Find the length of diagonal *SV* in square *SMVQ*, given that the measure of ∠ *SQT* is 30° and $\overline{ST}$ measures 6 cm.

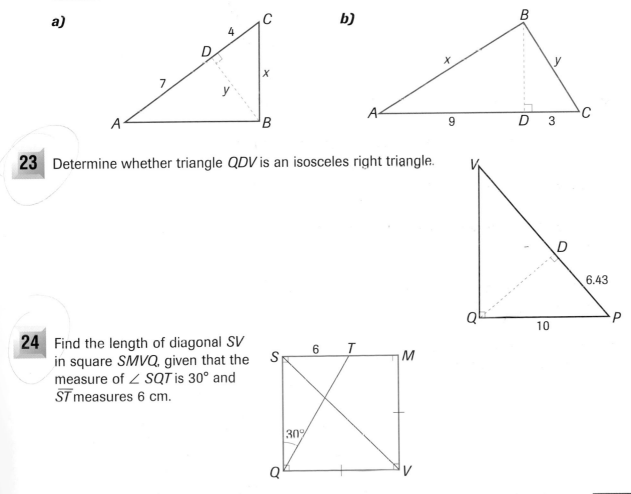

25 Diagonal *BD* is drawn in rectangle *ABCD*. The altitude of each triangle formed by the diagonal is then drawn. The rectangle measures 8 cm by 12 cm. Find the distance between the feet of the altitudes to the diagonal.

26 Find the values of *x*, *y* and *z* from the information in this figure.

27 A kite's lateral angles are right angles, and its diagonals intersect at right angles. Find the lengths of the diagonals in decimetres.

28 The ratio of the areas of two similar figures is equal to the square of the similarity ratio. If the area of triangle *BEA* is 1.53 cm², find the length of altitude *CH* in triangle *ECD*.

29 Chords *AB* and *BC* are congruent, as are chords *AD* and *CD*. Angle *B* measures 120°, and the circle has a radius of 6 units. Find the perimeter of quadrilateral *ABCD*.

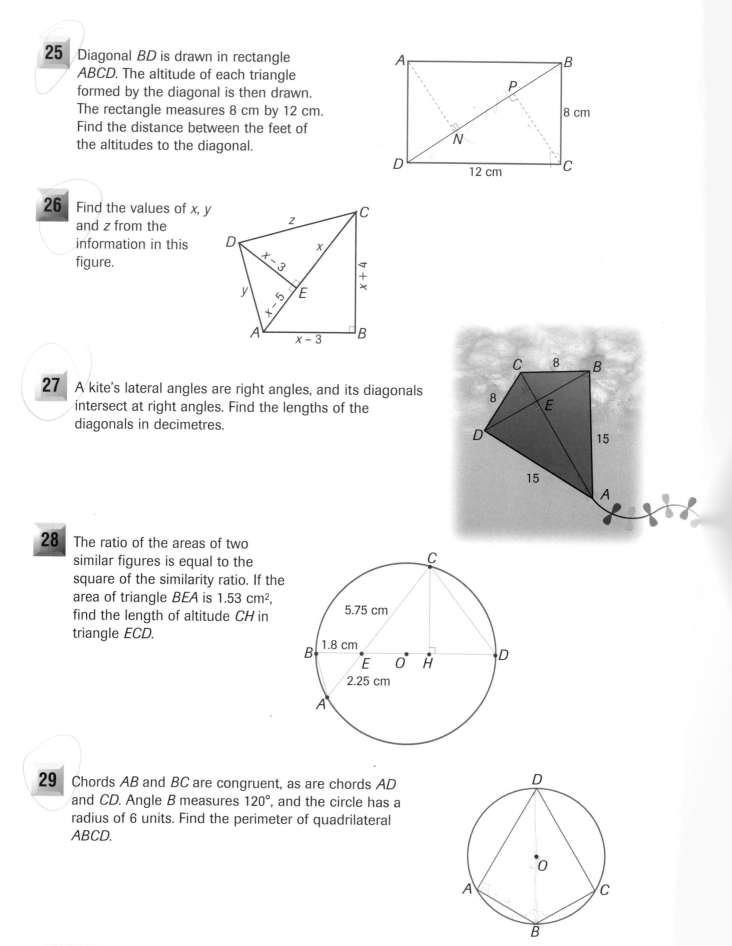

30 Calculate the area of triangle *ABC*. $\overline{AC}$ is a diameter, m ∠ *A* = 30° and side *BC* measures 6 cm.

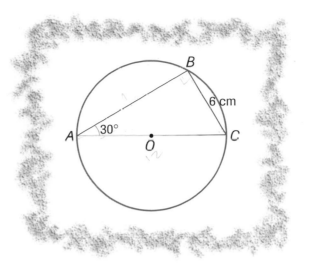

31 Express the side length of this equilateral triangle inscribed in a circle in terms of the radius *r*.

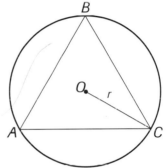

32 Express the side of a regular hexagon inscribed in a circle in terms of the radius *r*.

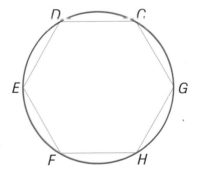

33 Find the measure of the intercepted arc in degrees.

a)

b)

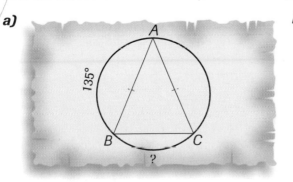

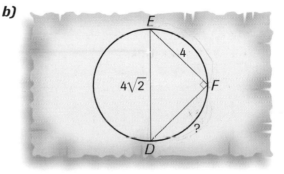

34 How far from the centre is an 8 cm chord in a circle with radius 6 cm?

35 A 2.3 m board is laid across a pipe with diameter 2.5 m, as shown. The water in the pipe just touches the board. How deep is the water?

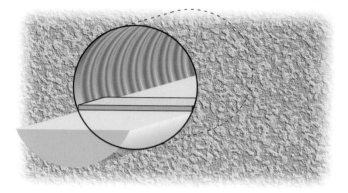

36 From a point *E* outside a circle, two secants are drawn that intersect the circle at *C* and *A* and at *B* and *D* respectively. Chord *AB* is then drawn perpendicular to chord *CD*. Chord *CD* passes through the centre, *O*. Find the following lengths, justifying each step:

a) m $\overline{AC}$

b) m $\overline{BD}$

c) m $\overline{CE}$

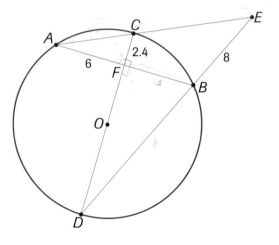

37 The profile of a cement structure is shaped like an isosceles trapezoid *ABCD*. A metal pipe passes through it. The points of tangency are *E, H, F* and *G*.

a) If segments *AG* and *DG* measure *x* and *y* units, express the diameter of the circle in terms of *x* and *y*.

b) If *x* = 0.8 m and *y* = 1.5 m, find m $\overline{OC}$.

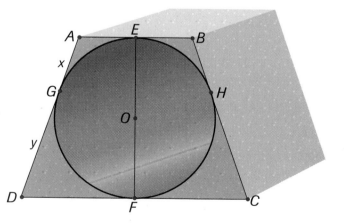

38 Point *P* is outside the circle with centre *O*. From point *P*, a tangent is drawn to point *T*, and a secant is drawn intersecting the circle at points *A* and *B*. *TD* bisects ∠ *ATB* and intersects *PB* at *C*. Prove that triangle *PTC* is isosceles with its apex at *P*.

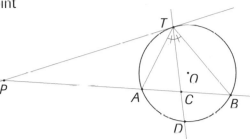

39 Triangle *ABC* is inscribed in a circle with centre *O*. Diameter *AE* and altitude *AD* are drawn. Prove that m $\overline{AB}$ • m $\overline{AC}$ = m $\overline{AE}$ • m $\overline{AD}$.

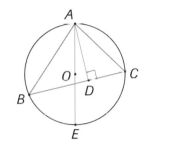

40 Point *P* is outside a circle with centre *O*. From *P*, a secant is drawn that intersects the circle at *A* and *B*. Prove that m $\overline{PA}$ • m $\overline{PB}$ = m $\overline{OP}^2$ − m $\overline{OA}^2$.

41 Two circles have radii of 1 m and 1 000 000 km respectively. If 3 m is added to each of the radii, is the increase in the circumference of the first circle greater than, equal to or smaller than the increase in the circumference of the second circle?

42 Write a calculator program that will use a number *r* and the coordinates of a point *P* to draw a circle with centre *P* and radius *r*. (Use the LINE command and a 20-sided regular polygon to approximate the circle.)

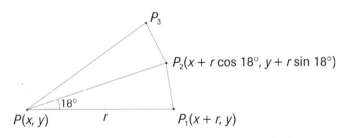

43

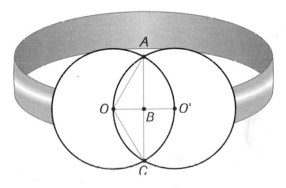

A piece of jewelry is shaped from two disks with radius 1 cm, whose centres are 1 cm apart. The top surface of the disks are to be covered with a thin layer of gold. Find the area of the faces.

44 Triangle *ABC* is right-angled at *A*, and $\overline{BE}$ divides angle ABC into two congruent parts. m $\overline{AB}$ = 9 cm and m $\overline{BC}$ = 15 cm. Find the length of $\overline{BE}$.

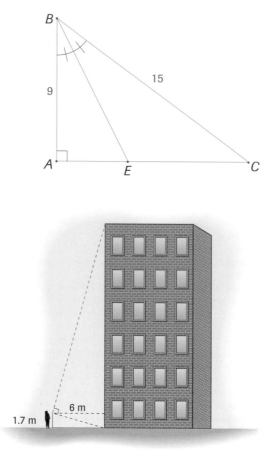

45 Nancy is looking at the base and the top of a building. She must stand 6 m back from the building for the two lines of vision to form a right angle. Her eyes are 1.7 m from the ground. How tall is the building? Justify each step.

46 **INHERITANCE**

Cindy and Marco's mother inherits a piece of land shaped like a right triangle with legs 120 m and 80 m. She wants to divide the land fairly between Cindy and Marco. Will the altitude, the bisector or the median at the right angle create the fairest division?

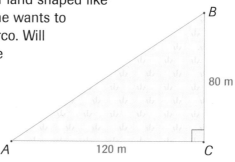

47 **FOUR QUARTERS**

A 25¢ coin has a diameter of 24 mm. Find the area of the surface between four quarters placed as shown.

48 HOOK

A hook is made from a quarter-disk with radius 1 cm from which a half-disk is removed. What is the area of one face of the hook?

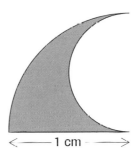

←————— 1 cm —————→

49 BALL IN A DITCH

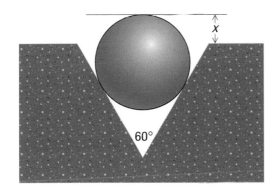

60°

A ball has fallen into a V-shaped ditch 24 cm deep. The angle of the V is 60°. The ball's radius is 10 cm. How many centimetres above the ground is the top of the ball?

50 PAPER CORNER

The corner of a 12 cm by 20 cm piece of paper is folded as shown. Point A ends up at point A'. What is the distance between points A and A'?

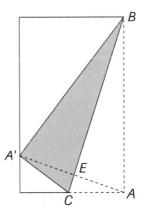

51 STARMAKER

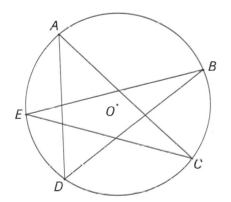

A manufacturer creates decorative stars by placing points on a circle. He has noticed an interesting relationship between the sum of the angle measures of the angles formed by the points on the star.

a) Find this relationship.

b) Prove this relationship.

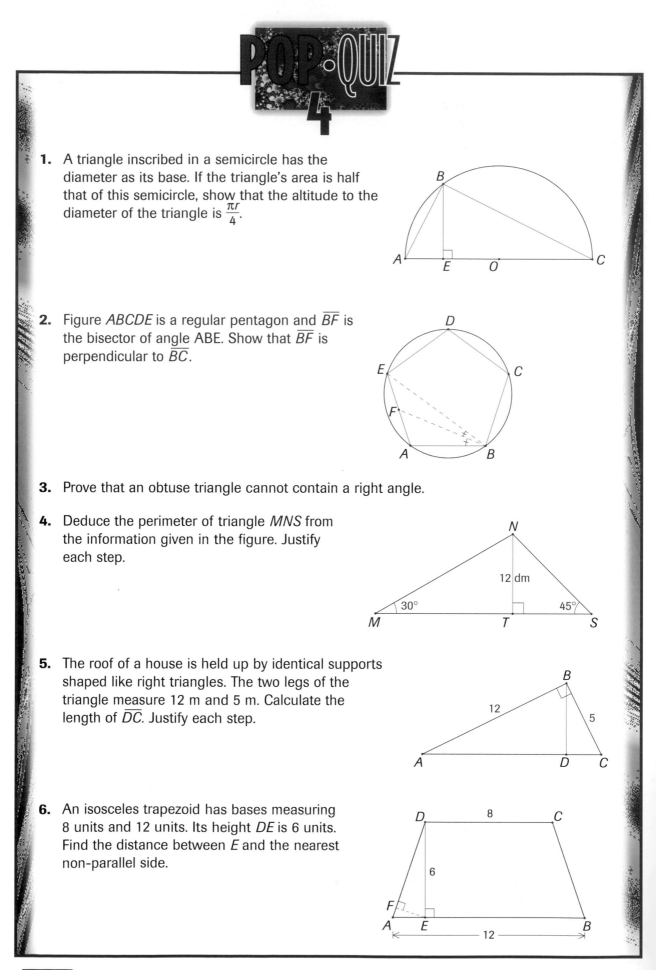

1. A triangle inscribed in a semicircle has the diameter as its base. If the triangle's area is half that of this semicircle, show that the altitude to the diameter of the triangle is $\frac{\pi r}{4}$.

2. Figure *ABCDE* is a regular pentagon and $\overline{BF}$ is the bisector of angle ABE. Show that $\overline{BF}$ is perpendicular to $\overline{BC}$.

3. Prove that an obtuse triangle cannot contain a right angle.

4. Deduce the perimeter of triangle *MNS* from the information given in the figure. Justify each step.

5. The roof of a house is held up by identical supports shaped like right triangles. The two legs of the triangle measure 12 m and 5 m. Calculate the length of $\overline{DC}$. Justify each step.

6. An isosceles trapezoid has bases measuring 8 units and 12 units. Its height *DE* is 6 units. Find the distance between *E* and the nearest non-parallel side.

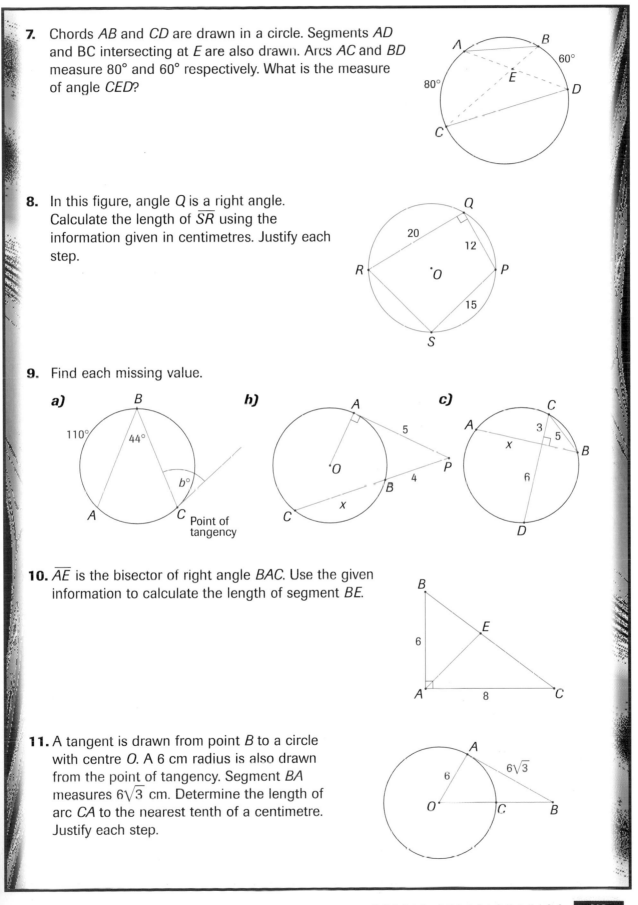

7. Chords *AB* and *CD* are drawn in a circle. Segments *AD* and *BC* intersecting at *E* are also drawn. Arcs *AC* and *BD* measure 80° and 60° respectively. What is the measure of angle *CED*?

8. In this figure, angle *Q* is a right angle. Calculate the length of $\overline{SR}$ using the information given in centimetres. Justify each step.

9. Find each missing value.

a)

b)

Point of tangency

c)

10. $\overline{AE}$ is the bisector of right angle *BAC*. Use the given information to calculate the length of segment *BE*.

11. A tangent is drawn from point *B* to a circle with centre *O*. A 6 cm radius is also drawn from the point of tangency. Segment *BA* measures $6\sqrt{3}$ cm. Determine the length of arc *CA* to the nearest tenth of a centimetre. Justify each step.

12. In a circle with centre *O*, two congruent chords *AB* and *DC* are drawn. Diameter $\overline{EF}$ is perpendicular to $\overline{AB}$, m $\overline{DG}$ = 2 cm and m $\overset{\frown}{DC}$ = 90°. Find the length of $\overline{OF}$, justifying each step.

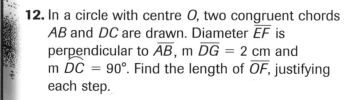

13. Point *B* on a semicircle is joined to the endpoints of the semicircle's diameter. $\overline{BH}$ is drawn perpendicular to the diameter. Chord *AB* has the same length as *HC*. Find the length of these two segments and calculate the height *BH*.

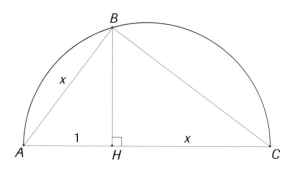

14. A circle with centre *O* has a 20 m diameter *AB* that is perpendicular to a 10 m chord *DC*. Determine the degree measure of arc *DC*, justifying each step.

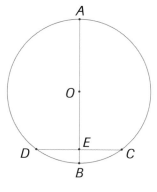

Interview with...

Archimedes
(c. 287–212 BC)

Archimedes, even in your own time, you were thought to be a great mathematician. They say that King Hieron asked you to solve a problem, and this process led you to a great discovery. What was the problem?

The king thought that a goldsmith had replaced some of the gold in his crown with silver. He wanted to know how much gold had been removed without having to take the crown apart.

How did you solve the problem?

By taking a bath! I was pondering the question, and suddenly realized that the same mass of gold and silver did not displace the same amount of water: the silver would have to have a greater volume than the gold, and would therefore displace more water. I climbed out of the bath, shouting "Eureka! Eureka!"

ng Hieron provided you with several challenges. Tell me hy you declared: ive me a fulcrum d I will move the world."

King Hieron had built a huge boat for King Ptolemy of Alexandria. But he couldn't get it into the water! With some help, I installed a system of levers and pulleys. Then, sitting alone on the beach, I pulled on the first cord attached to the first pulley, and the boat slid gently into the ocean.

rchimedes, you eveloped many mechanical ntions. Did you e any sketches of these nventions?

I believed these inventions were frivolous things. It was a combination of circumstances, people's requests and the need to defend my homeland that led me to explore the practical side of geometry. I did not keep any record of my inventions, but I wrote more than 10 books on geometry!

Is it true that your mechanical inventions helped King Hieron hold out under a two-year Roman siege in 214 BC?

Indeed! I protected my homeland by inventing weapons that terrified the enemy: catapults, parabolic mirrors that set their ships on fire, and such. The Romans were so afraid of my inventions that the mere sight of a rope thrown from the ramparts made them flee in fear of another diabolical contraption!

ARCHIMEDES

Why did you have a sphere and a cylinder carved on your tombstone?

Because I had discovered such beautiful relationships between them. These figures symbolized my life in geometry.

Archimedes is considered to be the greatest mathematician of ancient times. His treatises were carefully written, very rigorous and original. He was a brilliant inventor whose fame extended throughout the Greek world. His work on areas, volumes, circle measures and conics, among other things, made him a great geometer.

Archimedes observed the following relationship, and used it to divide an angle into three congruent parts:

"An extension *BC* of chord *AB* is congruent to the radius of a circle with centre *D*. Angle *C* is formed by drawing the secant that passes through *C* and the centre of the circle, and intersects the circle at *F* and *E*."

Show that the measure of angle *ADE* is three times the measure of angle *C*.

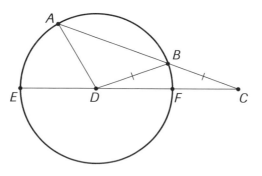

MY PROJECTS

PROJECT 1 The derivation of π

This project involves discovering the origin of the famous formulas for the circumference of a circle and the area of a disk. These formulas are based on a principle of invariance; that is, the ratio between the circumference and diameter of a circle does not depend on the size of the circle. This ratio is a constant and is valid for all circles; since antiquity, it has been known by the famous symbol π. In other words, stating that circumference C of a circle with radius r is $C = 2\pi r$ is the same as stating:

$$\frac{C}{2r} = \frac{\text{circumference}}{\text{diameter}} = \pi.$$

Starting with a square inscribed in a given circle, we can closely approximate a circle by repeatedly doubling the number of sides, producing a regular polygon with 8, then 16, 32, 64 … sides. Calculating the perimeter of the first four polygons shows that the ratio of this perimeter to the diameter of the circle is constant, and that the value of this constant tends toward π. (Use trigonometric ratios to simplify the calculations.)

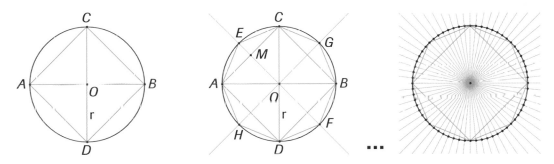

You could also write a computer program to accomplish this task simply by increasing the number of sides in the polygon.

PROJECT 2 The area of a disk

This project involves explaining how the area of the polygon shown here tends toward πr^2 if the number of its sides is increased.

To complete this project, observe how the lengths of each side (represented by $\overline{PQ}$) and the altitude (represented by $\overline{OM}$) evolve as the number of sides is increased indefinitely.

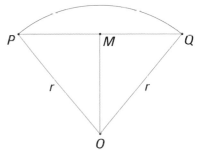

Enrich your project by doing some Internet research on π, as well as on formulas for the circumference of a circle or the area of the interior of a circle, or disk.

I UNDERSTAND THE MEANING OF THE FOLLOWING EXPRESSIONS:

Basic term:	Term that is used without being defined.
Axiom:	Statement that is accepted as true without proof.
Theorem:	Conjecture that is proved to be true.
Aligned adjacent angles:	Adjacent angles whose external sides are collinear.
Opposite rays:	Two rays contained in the same line with only the endpoint in common.
Distance between two points:	Function that associates a positive real number and a unit with any pair of points.
Angle measure:	Function that associates a positive real number and a unit with any angle. The number varies within an interval determined by the unit.
On the same side of a line:	Two points are said to be on the same side of a line when they belong to the same half-plane determined by the line, and are not on the line itself.
On opposite sides of a line:	Two points are said to be on opposite sides of a line when they belong to opposite half-planes determined by the line and are not on the line itself.
Median of a triangle:	Line segment that joins the vertex of a triangle to the midpoint of the opposite side.
Right bisector of a line segment:	Perpendicular line that divides a line segment into two congruent parts.
Bisector of an angle:	Line that divides an angle into two congruent angles.
Isometric (congruent):	Term that implies that an isometry exists between two figures.
Hypotenuse:	Longest side of a right triangle, or the length of that side.
Orthogonal projection:	Plane transformation that maps any point P in the plane onto point P', the foot of the perpendicular segment drawn from P to a given line l.
Projection:	Image of another point under an orthogonal projection.
Tangent:	Line in the same plane that intersects a circle at only one point.
Secant:	Line that intersects a circle at two distinct points.
Central angle:	Angle whose vertex is the centre of a circle.
Inscribed angle:	Angle whose vertex is a point on the circle and whose sides are secant or tangent to the circle.
Power of a point:	Number corresponding to the product of the distances from a given point to each of the points of intersection of a line through that point and a given circle.

Reflection 4

EXPONENTIAL AND LOGARITHMIC FUNCTIONS ....

THE MAIN IDEAS

- ▶ Laws of exponents and exponential functions
- ▶ Laws of logarithms and logarithmic functions
- ▶ Solving exponential and logarithmic equations

TERMINAL OBJECTIVE

- ▶ To solve problems using exponential and logarithmic functions as models for a situation.

INTERMEDIATE OBJECTIVES

- ▶ To **construct** a Cartesian graph of an exponential or logarithmic function and **describe** its characteristics.

- ▶ To **determine** the properties of an exponential or logarithmic function.

- ▶ To **make the connection** between the change in a parameter of the rule for an exponential or logarithmic function and the change in the corresponding graph.

- ▶ To **find** the rule for an exponential or logarithmic function using the values of given parameters, the coordinates of certain points, a table of values or a graph.

- ▶ To **represent** a situation using an exponential or logarithmic function.

- ▶ To **explore** different operations on exponential or logarithmic functions algebraically and graphically.

- ▶ To **apply** the properties of logarithms in simplifying logarithmic expressions and finding the solution set of an equation in one variable involving logarithmic and exponential expressions.

EXPONENTIAL FUNCTIONS

THE CONCEPT OF AN EXPONENT
AN EXPONENTIAL MODEL
THE BASIC EXPONENTIAL FUNCTION
TRANSFORMED EXPONENTIAL FUNCTIONS
ZEROS AND EQUATIONS
SIGN AND INEQUALITIES
NATURAL LOGARITHMS
FINDING THE RULE

THE CONCEPT OF AN EXPONENT

Creating camera effects

By attaching filters to their camera lenses, professional photographers can create spectacular photographs. Colour filters will either enhance or block some colours from appearing in the picture. Taken through these filters, photographs of people or scenery reveal some very imaginative special effects.

Three red filters are attached to a camera lens. Each filter allows 4/5 of the ambient light to pass through.

In 1553 a German named Michael Stifel introduced exponential notation as a simpler, more convenient means of mathematical expression.

How do photographic filters work? It's simple. The filter allows light wavelengths of the matching colour to pass through while absorbing or blocking the wavelengths of contrasting colours. In this case, a red filter allows only red light wavelengths to pass through and blocks all other light wavelengths.

a) Express, as a product, the fraction of light that passes through this set of filters.

b) Rewrite this fraction using:

1) A single exponent.

2) The same exponent twice.

c) What fraction of light would pass through a series of:

1) 4 filters of factor 3/5?

2) 3 filters of factor 1/2?

d) How many filters of factor 2/3 must be superimposed to get the same result as a set of 3 filters of factor 4/9? Or as a set of 2 filters of factor 8/27?

Working with **exponents** involves assigning an exponent to a **base** in order to obtain a **power**. In the expression $a^m = p$, a is the base, m is the exponent and p is the power.

Analysing the table of values below will enable you to draw some conclusions and identify some restrictions on the values that can be assigned to bases and exponents.

e) In each of the following, identify any restrictions that may exist.

1) **Base of zero**   2) **Unit base**   3) **Negative base**

4) **Negative exponent**   5) **Fractional or rational exponent**   6) **Irrational exponent**

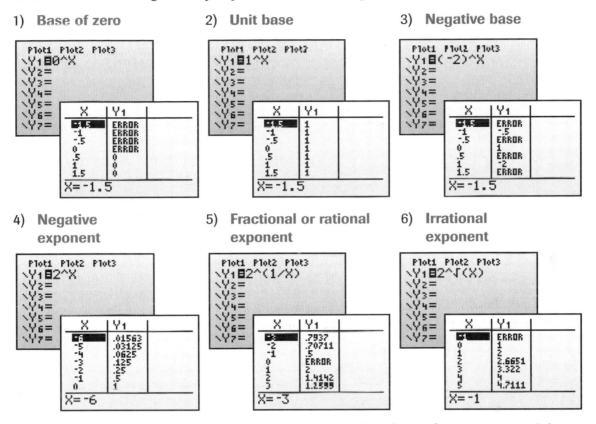

Note that all **base values** that are **strictly positive** and assigned a **real exponent** result in a **real power.** More specifically, the following rules apply:

$$a^0 = 1 \text{ when } a \neq 0 \qquad a^1 = a \qquad a^{-m} = \frac{1}{a^m} \text{ when } a \neq 0$$

$$a^{\frac{1}{m}} = \sqrt[m]{a} \text{ (except when } m \text{ is even and } a < 0)$$

Fractional powers were introduced by Simon Stevin in 1585.

Knowing the laws of exponential expressions makes them easier to work with and simplify.

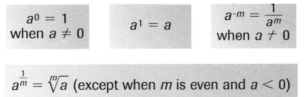

Laws of exponents

For $a, b \in \mathbb{R}^+$ and $m, n \in \mathbb{R}$, we have:

1. The product of powers with the same base: $a^m \cdot a^n = a^{m+n}$

2. The quotient of powers with the same base: $a^m \div a^n = \frac{a^m}{a^n} = a^{m-n}$

3. The power of a product: $(ab)^m = a^m b^m$

4. The power of a power: $(a^m)^n = a^{mn}$

5. The power of a quotient: $\left(\frac{a}{b}\right)^m = \frac{a^m}{b^m}$

1. Find the values of the missing numbers mentally.

   a) $5^3 = \blacksquare$

   b) $2^{-3} = \blacksquare$

   c) $11^0 = \blacksquare$

   d) $4^6 \times 4^{-3} = 4^{\blacksquare}$

   e) $3^{\blacksquare} = \dfrac{1}{27}$

   f) $7^{(5-\blacksquare)} = \dfrac{1}{49}$

   g) $\blacksquare^2 \times 3 = 64$

   h) $10^{\blacksquare} = 0.0001$

   i) $\blacksquare^2 = \dfrac{1}{9}$

   j) $(5^2)^{\blacksquare} = 625$

   k) $(5^{\blacksquare})^3 = \dfrac{1}{125}$

   l) $99^{\blacksquare} = 99$

2. Fill in the missing values in the following series of numbers.

   a) 6, 18, 54, 162, $\blacksquare$, $\blacksquare$, $\blacksquare$, ...

   b) 2916, 324, 36, $\blacksquare$, $\blacksquare$, $\blacksquare$, ...

   c) 0.0025, 0.025, 0.25, $\blacksquare$, $\blacksquare$, $\blacksquare$, ...

   d) 768, 192, 48, $\blacksquare$, $\blacksquare$, $\blacksquare$, ...

3. For each series in the previous exercise, identify the rule that makes it possible to find value v of the nth term in the series.

4. In the following series, find the values of the two missing terms. Each term is related to the next by the same multiplication factor.

   a) 13, $\blacksquare$, $\blacksquare$, 1625, ...

   b) 4, $\blacksquare$, 324, $\blacksquare$, 26 244, ...

   c) $\blacksquare$, 10, $\blacksquare$, 2560, ...

   d) 3.5, $\blacksquare$, 56, $\blacksquare$, 896, ...

5. Simplify the following algebraic expressions where $x \neq 0$.

   a) $\left(\dfrac{x^5}{x^3}\right)x^{-1}$

   b) $\left(\dfrac{x}{x^{-2}}\right)^3$

   c) $x^7\left(\dfrac{x^{-2}}{x^{-5}}\right)^3$

   d) $x^{-2}x^{-7}(x^3)^2 + x^{11}$

6. Express each product in exponential form with a base that is a prime number.

   a) $-5 \times -5 \times -5 \times -5 \times 5 \times 5 \times 5 \times 1$

   b) $-2 \times -2 \times 2 \times 2 \times -3 \times 3$

   c) $2 \times 4 \times 8 \times 12 \times 16 \times 24$

   d) $-12 \times -3 \times -2 \times 6 \times 18$

7. The Moon's radius measures about 1.7×10^3 km. The Earth's radius is 3.75 times larger than the Moon's. Saturn's radius is 9.4 times larger than the Earth's.

   a) Calculate the volume of the Moon.

   b) Calculate the area of the Earth's surface.

   c) How many times is Saturn's volume larger than the Moon's volume?

   Saturn is an enormous planet surrounded by a layer of icy debris that forms an impressive system of concentric rings. Almost entirely composed of hydrogen and helium, Saturn has a lower relative density than water (0.69). If Saturn were dropped into a large enough ocean, it would float!

8. A minicomputer is used to test the equality of various expressions. For each of the following, explain the cause of the error, then give the right answer.

```
F1        F2       F3     F4     F5           F6
  Algebra Calc  Other  PrgmIO Clear  a-z...
```

a) $\blacksquare (-1)^5 = -5$ false

b) $\blacksquare 3^8 = 8^3$ false

c) $\blacksquare -2^{-2} = 4$ false

d) $\blacksquare 3 \cdot x^2 = (3 \cdot x)^2$ false

e) $\blacksquare 7^0 = 0$ false

f) $\blacksquare 2^{-1} = \sqrt{2}$ false

```
MAIN         RAD AUTO         FUNC 6/30
```

9. Assuming that the denominators are not zero, simplify the following expressions.

a) $a^3 b^{-2}(a^{-1}b + b^6)$

b) $6\left(\dfrac{a^2}{b^6}\right)\left(\dfrac{b^{-2}}{a^4}\right)$

c) $(-3a)^4(a^4 b^7)$

d) $\dfrac{-a^3 b^7}{(a^{-1}b^3)^3}$

e) $a^{-4}b^7(-ab)^2(b^3)^{-1}$

f) $\dfrac{(ab + b)^2(b - a)}{(ab)^2(a + 1)^2}$

10. Examine the dimensions of the right prism below.

What algebraic expression can be used to find:

a) The total area of this prism?

b) The total area of a right prism whose dimensions are twice the size of this one?

c) The volume of a right prism whose dimensions are three times the size of this one?

11. A calculator has many buttons and functions that deal with exponents. Describe how to use the following buttons with your particular type of calculator. Explain their uses.

a) y^x **b)** $\wedge$ **c)** 10^x **d)** x^2 **e)** x^{-1} **f)** e^x

THINK TANK

a) Under what conditions are the following statements true?

1) $-x^m = (-x)^m$ 2) $0^m = 0$ 3) $\left(\dfrac{1}{x^m}\right)^n = \left(\dfrac{1}{x^n}\right)^m$ 4) $(-x)^m = x^{-m}$

b) What values of n would give you: $2(4^{n^n}) = (2^n)^n$?

c) Provide the rule that would allow you to calculate the nth term in a series where the first three terms are 2, 0.25 and 16.

AN EXPONENTIAL MODEL

A cure for computer viruses

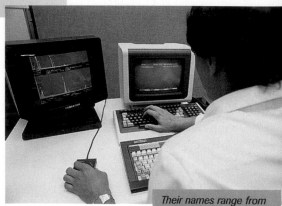

Computer viruses target various parts of a computer. The problems they cause vary from annoying to disastrous. Some viruses can render a computer totally inoperable. Fortunately, there are specialized programmers whose job is to detect and eliminate viruses. After discovering how to destroy a virus that had been preventing on-screen mouse movements, a programmer sends a warning message to three colleagues via Internet. She asks them to relay this message via Internet to three of their colleagues on the next day. The cycle continues and the message spreads.

Binary sabotage! Often consisting of merely a few lines of code, a virus is a program that duplicates itself and infects large software programs. Diskettes are the most widespread carriers of viruses.

Their names range from silly to sinister: No-Name, Data Crime, The Devil's Dance, Black Avenger.... Some of them are relatively harmless, while others can ravage an entire network. Computer viruses have become an everyday occurrence, and nearly every computer is at risk.

a) If the cycle is uninterrupted, how many people will receive the message:

1) on the 3rd day?   2) on the 6th day?   3) on the 10th day?

b) Continue the cycle shown on the screen and find the first day on which more than one million people will receive a copy of the message.

```
1*3
              3
Ans*3
              9
             27
             81
            243
■
```

This situation introduces a **mathematical model involving exponents.**

In the rule for an **exponential function,** the independent variable *x* appears as an **exponent.**

Here is the table of values for the mathematical model and the graph that shows the relation between the number of days and the number of people who receive the message each day.

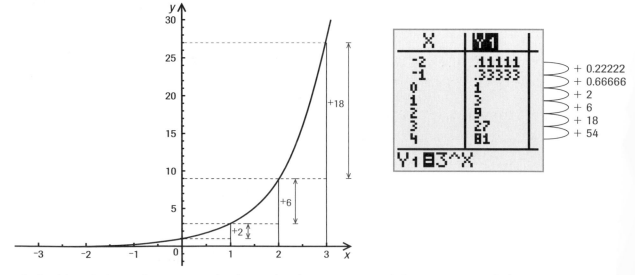

c) In this relation, what pattern is shown by the sequence of the unit rates of change?

d) Would you find the same pattern in the following tables of values?

1)

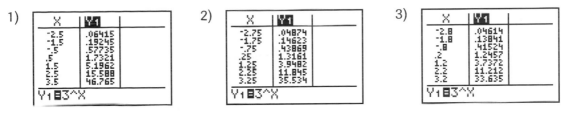

For each function f of the exponential model, we have:

$$\frac{f(x + 2) - f(x + 1)}{f(x + 1) - f(x)} = \textbf{base}$$

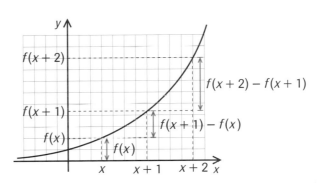

THE BASIC EXPONENTIAL FUNCTION

Expansion and reduction

Architects use a drawing program that allows them to expand or reduce images. Expanding an image allows them to draw tiny objects with precision. Reducing allows them to get an overall view of a large image. Architects using the program select the image's expansion or reduction factor. Here are the available options:

EXPANSION	2	3	5
REDUCTION	1/2	1/3	1/5

a) Consider the functions that associate a size change with the number of times the factors above are selected. What is the rule for each factor?

b) Among the previous function rules, indicate which ones have a base with:

1) A factor of exponential growth.

2) A factor of exponential decay.

The resulting rules produce **simple** exponential functions that differ only in their **bases.**

c) An exponent's base can be any real number producing a function that is always defined.

Plot1 Plot2 Plot3
\Y1⊟(-2)^X
\Y2⊟0^X
\Y3⊟0.25^X
\Y4⊟1^X
\Y5⊟4^X
\Y6=
\Y7=

1) Using a table of values, determine whether the functions shown on the right are always defined. (Use a step variation of 0.1.)

2) What type of function is associated with the rule $Y_4 = 1^x$?

The rule for a basic exponential function is $f(x) = c^x$ where c is a constant other than 1 and greater than 0.

d) Study the tables of values of the exponential functions shown on the right to determine whether their ranges could contain negative numbers. Justify your answer.

Plot1 Plot2 Plot3
\Y1⊟(1/2)^X
\Y2⊟(1/3)^X
\Y3⊟(1/5)^X
\Y4⊟2^X
\Y5⊟3^X
\Y6⊟5^X
\Y7=

The following graphs of basic exponential functions were sketched from the previous tables of values.

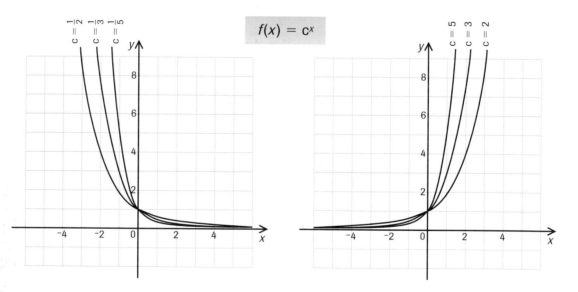

$f(x) = c^x$

e) Observe these graphs closely.

1) Explain how the base c affects the general appearance of the curve.

2) What is the y-intercept of these curves? How can you explain this result?

3) What is the image of 1 under each of these functions?

4) It looks like the curves will meet the x-axis. Will they really? Justify your answer.

f) Two exponential functions along with their inverses have been sketched. Give the domain and range for the inverse of all basic exponential functions.

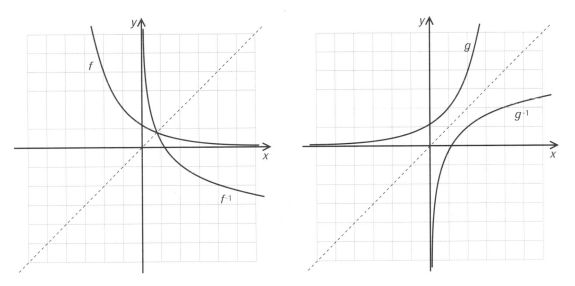

g) Is the inverse of an exponential function also a function? Explain.

To find the rule for an inverse function, invert the variables in the rule for the basic exponential function $y = c^x$ to obtain the rule $x = c^y$.

h) In your own words, explain the role of y in the rule for the inverse.

An exponent assigned to a base is called a **logarithm.**
Therefore, y is the logarithm of x in base c. In symbols, this is written. $y = \log_c x$.

> A logarithm is an **exponent.**
>
> $$y = c^x \Leftrightarrow x = \log_c y$$

Exponent $= \log_{base}(\text{power})$

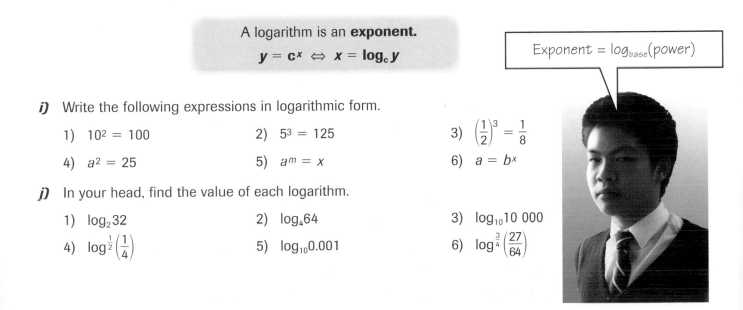

i) Write the following expressions in logarithmic form.

1) $10^2 = 100$

2) $5^3 = 125$

3) $\left(\dfrac{1}{2}\right)^3 = \dfrac{1}{8}$

4) $a^2 = 25$

5) $a^m = x$

6) $a = b^x$

j) In your head, find the value of each logarithm.

1) $\log_2 32$

2) $\log_4 64$

3) $\log_{10} 10\ 000$

4) $\log_{\frac{1}{2}}\left(\dfrac{1}{4}\right)$

5) $\log_{10} 0.001$

6) $\log_{\frac{3}{4}}\left(\dfrac{27}{64}\right)$

k) Complete the table of **properties** for the **basic exponential function.**

Rule	$f(x) = c^x$ (c > 0 and c ≠ 1)
Graph	- Asymptote at ▬▬▬▬▬ - Curve passing through (0, ▮) and (1, ▮)
Domain	▬▬▬▬
Range	▬▬▬▬
Zero	▬▬▬▬
Extremes	▬▬▬▬
Sign	▬▬▬▬
Variation	If c > 1: ▮ and if 0 < c < 1: ▮
Inverse	▬▬▬▬

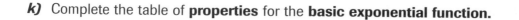

1. The screen images below show the first few terms in an exponential series. The first term of each has been blacked out.

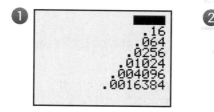
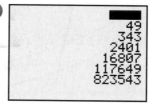
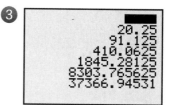

a) For each:

1) Give the multiplying factor.

2) Find the next two terms.

b) State the rule for the function you would get if you considered the relation between the term's row and its value.

2. Indicate which situations call for an exponential model.

a) A city's population increases by 2.8% each year.

b) Filling a pool using a water source with a constant flow.

c) The speed of a ball in free fall over time.

d) A bacteria's population triples every thirty minutes.

e) The value of a house over time.

3. Sketch the curves of the following functions:

a) $f_1(x) = 0.5^x$

b) $f_2(x) = 3^x$

c) $f_3(x) = 5^x$

4. Which of the following tables of values represents an exponential function?

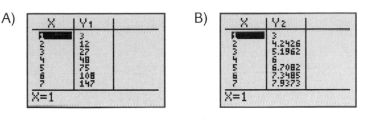

A)

X	Y₁
1	3
2	12
3	27
4	48
5	75
6	108
7	147

X=1

B)

X	Y₂
1	3
2	4.2426
3	5.1962
4	6
5	6.7082
6	7.3485
7	7.9373

X=1

C)

X	Y₃
1	3
2	-3
3	-21
4	-75
5	-237
6	-723
7	-2181

X=1

5. What is the relationship between the graphs of function f and function g?

a) $f(x) = 0.125^x$ and $g(x) = 8^x$

b) $f(x) = 0.0625^x$ and $g(x) = 16^x$

6. Some rules for basic exponential functions are given below.

$f(x) = 0.25^x$ $g(x) - (1/2)^x$ $h(x) = 0.9^x$ $i(x) = 1.5^x$ $j(x) - 4^x$

For each one, determine:

a) Whether it represents a case of growth or decay.

b) The domain and range.

c) The y-intercept of the function's curve.

d) The image of -1 and 1.

e) The equation of the asymptote to the curve.

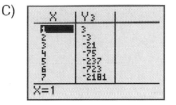

An exponential function with base c can also be written as $\exp_c(x)$

7. What can be concluded about the zero, the extremes and the sign of every basic exponential function?

8. In the graph below, the inverse of an exponential function has been drawn.

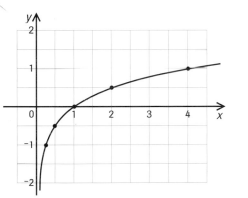

a) Give the rule for the exponential function associated with this inverse.

b) Give the rule for the function shown on this graph.

c) Find the domain and range of this function.

9. Write the following exponential functions in logarithmic form:

a) $3^2 = 9$

b) $5^3 = 125$

c) $2.5^s = t$

d) $y = \left(\dfrac{1}{8}\right)^x$

e) $s^v = w$

f) $y = c^x$

10. Find the exponential expression that is equivalent to the following:

a) $\log_6 36 = 2$

b) $\log_n 100 - z$

c) $\log_{0.75} y = x$

d) $\log_t s = r$

11. For each of the functions defined below, find the rule for the inverse and graph it.

    a) $f_1(x) = 3^x$ **b)** $f_2(x) = (0.5)^x$ **c)** $f_3(x) = 10^x$

12. Compare the images of the functions defined by $f(x) = x^3$ and $g(x) = 3^x$ over the interval $[0, +\infty[$.

a) Is it possible:

    1) For a strictly positive base to have a negative power?

    2) For a strictly positive base to have zero power?

b) If $f(x) = c^x$, prove the following:

    1) $\dfrac{f(x + 2) - f(x + 1)}{f(x + 1) - f(x)} = c$ 2) $f(x_1 + x_2) = f(x_1) \cdot f(x_2)$ 3) $f(x_1 - x_2) = \dfrac{f(x_1)}{f(x_2)}$

TRANSFORMED EXPONENTIAL FUNCTIONS

Rheumatism and aspirin

Rheumatism is a painful condition that can cause stiffness or inflammation of the joints, bones and even muscles. There are a number of ways to treat rheumatism. In some cases, patients are advised to take aspirin. After the aspirin has had time to take effect, its concentration in the bloodstream decreases at an exponential rate. Consider the aspirin's concentration in the bloodstream over time, from the point when the aspirin has reached its maximum effect.

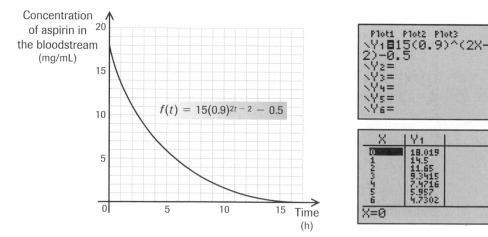

$$f(t) = 15(0.9)^{2t - 2} - 0.5$$

a) Use the table of values to confirm whether this relation is exponential.

The rule for this function features several parameters. The introduction of **parameters a, b, h** and **k** can transform the basic exponential function to produce a rule in the form $f(x) = ac^{b(x - h)} + k$ for a ≠ 0, b ≠ 0, c > 0 and c ≠ 1.

b) Give the values of parameters **a, b, h** and **k** in the rule $f(t) = 15(0.9)^{2t - 2} - 0.5$.

Introducing parameters **a, b, h** and **k** into the rule for an exponential function generates transformations that affect the graph of the basic exponential function. Here is a series of transformations applied to the graph of the function defined by $f(x) = 2^x$ to produce the graph of the function defined by $g(x) = 3(2)^{0.5(x - 4)} - 3$.

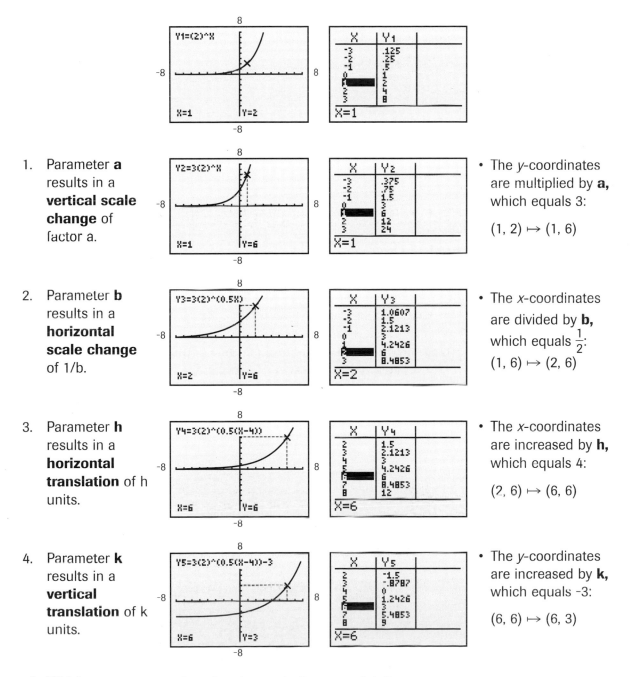

1. Parameter **a** results in a **vertical scale change** of factor a.

• The *y*-coordinates are multiplied by **a,** which equals 3:

$(1, 2) \mapsto (1, 6)$

2. Parameter **b** results in a **horizontal scale change** of 1/b.

• The *x*-coordinates are divided by **b,** which equals $\frac{1}{2}$:

$(1, 6) \mapsto (2, 6)$

3. Parameter **h** results in a **horizontal translation** of h units.

• The *x*-coordinates are increased by **h,** which equals 4:

$(2, 6) \mapsto (6, 6)$

4. Parameter **k** results in a **vertical translation** of k units.

• The *y*-coordinates are increased by **k,** which equals -3:

$(6, 6) \mapsto (6, 3)$

c) Which parameter produced a change in the asymptote?

d) Find the values of **k** in the functions below.

1)

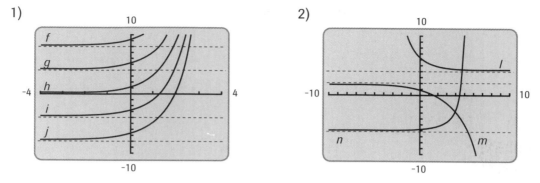

2)

e) Determine the equations of the asymptotes mentally.

1) $f_1(x) = -2(10)^x - 1$

2) $f_2(x) = (5)^{x+8} + 11$

3) $f_3(x) = -(4)^{7x-6} - \dfrac{1}{3}$

4) $f_4(x) = -22.5(1.25)^x$

Applying the parameters to the critical ordered pairs in the basic function: $\left(-1, \dfrac{1}{c}\right)$, **(0, 1)** and **(1, c)**, yields the critical ordered pairs of the transformed function. Finding the asymptote and these ordered pairs makes it easy to sketch the curve of the transformed function.

f) For the function defined by $f(x) = -2(2)^{0.5(x-1)} + 3$, find the asymptote and the critical ordered pairs, then sketch its curve.

> If (x, y) is an ordered pair in a basic exponential function, then $\left(\dfrac{x}{b} + h,\ ay + k\right)$ is an ordered pair in the transformed function defined by $f(x) = ac^{b(x-h)} + k$, where c is the base.

g) The rule for a **transformed exponential function** can be **reduced to three parameters.** Which law of exponents allows you to perform this algebraic transformation?

$$f(x) = ac^{b(x-h)} + k$$

$\updownarrow$ (▬▬▬▬)

$$f(x) = a(c^b)^{x-h} + k$$

$\updownarrow$ (Considering c^b as the new base.)

$$f(x) = ac^{x-h} + k$$

Thus, the standard form of an exponential function
- with 4 parameters is $f(x) = ac^{b(x-h)} + k$.
- with 3 parameters is $f(x) = ac^{x-h} + k$.

h) Rewrite the following rules using three parameters. Use a calculator to check if these new rules are equivalent to the original ones.

1) $f_1(x) = 7(0.5)^{-2(x-10)} + 6$

2) $f_2(x) = -(3)^{4x-8} - 1$

3) $f_3(x) = 3(0.25)^{-0.5x+1} + 2$

i) What is the domain of every exponential function?

j) Examine the graphs below.

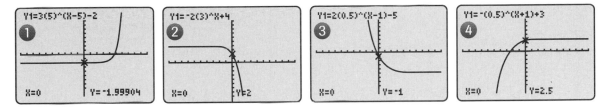

Explain:

1) How the base and parameter **a** in the function's rule, written in standard form with three parameters, allow you to determine whether the function is increasing or decreasing.

2) The role that parameter **k** plays in finding the range of an exponential function.

ZEROS AND EQUATIONS

The virtual chess player

A computer game designer claims to have built a computer that can beat the best chess players in the world. Unlike a human, this computer does not get tired or suffer stress, and most importantly, it has an unprecedented ability to calculate. In the most complex chess scenarios, the computer evaluates 42 598 400 possible moves before making a decision. The decision-making process does take a certain amount of time, however. With each passing minute, the computer retains only one quarter of the possibilities deemed most advantageous.

Deep Blue is a computer capable of calculating more than 50 billion moves per minute, but it lacks the one thing that makes a master chess player: intuition. Deep Blue won the first game, but Kasparov was able to identify its weak spots and came back to win the rematch.

a) Given the above situation, what is the significance of the rule $f(x) = 42\ 598\ 400\left(\dfrac{1}{4}\right)^x$?

b) After 3 minutes of play, how many possible moves does the computer retain?

c) Write the equation that must be solved to find the time it would take for the computer to retain 650 of the initial 42 598 400 possibilities.

The use of algebra to solve an exponential equation and the search for a zero of an exponential function are operations that rely on the following property:

$$\text{For } c > 0 \text{ and } c \neq 1,\ c^m = c^n \Rightarrow m = n$$

d) Complete this series of operations, which expresses both sides of the previous equation using the same base.

$$42\ 598\ 400\left(\frac{1}{4}\right)^x = 650 \qquad (1)$$

$$\left(\frac{1}{4}\right)^x = \frac{650}{42\ 598\ 400} \qquad (2)$$

$$\left(\frac{1}{4}\right)^x = \frac{1}{65\ 536} \qquad (3)$$

$$\left(\frac{1}{4}\right)^x = \left(\frac{1}{4}\right)^{\blacksquare} \qquad (4)$$

This strategy reflects the following method for solving exponential equations.

1. Express both sides of the equation using the **same base.**

2. If the bases are equal, the **exponents must be equal.**

3. Solve the final equation.

e) Use a calculator to estimate the amount of time the computer takes to make its decision.

For some exponential equations, it may be difficult to express both sides using the same base. When this happens, you can turn to another algebraic operation that uses logarithms, which will be discussed in a later section. Until then, use your calculator and make estimations.

EXAMPLE 1

We want to calculate the zero of function f defined by $f(x) = 3(4)^{x-2} - 192$.

We have: $f(x) = 0 \implies 3(4)^{x-2} - 192 = 0$.

$$3(4)^{x-2} = 192$$

$$(4)^{x-2} = 64$$

$$(4)^{x-2} = 4^3$$

$\Downarrow$ (Since the bases are equal, the exponents must be equal.)

$$x - 2 = 3$$

$$x = 5$$

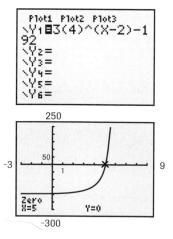

The zero of this function is therefore 5.

EXAMPLE 2

We want to find the zero of function g defined by $g(x) = \left(\frac{1}{2}\right)^x + 4$.

We have: $g(x) = 0 \Rightarrow \left(\frac{1}{2}\right)^x + 4 = 0$

$$\text{or } \left(\frac{1}{2}\right)^x = -4.$$

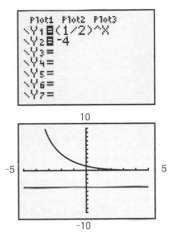

f) Explain why such an equation cannot have a solution:

1) By examining the graph.

2) By trying to express both sides using the same base.

EXAMPLE 3

We want to solve equation $(3^{(x+4)})^2 = \left(\frac{1}{9}\right)^x$.

The graphs for both functions on either side of the equation show that this equation does have a solution.

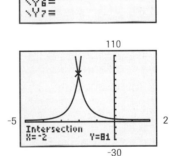

Algebraically we have:

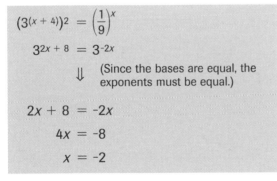

$$(3^{(x+4)})^2 = \left(\frac{1}{9}\right)^x$$

$$3^{2x+8} = 3^{-2x}$$

$\Downarrow$ (Since the bases are equal, the exponents must be equal.)

$$2x + 8 = -2x$$

$$4x = -8$$

$$x = -2$$

The solution is therefore -2.

g) Use algebra to find the zeros of the following functions:

1) $f_1(x) = 0.5(6^{x+1}) - 108$

2) $f_2(x) = 625\left(\frac{1}{5}\right)^{3x} - 1$

h) Solve these exponential equations algebraically.

1) $539 = 11(7^{2x-1})$

2) $\left(\frac{1}{4}\right)^{8x} = 2^{-10x+18}$

SIGN AND INEQUALITIES

My soup is cold!

On an expedition in Antarctica, an explorer heats some soup over a fire. At the moment the pot is removed from the fire, its metal has reached a temperature of 208°C. Subsequently, the pot's temperature changes according to the rule $T = f(t) = -26 + 234(3)^{-0.08t}$, where t is the time in minutes.

a) Examine the curve of this situation and describe the change in temperature.

b) What was the outdoor temperature when the pot was removed from the fire?

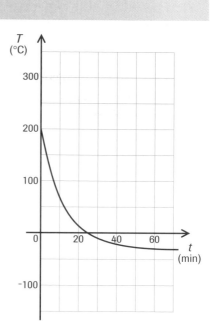

Antarctica has special status. It is a demilitarized zone owned by no single country. Some 40 countries signed a treaty reserving Antarctica for scientific research alone. Right now Antarctica is a place where scientists from around the world gather, work together and share their findings.

c) What is the zero of function f?

d) Find the solution set of the following inequalities:

   1) $T < 0$ 2) $T > 0$

e) Explain a method that can be used to solve exponential inequalities.

f) Using the screen images, solve the inequality $-26 + 234(3)^{-0.08t} < 52$.

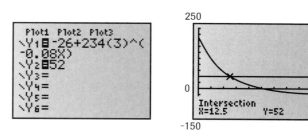

Once again, the usefulness of **graphs** in **examining the signs** of a function and **solving inequalities** is evident.

g) Here are the graphs of function f and its inverse f^{-1}:

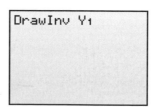

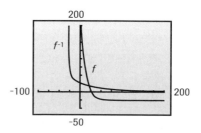

Referring to the mathematical model, state:

1) The domain and range of f.   2) The domain and range of f^{-1}.

You can also perform **operations** on exponential functions.

h) Functions f and g are defined by $f(x) = (3)^{2x}$ and $g(x) = -0.5(3)^{x+2}$. Using a calculator, graph the following functions and find the interval over which each one is increasing:

1) $f + g$ 2) $f - g$ 3) $f \cdot g$ 4) $\dfrac{f}{g}$

i) You can also find the composites of exponential functions and other types of functions. Functions f and g are defined by $f(x) = 1.5(2)^{x-3} + 8$ and $g(x) = -2x + 1$. State the rule for the composites:

1) $f \circ g$ 2) $g \circ f$

Transformed exponential functions have the following **properties:**

Rule	Standard: $f(x) = ac^{b(x-h)} + k$ or $f(x) = ac^{x-h} + k$ ($c > 0$ and $c \neq 1$)
Graph	The asymptote is a horizontal line defined by the equation $y = k$
Domain	IR
Range	If $a < 0$: $]-\infty, k[$ If $a > 0$: $]k, +\infty[$
Zero	Exists if $\begin{cases} a < 0 \text{ and } k > 0 \\ a > 0 \text{ and } k < 0 \end{cases}$
Extremes	None
Sign	Related to the existence of a zero
Variation	Always decreasing or always increasing
Inverse	The inverse is a function.

1. Here are some exponential functions:

1) $f_1(x) = 5^{\frac{1}{3}x}$ 2) $f_2(x) = -3(5)^{2x}$ 3) $f_3(x) = 5^{x-2}$

4) $f_4(x) = 5^x + 18$ 5) $f_5(x) = 0.5(5)^{0.5x} - 3$ 6) $f_6(x) = -(5)^{2(x+6)} + 20$

a) For each of these functions, find the values of parameters **a, b, h** and **k**.

b) Indicate the transformations that map the curve of the basic function $f(x) = 5^x$ onto each of the given functions.

2. For each of the functions defined below, find the *y*-intercept and the asymptote to the curve.

   a) $f(x) = -0.1(3)^x$

   c) $h(x) = 90 - (7)^{-2x + 8}$

   b) $g(x) = 5(2.5)^{2x} - 6$

   d) $i(x) = -2(2)^{2x + 2}$

3. A transformed exponential function is defined by $f(x) = -3(10)^{-2x + 10} + 7$.

   a) Identify its basic function.

   b) What are the three critical ordered pairs of this basic function?

   c) Give three ordered pairs of the transformed function.

   d) Give the equation for the asymptote of function *f*.

   e) Graph function *f*.

4. Graph the following functions:

   a) $f_1(x) = -(2)^x + 5$

   c) $f_3(x) = -(3)^{3x - 6} - 1$

   b) $f_2(x) = 4(0.5)^{x + 8} - 4$

   d) $f_4(x) = -2(0.25)^{-x}$

5. Write these rules in standard form with three parameters:

   a) $f(x) = -(6)^{2(x - 1)} + 1$ **b)** $g(x) = -2\left(\dfrac{1}{3}\right)^{-3x + 12} - 5$ **c)** $h(x) = 0.25(0.5)^{2x + 8}$

6. Compare the curves of the three functions below. Justify your response algebraically.

   $Y_1 = -5\left(\dfrac{1}{2}\right)^{3x - 9} + 30$ $Y_2 = -5(8)^{3 - x} + 30$ $Y_3 = -2560\left(\dfrac{1}{8}\right)^x + 30$

7. Graph the four functions given, then determine:

   a) The domain and range of each function.

   b) Whether the function is increasing or decreasing.

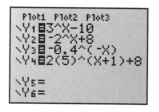

8. Here are the graphs of four exponential functions whose rules are in the form $f(x) = ac^{b(x - h)} + k$:

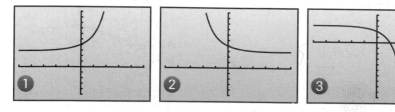
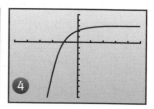

   In each case, determine the sign of parameters **a** and **b** when:

   a) $0 < c < 1$

   b) $c > 1$

9. Using the information shown below:

a) Find the coordinates of the points where the curves intersect.

b) State the equation that defines the asymptote of the inverse.

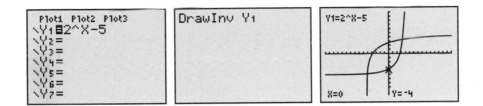

10. The rule for an exponential function is given in standard form: $f(x) = ac^{x-h} + k$. Based on this rule, indicate whether the following statements are true or false.

a) Only parameter **k** influences the position of the asymptote.

b) If the value **a** is negative, then the function is decreasing.

c) Function f has an extreme whose value matches the value of **k**.

d) The asymptote of the inverse function is vertical.

11. In your head, find the value of x that makes the following equations true.

a) $4^x = 4^0$

b) $3^{-0.5} = 3^{x+1}$

c) $\left(\frac{1}{3}\right)^x = 3$

d) $121^x = 11$

e) $\frac{1}{16} = 2^x$

f) $(\sqrt{5})^x = 25$

g) $8^x = 4^3$

h) $(\sqrt[4]{2.3}) = 2.3^x$

12. Find the zeros (if they exist) for the functions defined by the following rules:

a) $f_1(x) = 3(2)^{x-3} - 96$

b) $f_2(x) = 10 - 15\left(\frac{2}{3}\right)^{x-2}$

c) $f_3(x) = 7.5\,(6)^{-x} + 6$

d) $f_4(x) = 0.2(0.85)^{x-5} - 0.2$

13. Find the signs of the functions in question 12.

14. Solve the following equations algebraically:

a) $5^{6-x} = 25^{2x+13}$

b) $\left(\frac{1}{2}\right)^x = 4^{10}$

c) $(\sqrt{2})^{x+1} = 8^{-3x}$

d) $2\left(\frac{1}{3}\right)^{7^{2x}} = 162$

e) $4^{5x+7} = 8^{x-7}$

f) $125(25^x) = 5^8$

15. The radius of a megaphone increases exponentially. The resulting shape of the megaphone enables sound to travel uniformly.

a) On a Cartesian graph, draw the profile of a megaphone using the curves whose equations are $y = 0.5(1.5)^x$ and $y = -0.5(1.5)^x$ over the interval $[-1, 4]$.

b) What is the diameter of each end of the megaphone in decimetres?

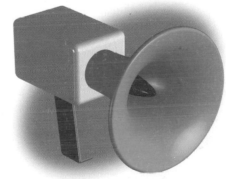

16. A fur dealer tells a customer that since her store opened 15 years ago, the average price of a lynx skin has risen from $30 to $850. Over the past 15 years, the price of a lynx skin has increased according to the rule $p = 30(1.25)^t$, where t is the time in years.

    a) What was the price of a lynx skin:

        1) 2 years after the store opened?   2) 10 years after the store opened?

    b) Graph this situation.

17. Given functions f and g defined by $f(x) = 2(3^{-2x} - 5)$ and $g(x) = 2\left(\frac{1}{9}\right)^{4x} - 10$. Determine the values of x for which:

    a) $f(x) = g(x)$ **b)** $f(x) > g(x)$ **c)** $f(x) < g(x)$

The lynx is a small feline found in parts of Europe, Asia and North America where the snow is thick for most of the year. It takes many lynx skins to produce just one piece of clothing. Commer-cial fur sales pose a serious threat to the lynx population.

18. Here are the rules for four functions:

$$Y_1 = -0.5^{-2x} + 1 \qquad Y_2 = 4^{0.5x} - 5 \qquad Y_3 = 2x - 10 \qquad Y_4 = 3$$

Using a calculator, solve these three inequalities:

    a) $Y_1 \geqslant Y_2$

    b) $Y_2 \geqslant Y_4$

    c) $Y_1 \leqslant Y_3$

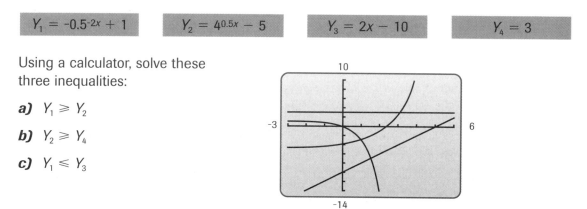

19. Functions f and g are defined by the following rules:

$$f(x) = (2)^{3x} \qquad\qquad g(x) = -0.25(2)^{x+5}$$

    a) State the rules for the functions that result from these operations:

        1) $f \cdot g$ 2) $\dfrac{f}{g}$

    b) Find the minimum and maximum of function $f + g$.

    c) Find the zero of function $f + g$.

20. A financial analyst uses this graph to examine the assets of two companies founded 5 years ago.

    a) At what point did Company 1 have twice the assets of Company 2?

    b) How much time had elapsed before the companies had equal assets?

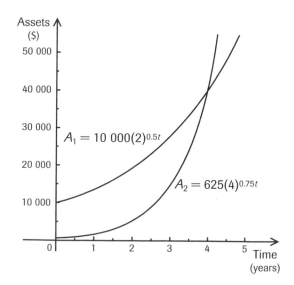

21. Functions f and g are defined by the rules

$$f(x) = 3(0.5)^{x-2} + 10 \qquad g(x) = -3x - 5$$

a) Find the rule for the composite $f \circ g$.

b) Graph the composite $f \circ g$.

c) Find the domain and range of composite $f \circ g$.

22. Find all the properties of the following exponential functions (graph, domain, range, intercepts, asymptote, sign and variation).

a) $f_1(x) = 2(5)^{x+10} - 250$

b) $f_2(x) = -3.5(0.5)^{-2(x+5)} + 56$

a) Consider the composite $f \circ f$ where f is defined by $f(x) = 2^x$. Make a graph and a table of values to determine whether the composite is an exponential function.

b) Find the possible values for base c and parameters **a, b, h** and **k** in the rule for an exponential function so that the function is:

I) Increasing.   2) Decreasing.   3) Positive.   4) Negative.

c) Is it possible to reduce an exponential function written in standard form with four parameters to a rule with two parameters? Justify your answer.

NATURAL LOGARITHMS

A mysterious little number

Just like people, some numbers are more famous and interesting than others. For example, the number π is known for its ability to relate a circle's diameter to its circumference. In the world of exponents, there exists another famous number, a number that has long been one of nature's secrets. This number is now essential to mathematics and science. It has become so important that it has been granted a place on your calculator.

a) Evaluate the expression $\left(1 + \dfrac{1}{x}\right)^x$ when x equals:

1) 10^6 2) 10^8 3) 10^{10}

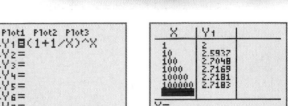

Notice that as the value of x gets larger, the expression $\left(1 + \frac{1}{x}\right)^x$ approaches the number e, whose value is 2.718 281…. The number e has a non-terminating, non-repeating decimal.

b) Evaluate the following expressions:

1) $1000e - 2718$ 2) $8e^2 \div 12e^6$ 3) $(3e^4)^2$

c) Match up each curve with the rule for its corresponding exponential function.

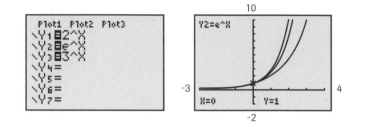

d) The graph below shows the function defined by $f(x) = e^x$ and its inverse f^{-1}.

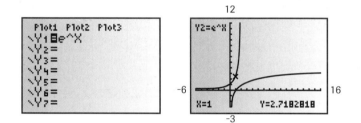

Find the rule for function f^{-1} as well as its domain and range.

The exponent with base e is called a natural logarithm or a Napierian logarithm.

The **natural logarithm** of x is written **ln x**. Algebraically, we have: $\log_e x = \ln x$.

Therefore, we have: $e^y = x \Rightarrow y = \log_e x = \ln x$

e) Use an exponential expression to justify the value of each logarithm shown below.

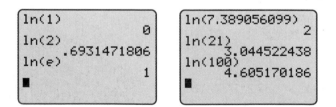

Space: What a dump!

A communications satellite draws from an energy source whose power P, in watts, follows the rule $P = 65e^{\frac{-t}{300}}$, where t is the time elapsed, in days, since the launch into orbit. Let f be the function defined by this rule.

From 1957 to 1997, more than 23 000 objects (satellites, rocket parts, etc.) have been placed in earth's orbit. About two thirds of these objects have fallen to earth or were disintegrated by the earth's atmosphere. The other objects, including the 500 active satellites, are still orbiting the earth or were destroyed in collisions.

a) What is the power of the satellite:

   1) When it is sent into orbit?

   2) One year after being sent into orbit?

b) Is it an increasing or decreasing function?

c) If a satellite's life span is 1000 days, find the domain and range of function f.

d) Use a graph to determine when the energy source depletes to:

   1) Half

   2) 8 W

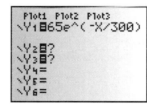
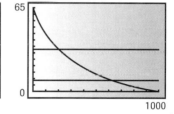

FINDING THE RULE

The elasticity of rubber

The properties of rubber make it an ideal substance for car tires. It is elastic, resistant and impermeable.

To test a new rubber compound, researchers make a ball of it and drop it from a height of 2 m above a table. After examining its bounces, they conclude that the ball's maximum height above the table diminishes by 20% after each bounce.

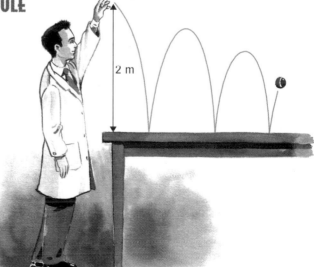

2 m

a) Explain why the relationship between the number of bounces and the maximum height of the ball after each bounce is exponential.

b) In this scenario, what is the function's base?

c) Give the rule for function *f,* which, for the xth bounce, gives the ball's height from the table in centimetres.

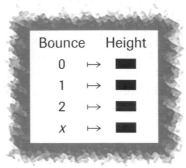

d) Give the rule for function *g,* which, for the xth bounce, gives the ball's height from the ground in centimetres. The tabletop is 1 m from the ground.

To find the rule for an exponential function in a given situation, you should identify the **following elements:**

> 1. The initial value (a).
> 2. The base (c).
> 3. The value of a constant (k).
>
> The resulting rule is in the form
> $$f(x) = ac^x + k$$

This form is equivalent to the rule in the form $f(x) = ac^{x-h} + k$. In effect, you can write $f(x) = \dfrac{ac^x}{c^h} + k$ by applying the quotient of powers rule. Considering $\dfrac{a}{c^h}$ as a new parameter **a,** we get $f(x) = ac^x + k$.

e) The researchers examine another rubber compound. This ball bounces 80 cm above the table after its 1st bounce and 5.12 cm above the table after its 4th bounce.

Explain how the compound's elasticity factor c can be calculated from this table of values.

Number of bounces	0	1	2	3	4	5	6
Height of the ball above the table (cm)	a	80	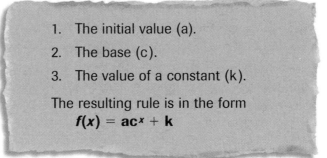		5.12		

f) Based on these data, find the rule that describes the relation between x number of bounces and the maximum height after each bounce.

Finding the rule for an exponential function in the form $f(x) = ac^x + k$ using two of its ordered pairs and the value of **k** involves **solving a system of two exponential equations in two unknowns.**

Calling all cell phone owners...

From 1990 to 1996, the number of cellular telephone subscribers in Canada increased at an exponential rate. The number of subscriptions rose from 584 000 in 1990 to 3 420 000 in 1996. The table of values below shows how many people have subscribed each year. Based on these data, find the rule that calculates the number of Canadians who have subscribed in relation to the number of elapsed years.

Years (since 1990)	Number of sub-scribers (thousands)
0	584
1	776
2	1027
3	1333
4	1866
5	2590
6	3420

a) Use the screens below to find the rule for the regression curve of this function.

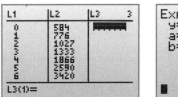

b) Assuming that the pattern has not changed, how many people subscribed in 1997?

Real-life scenarios do not always lend themselves to perfect mathematical models. Sometimes you must idealize the situation. The curve that passes closest to a set of points and seems to be most representative of the trend is called the **regression curve.**

1. Estimate the answers to the following operations (in numbers):

   a) $5 - e$ **b)** $4e$ **c)** e^2 **d)** πe **e)** e^{-1}

2. Using a calculator, find the values of these expressions to the nearest thousandth.

   a) $\frac{e}{2}$ **b)** $\sqrt{e}$ **c)** $0.5e^3$ **d)** e^e **e)** $\ln(10)$

3. Functions f, g and h are defined by the following rules:

   $$f(x) = 1.5e^{x+3} - 6 \qquad g(x) = -2e^{x-1} + 3 \qquad h(x) = -3\left(\frac{1}{e}\right)^{-2x} + 8$$

   a) Find the equation that defines the asymptote of each of these functions.

   b) For each function, identify:
   1) The domain.   2) The range.   3) The value at $x = 0$.
   4) The intervals of growth and decay.

4. Are the following statements true?

    a) The y-intercept of $y = e^x$ is e.

    b) The curve of the function defined by $f(x) = e^x$ is symmetric with the function defined by $g(x) = \left(\dfrac{1}{e}\right)^x$ about the y-axis.

5. Sketch a graph for each of the functions defined below:

    a) $f_1(x) = e^x + 4$ **b)** $f_2(x) = -(e)^{x+8} - 10$ **c)** $f_3(x) = 2(e)^{x-6}$

6. A company's financial report shows that the payroll p for the years 1987 to 1997 varies according to the rule $p = 0.8e^{0.245t} + 1.4$, where p is expressed in millions and t is the time elapsed since 1987.

    a) What was the payroll increase during this period?

    b) In what year did the payroll surpass $6 million?

    c) Give the equation of the asymptote for this function.

7. Solve the following equations algebraically:

    a) $e^{2x+3} = \left(\dfrac{1}{e}\right)^{-19}$ **b)** $e^6 + 2 = (e^{2x})^3 + 2$ **c)** $\dfrac{(2e)^3}{e^2} = 8e^{x+3}$

8. Solve the following equations using a graphing calculator.

    a) $e^x = x + 1$ **b)** $0.2e^{x-2} - 5 = -0.6x + 2$

    c) $3^{x+1} - 2 = e^{x+1} - 2$ **d)** $e^x = x^e$

9. A pharmaceutical company launches a new television ad campaign. The company estimates that over a period of 40 d, the number n of people who see their commercial will follow the rule $n = 1.6(1 - e^{-0.15t})$, where n is expressed in millions and t is the number of days since the beginning of the campaign.

    a) Based on this estimate, how many people will be exposed to the commercials?

    b) In how many days will the commercial reach one million viewers?

    c) Compare the function's rate of change in the first five days and the last five days of the campaign.

10. Use algebra to solve the following equations:

    a) $0.75 = mn^{-2}$ **b)** $25.25 = mn^3 + 5$ **c)** $247 = mn^{-1} - 3$

        $-96 = mn^5$ $\dfrac{23}{3} = mn^{-2} + 5$ $3.4 = mn^3 - 3$

11. The table of values below shows functions whose rules are in the form $f(x) = ac^x$. Write the rule for each of these functions.

a)

X	Y₁
0	5
1	15
2	45
3	135
4	405
5	1215
6	3645

X=0

b)

X	Y₂
0	-4
1	-20
2	-100
3	-500
4	-2500
5	-12500
6	-62500

X=0

c)

X	Y₃
0	1
1	.75
2	.5625
3	.42188
4	.31641
5	.2373
6	.17798

X=0

12. Given the coordinates of the points below, find the rules for the exponential functions to which they belong. All the rules are in the form $f(x) = ac^x$.

a) $A(1, 24)$ and $B(4, 648)$

b) $A(-2, -0.16)$ and $B(4, -2500)$

c) $A(-6, 48)$ and $B(1, 0.375)$

d) $A(0, -1)$ and $B(1, -e)$

13. The rule for this function is in the form $f(x) = ac^x + k$. Based on the information provided, find the rule.

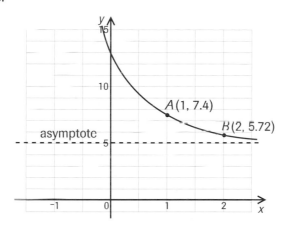

14. Today computer technology is evolving at a rapid pace. Computers are becoming immensely powerful, diskettes can store more and more information, and modem speeds are continually increasing. For all of these reasons, it is estimated that a computer's value depreciates by about 25% each year. Consider a computer purchased for $3200 today.

a) What is its initial value?

b) What percentage of its value does the computer retain from one year to the next?

c) How much will this computer be worth after:

1) 2 years?   2) 4 years?   3) 10 years?

In the shadow of high-speed hard drives, CD-ROMs and the new laser disks, the everyday 3.5-inch disk is often underestimated. With a storage capacity ranging from 700 kilobytes to 2.88 megabytes, floppy disks can hold the contents of an entire novel! These low-cost, practical disks are standard issue for any home computer.

15. An ice cube's volume is 20 cm³. At a temperature of 10°C, the ice cube's volume decreases by 40% each hour.

a) Complete the table of values on the right.

b) State the rule that calculates the ice cube's volume as a function of the number of hours it is exposed to a temperature of 10°C.

c) How many hours will it take for the ice cube's volume to become less than 1 cm³?

d) Can you infer that the ice cube's volume decreases by 20% every 30 min? If not, find the correct percent of decrease for every 30 min.

Time (h)	Volume (cm³)
0	▬
1	▬
2	▬
3	▬
4	▬

16. There are 500 bacteria per cubic centimetre in a container of milk. If this milk is left out in a room at a temperature of 22°C, the number of bacteria triples every hour. Once the milk contains 20 000 bacteria per cubic centimetre, it is considered spoiled. How long will it take the milk to spoil?

Some bacteria are good you. Yogurt contains at le 100 million bacteria per gram, most of it being Lactobacillus and Streptococcus. By fermenting the milk's lactose and by modifyin proteins and lipids, thes bacteria help transform into creamy yogurt.

In compound interest, the interest earned on an invested sum of money is reinvested so that it too earns interest. In short, you earn interest on your interest.

17. A sum of $1000 is invested for 5 years at an interest rate of 6% compounded annually.

a) Using a calculator, find the total amount accumulated after 5 years.

b) Using a calculator, find the sum that must be invested, under the same conditions, to accumulate $2709.91 on the due date.

18. Between 1984 and 1988, milk consumption in Québec decreased exponentially. This phenomenon has been attributed to the aging Québec population. The table below shows the amount of milk consumed per person during this time frame.

a) Use a calculator to find, by regression, the rule for the exponential function that best describes this situation.

b) According to this rule, what was the average milk consumption per person in 1991?

Year	Average consumption (litres/person)
1988	105
1990	98
1992	94
1994	92

19. Five hundred dice are tossed on a floor. Any die that lands with the number 6 face up is removed. The dice that are left are tossed on the floor again. Again, the dice that land with the number 6 face up are removed.

a) Let *n* represent the number of times the dice are tossed. Let *r* represent the number of dice that remain. State the rule that calculates the number of remaining dice based on the number of times the dice that landed with 6 face up were removed.

b) Using a calculator:

1) Graph this function.

2) Determine the number of times we must repeat the tossing of the dice before all the dice are removed.

20. When a chain is suspended by its ends and is not subjected to any force other than its own weight, the curve it forms is defined by the equation:

$$y = \frac{e^x + e^{-x}}{2}.$$

1) Give the properties of the function associated with this curve.

2) Is this curve a parabola? Justify your answer.

In 1980 environmentalists were testing the bottom of a waste pond near a metallurgical plant and detected 8 mg of mercury per cubic metre of sediment. When the environmentalists returned five years later, new tests revealed a mercury concentration of 10 mg/m³. The final test in 1995 revealed that the concentration of mercury at the bottom of the waste pond had increased exponentially since 1980.

a) What was the growth factor of the mercury concentration during the period:

1) 1985-1990?

2) 1987-1992?

b) What is the annual growth factor of the mercury concentration at the bottom of the pond?

Year	1980	1981	1982	1983	1984	1985
Mercury concentration (mg/m³)	8					10

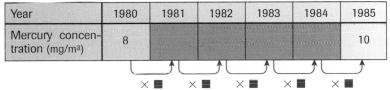

When mixed with water, mercury transforms into a highly toxic poison called methylmercury. This poison is not biodegradable, meaning it cannot be decomposed by nature. Every year approximately 10 000 tonnes of ionized or metallic mercury are dumped into our oceans by big industry.

c) The following rules will help you calculate the value of *M*, the mercury concentration, as a function of *t*, the amount of time elapsed since 1980. In each case, identify the unit of time that *t* represents.

1) $M = 8(1.25^2)^t$

2) $M = 8\left(1.25^{\frac{1}{5}}\right)^t$

3) $M = 8\left(1.25^{\frac{1}{60}}\right)^t$

d) What was the pond's mercury concentration:

1) In 1990?

2) In 1992?

3) 40 months after 1980?

In the rule for an exponential function, the independent variable appears as an exponent.

For each function f of the exponential model, we have:

$$\frac{f(x + 2) - f(x + 1)}{f(x + 1) - f(x)} = \textbf{base}$$

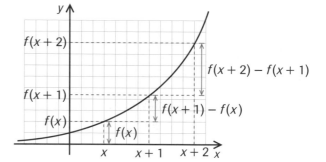

The **basic** exponential function is defined by the rule $f(x) = c^x$; a **transformed** exponential function is defined by $f(x) = ac^{b(x - h)} + k$. Sometimes you will encounter base e ≈ 2.7183.

By starting with the graph of a basic exponential function, you can sketch the graph of a transformed exponential function by considering the parameters **a, b, h** and **k.**

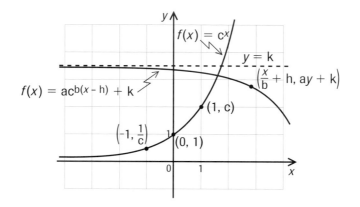

In an exponential expression, the exponent is also called a logarithm:

$$y = c^x \iff \log_c y = x$$

To solve an exponential **equation algebraically,** both sides of the equation are expressed using the **same base** in order to create **equal exponents.** This approach depends on the following property:

$$\text{For } c > 0 \text{ and } c \neq 1, c^m = c^n \Rightarrow m = n$$

To find the rule for an exponential function in the form $f(x) = ac^x + k$ for a given situation, identify the following: the initial value **a,** the base **c** and the value of **k.**

By identifying two ordered pairs in the rule $f(x) = ac^x + k$, you can determine the values of **a** and **c.** You can then solve a **system** of two exponential equations in two unknowns. You can also find the rule for an exponential function by regression using a calculator.

WORKOUT 5

1 Various bases have been given the exponent 4. Match up each base with its fourth power, which has been rounded to the nearest hundredth.

Base: 0.24; 1.8; 0.42; 1.6; 0.84; 0.38

Power: 0.5; 0.03; 6.55; 0.02; 0; 10.5

2 Calculate the following mentally:

a) $10^2 + 10^3$ **b)** $10^{-1} - 10^1$ **c)** $10^{-2} + 2 \times 10^{-3}$ **d)** $10^{-3} \div (10^{-2} + 10)$

3 Estimate the result of the following operations, then calculate the actual answer. Subtract your estimate from the actual answer. If the difference is less than 0.5, give yourself a point. What is your score?

a) 0.35×2.5 **b)** $0.75 \div 0.19$ **c)** 1.25×0.82 **d)** $3(0.09 + 0.59 + 0.49)$

e) $9.45 \div 0.69$ **f)** 18% of 47   **g)** 0.45×1.62 **h)** $0.35 \div 0.024$

4 Calculate the following in your head:

a) 0.1^2 **b)** 0.12^2 **c)** 0.5^3 **d)** 1.5^5

5 Estimate the cost of each purchase including taxes (15% = 10% + half of 10%):

a) 2 shirts worth $39.87 each.   **b)** 5 sweaters worth $87.95 each.

c) 1 dozen pencils worth $2.79 per unit.   **d)** 3 dozen balloons worth $15.99 per balloon.

6 Estimate the following by using a simpler fraction with roughly the same value, or by any other method you wish:

a) $\frac{4}{7}$ of 48   **b)** $\frac{11}{99}$ of 507   **c)** $\frac{8}{11}$ of 612

d) $\frac{23}{70}$ of 480   **e)** $\frac{17}{69}$ of 163   **f)** $\frac{18}{52}$ of 184

7 Calculate the following by estimating the unit price.

a) If 4 fish sell for $11.99, what is the price of 7 fish?

b) If 6 apples sell for 72¢, what is the price of 9 apples?

c) If oranges are purchased at $5.99 per dozen, what is the price of 28 oranges?

d) If 7 concert tickets cost $66.50, how much will 11 tickets cost?

8 The mechanics in a bicycle store are between 20 and 23 years old. If the product of their ages is 2 052 943 200, how many mechanics work in the store?

9 Look at the following statements and indicate whether they are true or false.

a) $\dfrac{5^8}{5^4} = 5^2$

b) $\sqrt[3]{-64} = -4$

c) $\sqrt[4]{4^2} = 2$

d) $100(1.25)^2 = (125)^2$

e) $e^4 + e^5 = e^9$

f) $3^{-\frac{2}{3}} = \sqrt{\left(\dfrac{1}{3}\right)^3}$

g) $((2^3)^4)^5 = 2^{12}$

h) $(1.8 \times 10^{13})^0 = 1$

i) $0^0 = 0$

10 Simplify the following expressions and express their exponents using positive integers.

a) $\left(\dfrac{2^4 - 2^0}{7^2 - 4^1}\right)^{-3}$

b) $7 \times \dfrac{(7^2)^{-3}}{(7^{-1})^{-7}}$

c) $-27 \times (9^3 \times 3^{-4} \times (5^0)^5)^4$

11 Simplify the following algebraic expressions after writing the restrictions:

a) $\dfrac{(-2a^2)^2(3a)^{-3}}{(2a)^{-2}}$

b) $\left(\dfrac{a^{\frac{5}{3}}}{a^{-\frac{2}{3}}}\right)^3$

c) $ab^3(a^{-1}b + a^2b^{-2} + 2a^{-1}b)$

d) $\left(\dfrac{a^{b+3}}{2a^{(4-2b)}}\right)^2$

e) $\left(\dfrac{ab^2}{a^3b^2}\right)^{-\frac{1}{2}}$

f) $(3a^3b - 12a^2b^4)(a - 4b^3)^{-1}$

12 Translate the exponential expressions into logarithmic expressions, and vice versa.

a) $7^2 = 49$

b) $(0.5)^a = b$

c) $\log_3 81 = 4$

d) $e^x = 50$

e) $a = \log_{0.25} b$

f) $r = s^x$

g) $\log_n v = w$

h) $\ln x = y$

13 Put the following statements into the form $a^x = b$.

a) b is the sixth power of a.

b) b is the square root of a.

c) b is the sixth root of a.

d) b is the reciprocal of a.

14 Indicate whether the following statements are true or false.

a) A negative number with a positive exponent is a positive number.

b) A positive number with a negative exponent is a positive number.

c) If $a > 1$ and $0 < n < 1$, then $a > a^n$.

d) If $a < b$ and a and b are positive, non-zero numbers, then $a^n < b^n$.

15 Below are graphs of functions whose rules have the form $f(x) = c^x$. For each graph, find the value of the base.

a)   **b)**   **c)**

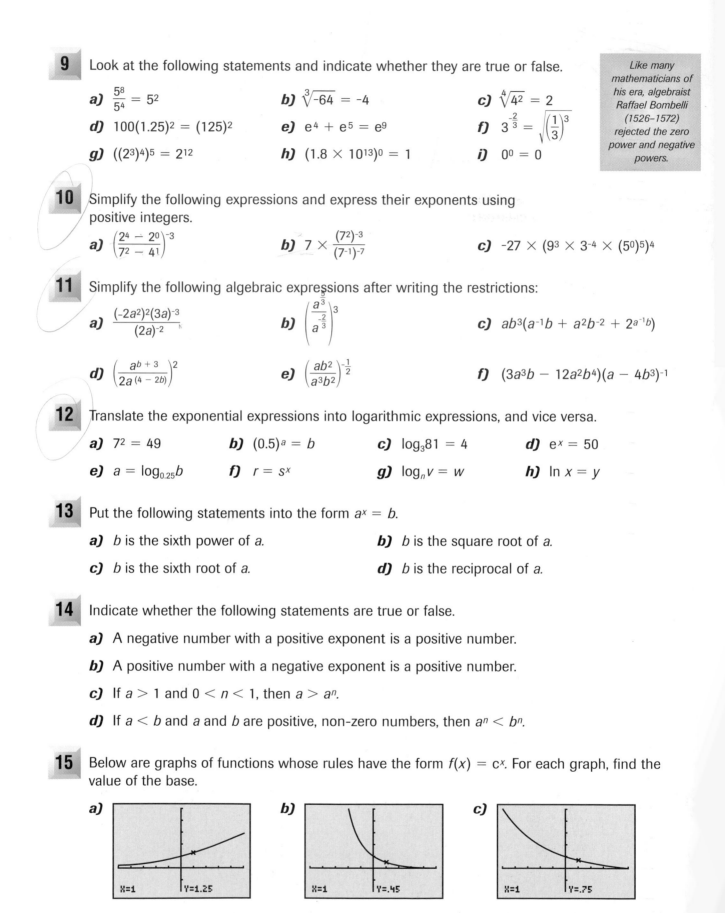

d)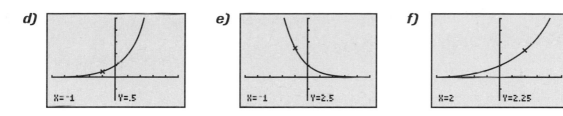

X= -1   Y=.5

e)

X= -1   Y=2.5

f)

X=2   Y=2.25

16 On January 1 of last year, at 12:02 a.m., Fred took a 10 mL sip of wine. He took another one at 12:04, then a third one at 12:08, and another one at 12:16, and he continued like this, always doubling the time interval between sips.

   a) State the rule for the exponential function that expresses the number n of minutes elapsed since January 1 as a function of the number x of sips that Fred takes.

   b) Graph the mathematical model for this situation.

   c) At this rate, what quantity of wine will Fred have consumed at the end of the year?

Vineyard at Saint-Émilion, in Bordeaux, France.

17 Here are the graphs of three functions.

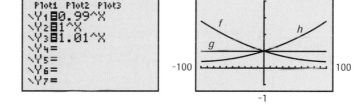

```
Plot1 Plot2 Plot3
\Y1 0.99^X
\Y2 1^X
\Y3 1.01^X
\Y4=
\Y5=
\Y6=
\Y7=
```

   a) Match up each rule with one of the curves.

   b) Explain why the rule $Y_2 = 1^x$ is not an exponential function.

   c) Give the rule for a function whose curve is situated between g and h and that passes through the same point of intersection as these two curves.

18 Indicate whether the following relations represent exponential models.

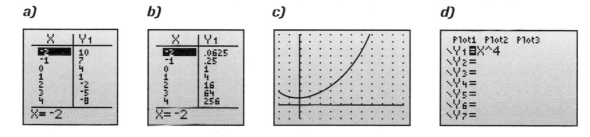

a)

X	Y1
-2	10
-1	7
0	4
1	1
2	-2
3	-5
4	-8

X= -2

b)

X	Y1
-2	.0625
-1	.25
0	1
1	4
2	16
3	64
4	256

X= -2

c)

d)

```
Plot1 Plot2 Plot3
\Y1 X^4
\Y2=
\Y3=
\Y4=
\Y5=
\Y6=
\Y7=
```

19 The table of values shows a quadratic function, a cubic function and an exponential function.

   a) Match each column with its function.

   b) For each unit change of x, what characteristics can be observed from the successive rates of change of:

      1) A quadratic function? 2) A cubic function? 3) An exponential function?

X	Y1	Y2	Y3
0	5	7	3
1	7	10	6
2	21	16	15
3	59	28	30
4	133	52	51
5	255	100	78
6	437	196	111

X=0

20 You might not think there is anything interesting about folding a piece of paper, but give this a try. Fold a piece of paper into two congruent sections eight times in a row. You will probably not be able to fold it more than 8 times.

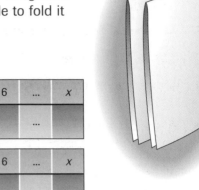

a) Complete the tables of values below:

Number of folds	0	1	2	3	4	5	6	...	x
Number of thicknesses	1	2	4					...	

Number of folds	0	1	2	3	4	5	6	...	x
Number of thicknesses	1	$\frac{1}{2}$	$\frac{1}{4}$					...	

b) Find the functions that will calculate how the number x of folds affects:

1) The number of thicknesses.

2) The fraction of the initial surface area.

c) Graph these two functions on the same axes.

d) What transformation of the plane transforms one of these curves into the other one?

21 The base of an exponential function cannot be negative or 1. Consider the function f defined by $f(x) = (-2)^x$.

a) Calculate the value of $f(-0.1)$, $f(0)$, $f(0.1)$, $f(0.2)$ and $f(0.3)$.

b) Explain why f is not an exponential function.

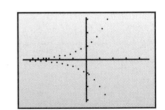

22 Here are rules for three exponential functions:

$$f_1(x) = 2^x \qquad f_2(x) = \left(\frac{1}{4}\right)^x \qquad f_3(x) = 6^x$$

a) What is the equation of each function's asymptote?

b) For each function, find the images of -1, 0 and 1.

c) Using your answers, graph these three functions.

d) Find the domain and range of each of these functions.

23 Graph functions f and f^{-1} on the same axes.

a) $f(x) = 4^x$ b) $f(x) = 0.2^x$ c) $f(x) = e^x$

24 Based on the rules $f(x) = 0.3^x$ and $g(x) = 0.7^x$, find the intervals over which:

a) $f(x) > g(x)$.

b) The curve of function g is above the curve of function f.

c) The two curves increasingly move away from one another as x gets larger.

d) The two curves increasingly approach one another as x gets larger.

25 The program shown below draws a circle whose radius is 16 mm.
It proceeds to draw concentric circles whose radii decrease by half each time.

a) In a table of values, show the relationship between the rank and the radius of the circle.

b) Graph this relationship.

c) On the computer screen, the curve that forms a circle is 0.32 mm thick. Therefore, when the program reaches a circle with radius 0.16 mm, you can only see a dot on the screen. How many circles were drawn before you see that final dot?

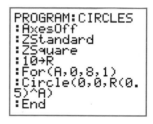

```
PROGRAM:CIRCLES
:AxesOff
:ZStandard
:ZSquare
:10→R
:For(A,0,8,1)
:Circle(0,0,R(0.5)^A)
:End
```

26 Give the rule for the basic exponential functions that contain these points:

a) $P(2, 2025)$ **b)** $P(-4, 1296)$ **c)** $P(-3, 0.008)$ **d)** $P(4, 14\ 641)$

27 For the past 4 years at Christmas, Anick has received $80 from her grandparents. She has always put this money directly in her piggy bank, which now contains $320. On the other hand, she could have placed this money in the bank where it would have accumulated interest.

a) Complete the following and calculate how much money Anick could have accumulated over 4 years at an interest rate of 8% per year.

	A	B	C	D
1	YEAR	PRINCIPAL AT THE START OF THE YEAR ($)	INTEREST DURING THE YEAR ($)	SUM ACCUMULATED AT YEAR'S END ($)
2	1	80.00	80.00 × 0.08 = 6.40	80.00 + 6.40 = 86.40
3	2	80.00 + 86.40 = 166.40	166.40 × 0.08 = 13.31	166.40 + 13.31 = 179.71
4	3	80 + 179.71 = 259.71	259.71 × 0.08 = ☐	259.71 + ☐ = ☐
5	4	80.00 + ☐	☐	☐

b) Check your answer using this annuities formula:

$$S = \frac{V((1 + i)^n - 1)(1 + i)}{i}$$

where S is the sum accumulated, P is the amount paid per period, n is the number of payments made and i is the interest rate per period.

Annuities are payments made at fixed intervals of time. These payments may go toward the reimbursement of borrowed capital (amortization) and its interest, or toward a particular savings plan.

28 From the critical points of the basic exponential function $f(x) = 3^x$, graph these functions:

a) $g(x) = 2(3)^x$ 　　　　 **b)** $h(x) = -3^x$ 　　　　 **c)** $i(x) = -3^x + 5$

d) $j(x) = 3^{x-5} - 4$ 　　 **e)** $k(x) = 4(3)^{x+2} + 10$ 　　 **f)** $l(x) = -3^{-x}$

29 A transformed exponential function is defined by $f(x) = ac^{b(x-h)} + k$. Explain why parameters **a, b** and **h** do not affect the position of the asymptote.

30 Describe the translations that must take place for the curve defined by $y = e^x$ to be mapped onto these curves:

a) $y = e^{x+3} + 10$ 　　 **b)** $y = e^{x-4} + 7$ 　　 **c)** $y = e^{x+1} - 5$

31 To create a design, an artist decreases the length of a plank of wood by successively cutting one third of its length. The table below shows the relationship between the number of cuts and the length of the wood.

a) What was the initial length of the plank?

b) Graph the mathematical model that represents this situation.

c) On the same graph, sketch the equation $y = 1$.

d) Using the graph, identify how many cuts must be made so that the plank is less than 1 m long.

	B5	▼	=10*(2/3)*(2/3)
		A	**B**
1		NUMBER OF CUTS	LENGTH (M)
2		*x*	*y*
3		0	10,00
4		1	6.67
5		2	4.44
6		3	2.96
7		4	1.98
8			
9		*x*	10*(2/3)*(2/3)
10			

32 For each of the functions defined by the rules below, determine:

a) Its range.

b) Whether it is increasing or decreasing.

c) Whether it has a zero.

d) The y-intercept.

```
Plot1  Plot2  Plot3
\Y1=3(2)^X+14
\Y2=-(3)^(2X+8)
\Y3=-(0.5)^(-X)
\Y4=(1/5)^(2X)+1
\Y5=
\Y6=
```

33 Using the parameters, graph the following functions:

a) $f_1(x) = -(3)^x + 8$ 　　　　 **b)** $f_2(x) = 2(1.5)^{x+5} - 8$

c) $f_3(x) = -(2)^{3x-12} - 5$ 　　 **d)** $f_4(x) = 4(0.5)^{-x}$

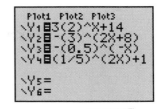

34 Here are four functions.

$$f_1(x) = 3^{x+8} - 12 \qquad\qquad f_2(x) = 4(5.5)^{2x} - 8$$
$$f_3(x) = -(0.3)^{x-1} + 1 \qquad\qquad f_4(x) = 100(14)^{-x}$$

For each of them, find:

a) The range.

b) The equation of its asymptote.

35 The temperature of a cup of tea decreases exponentially as time passes. The relation between the time x in minutes and temperature T is defined by:

$$T = \left(\begin{array}{c}\text{The tea's original}\\\text{temperature}\end{array} - \begin{array}{c}\text{Room}\\\text{temperature}\end{array}\right) \times 0.9^x + \begin{array}{c}\text{Room}\\\text{temperature}\end{array}$$

At precisely 6:00 p.m., one cup of tea is placed on a table and another is placed in a refrigerator. Both cups of tea are 100°C. The table is in a room whose temperature is 20°C. The refrigerator's thermometer reads 5°C.

a) On the same graph, draw the curves that represent the cooling of the tea in each cup.

b) What are the coordinates of the point of intersection of these two curves?

c) State the equation of the asymptote of each curve.

d) After 10 min, what is the difference in temperature between the two cups of tea?

36 For the curve defined by $y = \frac{1}{6}(3)^{x-1} - 13.5$, points A and B are the x- and y-intercepts. Calculate the distance between A and B.

37 Solve these exponential equations algebraically:

a) $5^{-2(x+3)} = 625$

b) $-\left(\frac{1}{3}\right)^x = -3^7$

c) $(\sqrt{4})^{x+1} - 64 = 0$

d) $4(\sqrt{3})^x = 108$

e) $2^{x-2} = 32^{x+2}$

f) $100^x = 0.000\ 01$

g) $4^{x^2-9} = 1$

h) $0.5^{x^2+x-7} = 2$

i) $2 \times 2^{x^2-5} = 8^x$

38 For $m \neq n$ in $a^m = a^n$, what must be the value of a for this equation to have a solution?

39 For $a \neq 0$, $b \neq 0$ and $a \neq b$ in $a^m = b^m$, what must be the value of m for this equation to have a solution?

40 Solve these equations:

a) $(x + 3)^{(x-3)^2} = (x + 3)^4$

b) $(x^2 + 1)^{2x+4} = 1$

41 NASA uses rockets composed of several sections to send a satellite into orbit. The main section is equipped with a giant reactor capable of overcoming the earth's gravitational pull and launching the rocket into space. At the moment of lift-off, the reactor's fuel tank contains 1.68×10^6 L of fuel. Once this fuel is ignited, the reactor consumes 5% of the fuel every 20 s.

a) State the rule for function *f*, which relates the number of 20 s periods since lift-off to the amount of fuel left in the combustion chambers.

b) Graph this function.

c) Restricted to this particular situation, what are the domain and range of function *f*?

d) How much fuel is left in the tank 1 min after lift-off?

e) Using a calculator, find out how much time it takes for the reactor to consume half of the fuel.

Space shuttle Columbia is an enormous spacecraft measuring 37 m long and weighing 70 t. It is attached to a giant tank containing 700 t of liquid fuel and flanked by two additional rockets full of solid fuel. The cargo hold contains a satellite. Unlike rockets, space shuttles return to earth and can be reused.

42 Given function *f* defined by $f(x) = 3(2)^{x+3} - 12$. What elements of the domain have images that are:

a) Strictly negative?

b) Between -6 and 12?

43 In nuclear medicine, patients are injected with a solution containing technetium, an element that emits weak gamma rays. With technetium injected in a body, radiologists can detect any abnormalities by using a scanner that picks up gamma rays. Once the solution is injected into the patient, the quantity (*Q*) of technetium decays over time according to the rule $Q = q_0 e^{-0.1t}$, where q_0 is the initial quantity of technetium in grams and *t* is the time, in hours, since the injection.

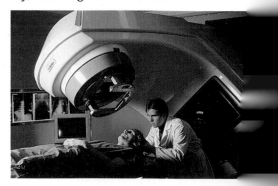

a) Use a table of values to show the decay of 5 g of technetium over a period of 10 h.

b) Using a calculator, find, to the nearest hundredth, the amount of time it would take for 5 g of technetium to decay by half.

c) Find all the properties of the theoretical model for the decay of 5 g of technetium.

Nuclear medicine uses radio-iso (radioactive substances) to diagnos treat illnesses. Injected or intravenously, these radio-isotop absorbed by tissues and organs in v concentrations. A scanner detects g rays and draws up a distribution map radiation in the organism. This proc uses infinitesimal quantities of radi subs

44 Solve these equations by taking out a common factor.

a) $25^{2x+1} - 25^{2x} = 600$ ~~impossible~~

b) $\dfrac{14^{10} + 14^{11}}{15} = 14^{x^2}$

c) $3^{10} + 3^{10} + 3^{10} = 3^x$

45 Here is the graph of an exponential function and its inverse.

a) Which of these curves is the inverse?

b) What is the x-intercept of the inverse?

c) Give the coordinates of three points on the curve of the inverse.

d) What are the coordinates of the point of intersection of the asymptotes to these curves? $(-5, -5)$

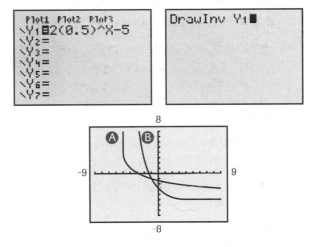

46 The screen images below show that the intersection between an exponential function and its inverse is the same as the intersection between an exponential function and the linear equation $y = x$.

a) Is the same thing true for all types of functions? Justify your answer.

b) Find the point of intersection of these functions to the nearest hundredth.

c) State the rule for an exponential function whose curve does not intersect the curve of its inverse.

47 It can be proved that $e^x = 1 + \dfrac{x}{1!} + \dfrac{x^2}{2!} + \dfrac{x^3}{3!} + \dfrac{x^4}{4!} + ...$, where 4! is read "factorial 4" and is calculated as $4 \times 3 \times 2 \times 1$. Likewise, $3! = 3 \times 2 \times 1$.

a) Using the first five terms of this sum, find the value of $e^{\frac{1}{2}}$.

b) Use a calculator to compare this value to the value of "e^0.5."

48 For $A = 2^x + 2^{-x}$ and $B = 2^x - 2^{-x}$, show that $A^2 - B^2 = 4$.

49 Here are the tables of values of two functions.

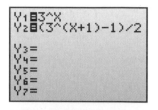

a) What do the numbers in column Y_1 represent?

b) Explain how you can obtain the numbers in column Y_2 from the numbers in column Y_1.

c) Using a graphing calculator, confirm that $S = \dfrac{a^{x+1} - 1}{a - 1}$ calculates the sum of the first $(x + 1)$ positive integral powers of a.

d) Calculate $6^0 + 6^1 + 6^2 + 6^3 + 6^4 + 6^5 + 6^6$.

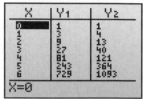

50 As legend has it, the inventor of chess asked the King of Persia for a "few grains of wheat" as compensation for his invention. The King, believing this to be a more than just reward, began to grant the inventor's request: one grain of wheat for the 1st square, two grains for the 2nd square, four grains for the 3rd square, and so on until the 64th square. But when the King asked the treasurer how much grain would be awarded, he realized how outrageous the request was.

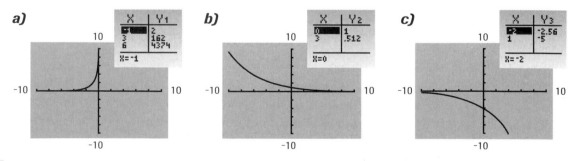

a) What rule defines the number of grains to be placed on the nth square?

b) How many grains will it take to fill the first 30 squares? Use the formula $S = 2^n - 1$, where n is the number of squares and S is the sum.

c) If one grain of wheat had a volume of 1 mm³, how many cubic metres of wheat would cover the 64th square?

51 From the information below, state the rule for all three exponential functions in the form $f(x) = ac^x$.

a)   *b)*   *c)*

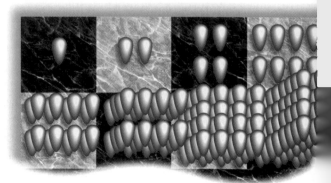

52 By identifying two ordered pairs belonging to an exponential function in the form $f(x) = ac^x$, the values of a and c can be found.

a) Show that the value of c can be calculated from the ordered pairs $(x_1, f(x_1))$ et $(x_2, f(x_2))$, where $x_1 < x_2$, using the formula $c = \left(\dfrac{f(x_2)}{f(x_1)}\right)^{\frac{1}{x_2 - x_1}}$.

b) Using this same formula, write a program that calculates the values of a and c in the rule $f(x) = ac^x$ from two of its ordered pairs.

53 One of these functions has the form $f(x) = ac^x$. Given that the curves are symmetrical about the line $x = 2$, find the two rules.

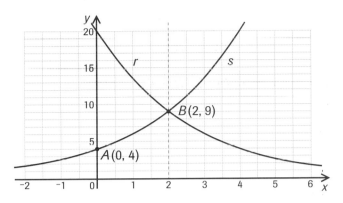

54 In 1960 Adrienne bought a shiny new convertible for $8000. Over the next 6 years, her car depreciated each year by 15% of the previous year's value. During the next 4 years, the value of her car remained the same. Then, because it was so rare and beautiful, her car was classified as a "collector's item." From this point on, the value of her shiny old convertible increased 10% each year.

a) State the rule that defines the car's annual value for the first 6 years.

b) What was the car worth 8 years after the purchase date?

c) In what year did the car's value return to the same price she paid for it?

55 Solve each of these inequalities algebraically:

a) $0.25(5)^x > 31.25$

b) $2\left(\frac{1}{3}\right)^{x+2} - 18 < 0$

c) $(e^{3x})^2 > \left(\frac{1}{e}\right)^3$

56 The inequality $c^{2x-7} < c^{2-x}$ must be solved. Determine whether $c > 1$ or $0 < c < 1$ when the solution is:

a) $x < 3$

b) $x > 3$

57 Functions f and g are defined by $f(x) = 3(2)^{x+5} + 2$ and $g(x) = -2x + 3$.

a) Find the rule for the composites:

1) $f \circ g$

2) $g \circ f$

b) Find the domain and range of each composite.

58 Functions f and g are defined by $f(x) = (0.5)^x$ et $g(x) = -3(0.5)^{x+2}$.

a) State the rule for the following functions:

1) $f + g$ 2) $f - g$ 3) $f \cdot g$ 4) $\dfrac{f}{g}$

b) Which of these functions are exponential?

59 PLANET EARTH: NO VACANCY

The table below shows the human population on earth in different years. It is apparent that the human population is increasing at an alarming rate, so much so that scientists are now looking for ways to deal with the problems of overpopulation. Maybe one day in the not-so-distant future, humans will begin inhabiting other planets.

Year	Population (billions)
1959	3
1974	4
1986	5
1997	6

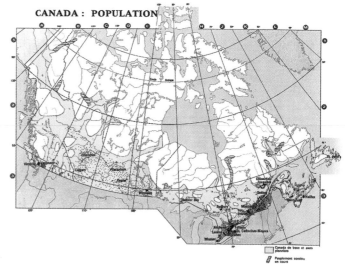

a) The rule $p(x) = 10^{(0.007953x - 15.1)}$ estimates the earth's population, in billions, on the first day of January in a given year. According to this empirical model, what will the earth's population be in 2010?

b) According to some scientists, the earth can support 27 billion people. In what year will the earth's population reach this critical point?

60 POPULATIONS COMPARED

On January 1, 1994, Canada had a population of 29 094 400 people, increasing by 1.1% each year. At the same time, Québec had a population of 7 258 400, increasing by 0.6% each year. On January 1, 2010, assuming this trend persists, what fraction of the Canadian population will the Québec population represent?

61 COMPOUND INTEREST

When a principal P is invested with compound interest, the interest is added to the principal after a specified time period. At the end of each period, when the interest is added, we say that the interest has been "capitalized" (turned into capital). Below is a formula that calculates the final amount A obtained when a principal P is invested for t years at an annual interest rate of r. The interest is compounded n times a year.

$$A = C\left(1 + \frac{r}{n}\right)^{nt}$$

One dollar is invested at an annual rate of 100% for one year. The final amount A of this investment is calculated when interest is compounded over different periods of time.

a) Complete the table.

b) What happens as the number of capitalization periods increases?

c) When you continually increase the number of capitalizations, what value does A approach?

Value A is calculated from a principal P invested at an annual interest rate r compounded continuously for t years according to the formula

$$A = C\,e^{rt}$$

Capitalization frequency	n	$A = C\left(1 + \frac{r}{n}\right)^{nt}$	A (\$) after 1 year
Yearly	1	$A = 1(1 + 1)^1$	2
Semi-annually	2	$A = 1\left(1 + \frac{1}{2}\right)^2$	2.25
Quarterly	4	$A = 1\left(1 + \frac{1}{4}\right)^4$	2.44141
Monthly	12	$A = 1\left(1 + \frac{1}{12}\right)^{12}$	2.61304
Weekly	52	$A = 1\left(1 + \frac{1}{52}\right)^{52}$	2.69260
Daily	365	▬	▬
Hourly	▬	▬	▬
Every second	▬	▬	▬

d) A sum of \$1000 is invested for 5 years at an interest rate of 8%. At the end of this period, what would the difference in returns be if the interest was compounded continuously as opposed to monthly?

e) A financial institution guarantees an interest rate of 8.5% for a 10-year period. How much capital must be invested to yield a return of \$15 000 at the end of this period:

1) If the interest is compounded every three months?

2) If the interest is compounded continuously?

YOUR FIRST JOB AS A FINANCIAL ADVISOR

Mike wants to put some money *M* in the bank. For each of the following situations, decide which option is best for Mike. Justify your decision by calculating each one.

a) Invest a sum of money at a rate of 6% compounded annually over 2 years or invest it with a simple interest rate of 6% for a period of two years.

b) Invest the sum of money at a rate of 7% the first year and 8% the second year, or invest it at 8% the first year and 7% the second year.

c) Over a one-year period, invest the money at an annual rate of 6%, or invest half the money at an annual rate of 5% and the other half at an annual rate of 7%.

d) Invest the money at a rate of 3% compounded annually for 8 years, or invest it at a rate of 8% compounded annually for 3 years.

Founded in 1935, the Bank of Canada is responsible for setting interest rates and issuing bank notes. Because it is governed by the State, the bank can enforce the government's monetary policies.

63 **EARTH: IS IT REALLY THAT SMALL?**

When the diameter of the Earth and its orbiting moon is compared to that of the universe, it is often said that the Earth is no larger than a dust particle. Inspired to illustrate this point, an astronomer produced the diagram below.

a) The diameter of the entire solar system is how many times greater than the diameter of the Earth-Moon system?

b) The diameter of our galaxy is how many times greater than the diameter of the Earth-Moon system?

c) A meteorite is travelling down the centre of our galaxy at a speed of 3×10^5 km/s. How many years will this meteorite remain within our galaxy?

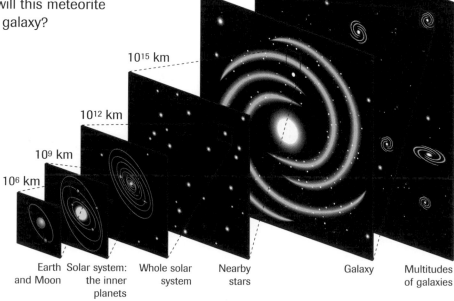

10^{21} km

From one drawing to the next, the dimensions are multiplied by 1000.

10^{18} km

10^{15} km

10^{12} km

10^9 km

10^6 km

Earth and Moon | Solar system: the inner planets | Whole solar system | Nearby stars | Galaxy | Multitudes of galaxies

64 HALLOWEEN AND H₂O

To make masks, thin sheets of plastic are lowered into a large vat of boiling water. The plastic is removed within a couple of seconds and laid out onto moulds so that it takes the desired shape. Every hour, 10% of the water evaporates. At the beginning of the day, the vat contains 85 L of boiling water.

a) Find the rule that will calculate how much water is in the vat as a function of:

   1) The number of hours elapsed since the beginning of the day.

   2) The number of half-hour periods elapsed since the beginning of the day.

b) Represent both of these functions on the same graph.

Why do people dress up on Oct. 31, Halloween? The ancient Celts believed that on this day, the lord of the dead summoned hosts of evil spirits from their graves. To prevent themselves from being harmed by these spirits, the Celts disguised themselves as ghosts and ghouls so that they would not be recognized as living people, and would not be harmed by the evil spirits.

65 FROM NEWTON TO ALUMINUM

According to Newton, the time t it takes for a warm body to cool is related to the difference in the body's temperature T_1 and the temperature T_2 of the surrounding air. This can easily be verified using a laboratory calculator and a temperature probe.

t (s)	T_1 (°C)	$T_1 - T_2$ (°C)
5	73	45
10	69	41
20	65	37
30	60	32
40	54	26
60	47	19
90	40	12
120	35	7
140	33	5
160	32	4
180	31	3

A sheet of aluminum foil was heated to 75°C with a hair dryer. After that, the data shown in the table were collected. At the time of this experiment, the ambient temperature was 28°C.

a) By regression, find the rule that defines the relation between the time t and the temperature difference $(T_1 - T_2)$.

b) Transform this rule so that it defines the relation between the time and the temperature of the aluminum foil.

c) Graph this last function with its asymptote.

Aluminum plant in Shawinigan.

1. The table of values represents two exponential functions. Find the base associated with:

a) Y_1 b) Y_2

X	Y₁	Y₂
1	12	52
2	18	160
3	27	484
4	40.5	1456
5	60.75	4372
6	91.125	13120
7		39364

Y₁=136.6875

2. A function is defined by the rule $f(x) = 3(2)^{x-3} - 24$.

a) Graph function f.

b) Find the domain and range of f.

c) Find the equation of the asymptote.

d) Find the zero of this function, if one exists.

e) Examine the sign of this function.

3. From 1990 up to and including 1995, the number of people hooked up to the Internet varied according to the rule $f(t) = 1.32e^{0.55t}$ where $f(t)$ is expressed in millions and t is the number of years elapsed since 1990.

a) Find the domain and range of function f restricted to this situation.

b) How many people were hooked up to the Internet in 1992?

c) From 1990 up to and including 1995, how many people were connected to the Internet?

d) Find the equation of the asymptote.

4. Determine the solution sets of the following equations algebraically:

a) $8^{3x} = 16^{x-1}$ b) $4^{1-3x} = 1$ c) $\left(\dfrac{9}{25}\right)^{x+1} = \left(\dfrac{125}{27}\right)^{-2x}$

5. The volume of water in an aquarium decreases due to evaporation. The table of values shows the volume of water in the aquarium over the last 6 weeks. An analysis of these data showed that the volume of water decreased according to a function whose rule is in the form $f(x) = ac^x$.

a) What is the rule for this function?

b) Given the context, find its domain and range.

X	Y₁
0	40
1	36
2	32.4
3	29.16
4	26.244
5	23.62
6	21.258

X=0

6. A forestry company owns land that it wants to completely reforest. It has already reforested 240 ha. It will increase its reforesting efforts by 20% each year.

a) Find the function rule that, for a specified number of years, can be used to calculate the area of reforested land.

b) In how many years will the reforested area be more than 1000 ha?

7. Since it was installed, a freezer's temperature varies according to a rule in the form $f(x) = ac^x - 12$. This situation is represented in the table of values below:

a) What rule defines the function associated with this situation?

b) Graph the function and its asymptote.

8. A sum of $5000 is invested for n years at an annual interest rate of 6%.

a) Find the function rule for f that, for a specified number of years, can be used to calculate the final amount A of the investment when the interest is compounded:

1) Annually.   2) Monthly.

b) What type of transformation will you see in the graph of function f if the sum is changed to $10 000 (assuming function f is compounded annually)?

LOGARITHMIC FUNCTIONS

BASIC LOGARITHMIC FUNCTIONS

The reproduction of bacteria

There are billions of bacteria around you. Some are harmful; others are essential to life. Bacteria reproduce through a process called fission. In this process, a bacterium doubles in length, then splits into two separate, identical cells. The time required for a bacterium to duplicate itself depends on the type of bacterium and the surrounding conditions. At normal temperatures, the bacterium *Microccocus* splits every 2 h. Thus the rule $y = 2^x$ tells how many bacteria came from a single *Microccocus* after x hours. In the graph below, the red curve depicts the model for this function. The blue curve shows the inverse.

A bacteria cultu... a lab. The first person to observe bacteria was Dute... naturalist Anton Van Leeuwenhoe... (1632–1723). He made this discov... in 1675.

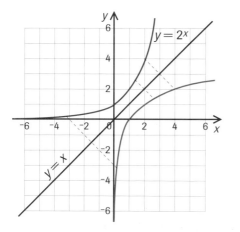

a) How many bacteria will there be after 10 h?

b) How long will it take for the bacteria population to reach 65 536?

c) By inverting the variables, write an algebraic expression for the inverse.

d) Describe in words what y is, in relation to x and 2 in this expression.

e) Given that the exponent of a base is called a "logarithm," state the rule for the inverse using a logarithm.

Every **logarithmic function** is the **inverse** of an exponential function. Knowing the arrangement of the terms in one form helps to convert the function into the other form.

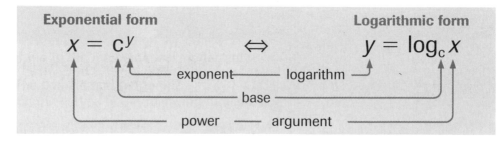

Exponential form $\qquad$ Logarithmic form

$$x = c^y \qquad \Leftrightarrow \qquad y = \log_c x$$

exponent — logarithm
base
power — argument

Thus, the rule for **basic logarithmic functions** has the form:

$$y = \log_c x \text{ or } f(x) = \log_c x \text{ with } c > 0 \text{ and } c \neq 1$$

Logarithmic functions in base **10** and base **e** are used most frequently. As a result, we do not indicate the base for any logarithm in base 10, and we give a special symbol to any logarithm in base e. Thus,

$$x = 10^y \Leftrightarrow y = \log x \text{ and } x = e^y \Leftrightarrow y = \ln x$$

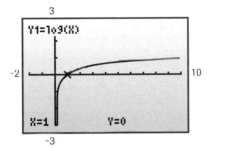

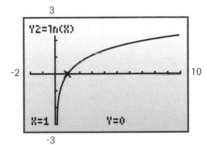

A logarithm in base 10 is called a **common** logarithm. A logarithm in base e is called a **natural** logarithm

Logarithmic functions can have different bases.

f) Study these graphs:

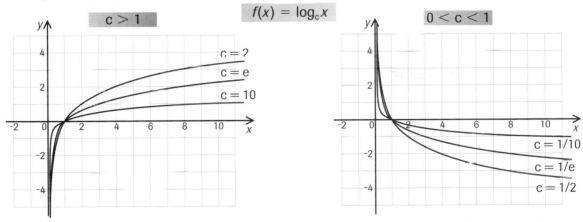

1) How does the value of base c affect the general appearance of the curve?

2) What is the x-intercept of each of these curves? How do you explain this result?

3) For $f(x) = \log_c x$, show algebraically that $f(c) = 1$ and that $f(1/c) = -1$.

4) The curves seem to merge into the y-axis. Is this really what is happening? Justify your answer.

5) Find the domain and range of every basic logarithmic function.

Examining these graphs allows you to see that:

The logarithm of 1 is zero:	The logarithm of the base is equal to 1:
$\log_c 1 = 0$	$\log_c c = 1$

Just before the death of John Napier (1617), Henry Briggs visited him in Edinburgh. After many lengthy discussions, they concluded that the logarithm of 1 must be equal to zero and that the logarithm of 10 must be equal to 1.

g) Complete the table of **properties** for **basic logarithmic functions**.

Rule	$f(x) = \log_c x$ (c > 0 and c ≠ 1)
Graph	- Asymptotic at � - the curve passes through $(c, ■)$ and $\left(\frac{1}{c}, ■\right)$.
Domain	████████
Range	████████
Zero	████████
Extremes	████████
Sign	████████
Variation	If c > 1 : ■ and if 0 < c < 1: ■
Inverse	The inverse is ████████.

INVESTMENT 5

1. Here are tables of values for a logarithmic function and an exponential function:

x	$y = 10^x$
-2	███
-1	███
0	███
1	███
2	███

x	$y = \log x$
███	-2
███	-1
███	0
███	1
███	2

a) Complete these tables.

b) Compare the domains and ranges of these functions.

c) Graph these functions on the same axes.

d) Draw the reflection line that maps one curve onto the other.

We now know that Jost Bürgi (1552–1632) was working with ideas very similar to John Napier's logarithms at about the same time. Claims have been made that he had developed the idea of logarithms around 1588. His work would only be published after Napier's however.

2. Write each statement in logarithmic form:

a) $2^5 = 32$
b) $12^2 = 144$
c) $10^{-3} = 0.001$
d) $e^{-1} = \frac{1}{e}$
e) $\left(\frac{1}{2}\right)^3 = \frac{1}{8}$
f) $\left(\frac{1}{5}\right)^{-4} = 625$
g) $10^0 = 1$
h) $3^1 = 3$

3. Evaluate the following logarithms mentally:

a) $\log_2 8$
b) $\log_3 9$
c) $\ln e$
d) $\log 1000$
e) $\log_{\frac{1}{2}} 16$
f) $\log_{11} 121$
g) $\log_2 0.25$
h) $\ln 1$

4. Write each statement in exponential form:

a) $\log_4 64 = 3$ **b)** $\log^{\frac{1}{3}} 9 = -2$ **c)** $2 = \log 100$

d) $\log_2 \left(\dfrac{1}{16}\right) = -4$ **e)** $\ln e^3 = 3$ **f)** $\log_c (a + 1) = b$

5. Represent the following statements as logarithms and evaluate them.

a) The exponent to which base 8 must be raised to obtain the power 512 is ■.

b) The exponent to which base $0.\overline{3}$ must be raised to obtain 243 is ■.

c) The logarithm of 16 in base ■ is 2.

d) The logarithm of ■ in base 0.5 is -3.

In physics applications, base e is used more often than all the other bases combined.

6. Find the missing values.

a) $3 = \log_■ 343$ **b)** $\log_2 \sqrt{8} = ■$ **c)** $\log_9 ■ = -2$

d) $\log_■ 25 = 4$ **e)** $■ = \log^{\frac{2}{3}} \left(\dfrac{8}{27}\right)$ **f)** $\ln ■ = -3$

7. Using a calculator, evaluate the following logarithms to the nearest thousandth.

a) $\log(5)$ ▬ **e)** $\ln(2)$ ▬
b) $\log(50)$ ▬ **f)** $\ln(5)$ ▬
c) $\log(0.125)$ ▬ **g)** $\ln(0.1)$ ▬
d) $\log(\pi)$ ▬ **h)** $\ln(\sqrt{(\pi)})$ ▬

Henry Briggs (1556–1630) and Edward Wright (1560–1615) worked together to produce the first table of common logarithms.

8. Are the following statements true? Justify your answer.

a) A logarithm can be negative.

b) A logarithm's argument can be less than zero.

c) For $f(x) = \log_c x$, we always have $f(c) = 1$.

d) For $f(x) = \log_c x$, we always have $f(0) = 1$.

9. Here are the rules for some basic logarithmic functions:

$$f(x) = \log_3 x \qquad g(x) = \log_4 x$$
$$h(x) = \log^{\frac{1}{5}} x \qquad i(x) = \log_{1.5} x$$

For each of the defined functions, determine:

a) Whether it is increasing or decreasing. **b)** The domain and range.

c) The zero. **d)** The image of $\dfrac{1}{c}$ and of c, if c is the base.

e) The equation of the asymptote to the curve.

10. The following graphs represent functions whose rules have the form $f(x) = \log_c x$. For each one, find the value of c.

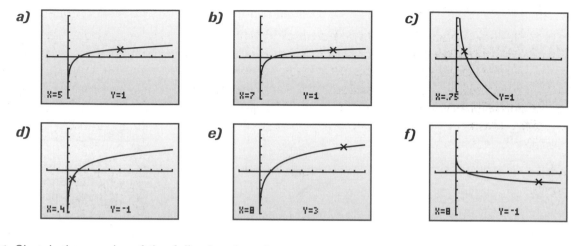

11. Sketch the graphs of the following functions:

a) $f(x) = \log_3 x$ **b)** $g(x) = \log_{\frac{1}{4}} x$ **c)** $h(x) = \log_6 x$

12. State the rule for the inverse of each of the functions defined below, then sketch its graph.

a) $f(x) = \log_4 x$ **b)** $g(x) = \log_{\frac{1}{3}} x$ **c)** $h(x) = \log_6 x$

$$y = \log_4 x$$
$$x = \log_4 y$$
$$f^{-1} \; (y = 4^x)$$

THINK TANK

a) What relationship exists between a and b if:

1) $\log_a b = \log_b a$?   2) $\log_a b > 0$?

b) A calculator features two different keys for logarithms. What relationship can you establish between log x and ln x?

c) Given that $10^{1.699} \approx 50$ and that $2^{3.322} \approx 10$, find a strategy that helps you calculate $\log_2 50$.

LAWS OF LOGARITHMS

Math in the olden days

In the late 16th century, long and laborious calculations were slowing down scientific progress. Consumed by this problem, mathematician John Napier set out to find ways of simplifying tedious calculations. The result was the compilation of the first table of logarithms. John Napier spent nearly 20 years of dedicated work on logarithms, but the impact on mathematical calculations was worth it.

Today we can discover the properties of logarithms in about 20 minutes.

John Napier
(1550-1617)

THE FUNDAMENTAL LAW

a) Justify this fundamental property:

$$c^{\log_c m} = m \text{ where } m \text{ and } c \in \mathbb{R}^*_+ \text{ and } c \neq 1$$

THE PRODUCT LAW FOR LOGARITHMS

b) Use the table on the right to identify the relationship between log 4, log 8 and log 32.

log 2 ≈ 0.301 03	log 16 ≈ 1.204 12
log 4 ≈ 0.602 06	log 32 ≈ 1.505 15
log 8 ≈ 0.903 09	log 64 ≈ 1.806 18

$$\log 32 = \log (4 \times 8)$$

$$\log 32 = \log 4 \blacksquare \log 8$$

c) In the same manner, express log 64 using:

1) log 2 and log 32   2) log 4 and log 16   3) log 2, log 4 and log 8

d) Are the following statements true or false?

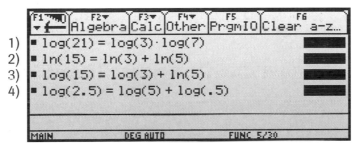

The situations above help prove that the logarithm of a product of positive numbers equals the sum of the logarithms of the factors. Algebraically, the **product law for logarithms** is expressed as:

$$\log_c mn = \log_c m + \log_c n \text{ where } m, n, c \in \mathbb{R}^*_+ \text{ and } c \neq 1$$

e) Proof of this law is given in the steps below. Justify each step.

$$mn = m \cdot n$$

$$c^{\log_c mn} = c^{\log_c m} \cdot c^{\log_c n} \qquad (\blacksquare)$$

$$c^{\log_c mn} = c^{\log_c m + \log_c n} \qquad (\blacksquare)$$

$$\log_c mn = \log_c m + \log_c n \qquad (\blacksquare)$$

f) Given $2^{3.322} \approx 10$, use the product law for logarithms to calculate $\log_2 80$.

THE QUOTIENT LAW FOR LOGARITHMS

g) By analysing the table of values on the right, identify the relationship between log 4, log 8 and log 32.

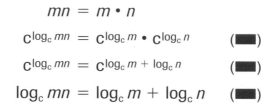

log 2 ≈ 0.301 03	log 16 ≈ 1.204 12
log 4 ≈ 0.602 06	log 32 ≈ 1.505 15
log 8 ≈ 0.903 09	log 64 ≈ 1.806 18

log 4 = log (32 ÷ 8)

log 4 = log 32 ■ log 8

h) In the same manner, express log 2 using:

1) log 4 and log 8

2) log 32 and log 64

i) From the same table, evaluate log 0.25.

j) Using a calculator, verify that:

1) log 6.25 = log 25 − log 4

2) $\ln\left(\dfrac{10}{3}\right) = \ln 10 - \ln 3$

The situations above help prove that the logarithm of a quotient with positive numbers equals the logarithm of the numerator minus the logarithm of the denominator. Algebraically, the **quotient law for logarithms** is expressed as:

$$\log_c\left(\frac{m}{n}\right) = \log_c m - \log_c n \text{ where } m, n, c \in \mathbb{R}_+^* \text{ and } c \neq 1$$

k) Proof of this law is given below. Justify each step.

$$\frac{m}{n} = m \div n$$

$$c^{\log_c\left(\frac{m}{n}\right)} = c^{\log_c m} \div c^{\log_c n} \qquad (\blacksquare)$$

$$c^{\log_c\left(\frac{m}{n}\right)} = c^{\log_c m - \log_c n} \qquad (\blacksquare)$$

$$\log_c\left(\frac{m}{n}\right) = \log_c m - \log_c n \qquad (\blacksquare)$$

l) Use $2^{3.907} \approx 15$ and the quotient law for logarithms to calculate $\log_2\left(\dfrac{32}{15}\right)$.

THE POWER LAW FOR LOGARITHMS

The product law for logarithms allows us to state the following:

$$\log(2^3) = \log(2 \times 2 \times 2) = \log 2 + \log 2 + \log 2 = 3 \log 2$$

m) Using the table on the right, identify the relationship between:

1) $\log(8^2)$ and $2 \log 8$

2) $\log(4^3)$ and $3 \log 4$

$\log 2 \approx 0.301\ 03$	$\log 16 \approx 1.204\ 12$
$\log 4 \approx 0.602\ 06$	$\log 32 \approx 1.505\ 15$
$\log 8 \approx 0.903\ 09$	$\log 64 \approx 1.806\ 18$

n) Evaluate $\log(2^{1000})$.

o) Using a calculator, verify that:

1) $\ln(2.5^3) = 3 \ln 2.5$

2) $\log(2^{6.3}) = 6.3 \log 2$

The above situations help prove that the logarithm of a strictly positive power equals the exponent of the power times the logarithm of the base of the power. Algebraically, the **power law for logarithms** is expressed as:

$$\log_c m^n = n \log_c m \quad \text{where } m, c \in IR_+^* \text{ and } c \neq 1$$

p) Proof of this law is given below. Justify each step.

$$m^n = (m)^n$$

$$c^{\log_c m^n} = \left(c^{\log_c m}\right)^n \qquad (\ \blacksquare\ )$$

$$c^{\log_c m^n} = c^{n \log_c m} \qquad (\ \blacksquare\ )$$

$$\log_c m^n = n \log_c m \qquad (\ \blacksquare\ )$$

q) Using the power law for logarithms, calculate $\log_2 8^7$.

CHANGE OF BASE LAW

We wish to solve the following exponential equation:

$$5^x = 7$$

r) Estimate the value of x.

s) Justify the following:

$$5^x = 7 \implies \log 5^x = \log 7$$

t) Isolate x in $\log 5^x = \log 7$.

u) Write $5^x = 7$ in logarithmic form.

v) Find the value of $\log_5 7$.

w) Using a calculator, check if the following equations are true:

1) $\log_6 36 = \dfrac{\log 36}{\log 6}$
2) $\log_2 64 = \dfrac{\ln 64}{\ln 2}$
3) $\log 36 = \dfrac{\ln 36}{\ln 10}$

Although most calculators calculate logarithms only in base 10 or e, you can use the change of base law to calculate logarithms in other bases. Algebraically, the **change of base law** is expressed as:

$$\log_c m = \frac{\log_s m}{\log_s c} \quad \text{where } m,\, c,\, s \in \mathbb{R}^*_+,\, c \neq 1 \text{ and } s \neq 1$$

x) The change of base law is derived below. Justify each step.

$$\text{Given } \log_c m = n \iff c^n = m \qquad (\blacksquare)$$

$$\log_s c^n = \log_s m \qquad (\blacksquare)$$

$$n \log_s c = \log_s m \qquad (\blacksquare)$$

$$n = \frac{\log_s m}{\log_s c} \qquad (\blacksquare)$$

$$\text{Therefore: } \log_c m = \frac{\log_s m}{\log_s c} \qquad (\blacksquare)$$

y) In the three screens shown below, $\log_c m$ was calculated. For each, express the result in the form $\log_c m$.

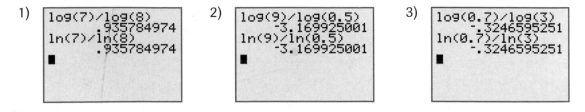

1)
```
log(7)/log(8)
          .935784974
ln(7)/ln(8)
          .935784974
■
```

2)
```
log(9)/log(0.5)
         -3.169925001
ln(9)/ln(0.5)
         -3.169925001
■
```

3)
```
log(0.7)/log(3)
          -.3246595251
ln(0.7)/ln(3)
          -.3246595251
■
```

1. Write the following expressions in expanded form:

   a) $\log_c 2mn$

   b) $\log_5 7(x + 2)^7$

   c) $\log_3 4x^2$

   d) $\log_2 \left(\dfrac{5a}{b^2}\right)$

   e) $\log_4 (4mn)^3$

   f) $\log_6 (2(x + 1))^2$

   g) $\log_4 16\sqrt{x}$

   h) $\log (x^2 - 4)$

2. Express each of the following as a single logarithm:

   a) $\log_2 5 + \log_2 8$

   b) $\log_4 45 - \log_4 3$

   c) $\ln 7 + \ln 8 - \ln 4$

   d) $2 \log 25 - 3 \log 5$

   e) $\log_2 0.5 + \log_2 4 + 3 \log_2 3$

   f) $\dfrac{\log_2 9}{\log_2 10} - \log 3$

3. Assuming that the following expressions exist, express each as a single logarithm:

   a) $\log (x^2 - 4) - 2 \log (x + 2)$

   b) $\log_a t - 3 \log_a 2t + 2 \log_a 3t$

   c) $\log_n m^3 - \log_n \sqrt{m}$

   d) $2 \log (x^2 - 1) - \log (x + 1) - 2 \log (x - 1)$

   e) $\log_5 x - 2 \log_5 \left(\dfrac{xy}{8}\right)$

   f) $3 \log s - 2 \log s + (\log s \cdot \log_s s \cdot \log_s 1)$

4. Given that:

$\log 2 \approx 0.301\ 03$	$\log 3 \approx 0.477\ 12$
$\log 5 \approx 0.698\ 97$	$\log 7 \approx 0.845\ 10$

   Around 1650 William Oughtred (1574–1660) clearly stated the following properties:

   $log(mn) = log(m) + log(n);$
   $log(m/n) = log(m) - log(n);$
   $log(x^n) = n\ log(x).$

   find the following logarithms by using the appropriate properties:

   a) $\log 9$

   b) $\log 14$

   c) $\log 45$

   d) $\log 90$

   e) $\log 50$

   f) $\log 7^5$

   g) $\log 0.5$

   h) $\log \sqrt{\dfrac{35}{6}}$

   i) $\dfrac{\log 20}{\log 40}$

   j) $\log 54 \times \log 70$

5. Express x as a function of a, b and c.

   a) $\log x = \log a + \log b + \log c$

   b) $\log x = \dfrac{2}{3} \log a - \dfrac{1}{2} \log b + 2 \log c$

6. Solve for x.

   a) $\ln (5 - x) - \ln (x - 3) = 0$

   b) $2 \ln a + \ln (x - a) = 1$

   c) $\log x^2 = \log x - 2$

   d) $\log bx = 2 \log a + \log b - \log c$

7. Simplify the following expression:

   $$\log 10 - \log \left(\dfrac{2}{5}\right) - \log \left(\dfrac{35}{2}\right) + \log \left(\dfrac{21}{2}\right) + \log \left(\dfrac{21}{63}\right)$$

8. The whole number part of a logarithm whose number is greater than 1 is called the "characteristic." What is the characteristic of each the following logarithms?

   a) $\log_8 100$

   b) $\log_5 344$

   c) $\log_2 24$

   d) $\log_{15} 850$

   e) $\log 3485$

9. Using the change of base formula, evaluate the following logarithms to the nearest thousandth:

a) $\log_6 50$ b) $\log_{15} 860$ c) $\log_{12} 1520$ d) $\log_{0.5} 35$ e) $\log_{2.75} 400$

10. Express:

a) 50 as a power of 25.

b) 80 as a power of 7.

c) 124 as a power of $\sqrt{2}$.

d) 0.75 as a power of 4.

11. We want to display the graph of a logarithmic function on a calculator.

a) Explain the steps involved in drawing the curve of a logarithmic function whose base is neither 10 nor e.

b) Sketch the curves of the functions defined by:

1) $Y_1 = \log_{20} x$ 2) $Y_2 = \log_{0.1} x$ 3) $Y_3 = \log_2 x$

12. Apply the laws of logarithms to isolate the variable N in the following equation:

$$\ln N = \ln N_0 - kt$$

13. Determine whether the following statements are true or false.

a) $\log_2 4 + \log_2 8 = 5$ b) $\log_5 16 - \log_5 2 = \log_5 8$ c) $\log_3 8 = 3 \log_3 2$

d) $\log_5 \left(\dfrac{8}{13}\right) = \dfrac{\log_5 8}{\log_5 13}$ e) $\log (4 + 11) = \log 4 \cdot \log 11$ f) $\dfrac{\log_c 7}{\log_c 12} = \log_7 12$

g) $\log_c \left(\dfrac{3}{2}\right) = \dfrac{1}{2} \log_c 3$ h) $\log 6 - 4 \log 2 = \log \left(\dfrac{6}{2}\right)$ i) $(\log 2.5^3)^2 = 6 \log 2.5$

14. For $m, n \in \mathbb{R}_+^*$, which of the following expressions are equal to one another?

A) $3 \log m - 2 \log n$ B) $\log 3m - \log 2n$ C) $3 \log n - 2 \log m$

D) $\log 2m - \log 3n$ E) $\log n^3 - \log m^2$ F) $1 + \log m - \log 15n$

15. Prove $\log^{\frac{1}{10}} x = -\log x$.

16. The intensity of light I that penetrates a lake varies exponentially depending on the depth d beneath the surface of the water. For a depth of up to 10 m, we can calculate the light intensity using the formula $\log I = -0.245 \log p + 3$ where I is expressed in candelas and d is expressed in metres.

a) Calculate the value of I at a depth of 8 m.

b) What is the function rule for expressing light intensity I in terms of depth d?

c) Why can this rule not be used to calculate the light intensity at the surface of the water?

17. Prove this property: $\log_c\left(\dfrac{x}{y}\right) = -\log_c\left(\dfrac{y}{x}\right)$.

18. True or false?

a) $\log MN = \log M + \log N$

b) $\log M + N = \log MN$

c) $e^{\ln e} = 1$

d) $\ln\,(\log 10) = 0$

e) $\dfrac{\log 1}{\ln 1} = 1$

f) $\ln x = \dfrac{\log x}{\log e}$

g) $p \log M = \log\sqrt[p]{M}$

h) $(\log x)(\ln y) = (\log y)(\ln x)$

19. The power P of sound refers to the amount of energy transported by sound waves and is expressed in watts per unit of area. The acoustic intensity level i, expressed in decibels, is calculated with the formula $i = 10 \log\left(\dfrac{P}{P_0}\right)$, where P_0 is the minimum power of sound perceptible to the human ear.

Type of sound	Intensity level (dB)
• whisper	20
• conversation	60
• horn	90
• jet engine	120
• sonic boom	150

The symbol for a decibel is dB.

a) If $P_0 = 10^{-16}$ W/cm², find the decibel level of a normal conversation if the corresponding intensity P is 10^{-10} W/cm².

b) To respect noise pollution by-laws, a factory must reduce its noise level by half. If i_1 is the current acoustic intensity and i_2 is the required intensity, the noise reduction corresponds to:

$$i_1 - i_2 = 10 \log\left(\frac{P}{P_0}\right) - 10 \log\left(0.5\,\frac{P}{P_0}\right)$$

Determine this reduction.

THINK TANK

Each logarithm consists of a whole number and a decimal fraction, called respectively the "characteristic" and the "mantissa."

a) What can you guess about the mantissas of the following logarithms:

1) log 5.1, log 51, log 510 and log 5100?

2) log 0.51, log 0.051, log 0.0051 and log 0.00051?

b) We know that a mantissa is positive. Explain how we can make the decimal parts of the previous logarithms positive and thus obtain their mantissas.

c) After expressing numbers 0.0051, 0.51, 5.1, 51 and 510 in scientific notation, what can you guess about the mantissas and characteristics of their common logarithms?

TRANSFORMED LOGARITHMIC FUNCTIONS

Are you experienced?

When tennis players break the strings on their rackets, it is nothing new. An avid player can break up to 300 strings in a year. Fortunately, racket strings are not hard to replace.

A stringer new to the job might take over an hour to string a racket. But the more experience the stringer gains, the less time it takes to fix a racket. The graph below shows the relationship between the number of rackets strung and the time required to string one racket.

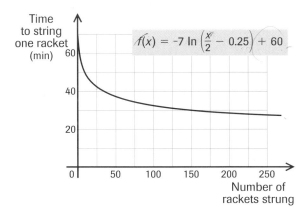

$$f(x) = -7 \ln\left(\frac{x}{2} - 0.25\right) + 60$$

a) How long did it take the stringer to string his:

1) First racket?

2) 1000th racket?

b) Using a calculator, find out how many rackets the stringer must repair before he can string one in about:

1) 30 min?

2) 20 min?

This scenario introduces the rule for **transformed logarithmic functions.** The function is transformed by parameters **a, b, h** and **k.**

> The rule for a **transformed logarithmic function** has the form:
> $$f(x) = a \log_c (b(x - h)) + k \quad \text{where } c > 0, c \neq 1, a \neq 0 \text{ and } b \neq 0$$

c) What are the values of parameters **a, b, h** and **k** in this situation?

Once again, these parameters behave as they do in other functions.

d) How does each parameter affect:

1) The graph of the basic function?

2) The ordered pairs of the basic function?

e) Given the screen images below, indicate which of the parameters affect(s) the asymptote of a logarithmic function.

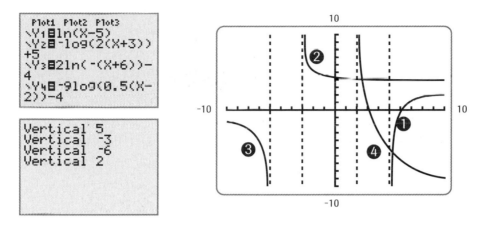

Using the parameters and the ordered pairs **(c, 1)**, **(1, 0)** and **(1/c, −1)** of the basic function defined by $f(x) = \log_c x$, you can obtain the critical ordered pairs of the transformed logarithmic function of the same base. With these ordered pairs and the asymptote, you can quickly sketch the transformed function.

f) Functions f and g are defined by $f(x) = 3 \log_2 (0.5(x − 6))$ and $g(x) = -\log_5 (x − 6) + 3$. For each function, find:

1) The equation of the asymptote to the curve.

2) The three critical ordered pairs of its basic function.

3) Its three critical ordered pairs.

g) What is the range of every logarithmic function?

h) From the graphs below, explain how parameters **b** and **h** affect the domain of a logarithmic function.

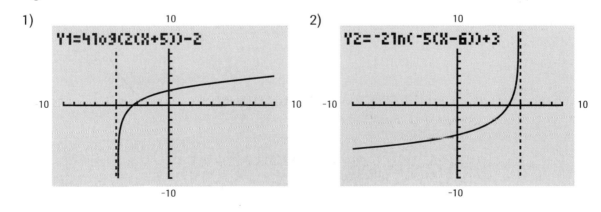

1) Y1=4log(2(X+5))−2

2) Y2=−2ln(−5(X−6))+3

i) Why must the inverse of a logarithmic function be an exponential function?

j) The method shown below describes how one can obtain the rule for the inverse of the function f defined by $y = 4 \log (2(x + 5)) - 2$. Justify each step.

$$x = 4 \log (2(y + 5)) - 2 \qquad (1)$$
$$x + 2 = 4 \log (2(y + 5)) \qquad (2)$$
$$0.25(x + 2) = \log (2(y + 5)) \qquad (3)$$
$$10^{0.25(x + 2)} = 2(y + 5) \qquad (4)$$
$$0.5 \times 10^{0.25(x + 2)} = y + 5 \qquad (5)$$
$$0.5 \times 10^{0.25(x + 2)} - 5 = y \qquad (6)$$

Therefore, the rule for the inverse is $f^{-1}(x) = 0.5 \times 10^{0.25(x + 2)} - 5$. We have come back to the rule for an exponential function.

You can also perform **operations** on logarithmic functions.

k) Functions f and g are defined by $f(x) = \log (2x + 7)$ and $g(x) = \log (x + 1)$.

1) State the rule for $f + g$ and $f - g$ as a single logarithm.

2) Determine whether $f \cdot g$ is increasing or decreasing.

3) Graph function $\dfrac{f}{g}$ using a calculator and find:

   i) The equation of its asymptote.   ii) The domain of this function.

That's one cool iguana

Iguanas live in the hot tropical areas of the Americas. Fortunately, nature has equipped these reptiles with a defense mechanism against the heat, whereby an iguana can actually control the increase in its body temperature. To study this phenomenon in a lab, researchers exposed an iguana to a temperature of 50°C. Each minute, the increase in body temperature was recorded. Some of the results of this experiment are shown here.

Time (min)	Increase in body temperature (°C)
1	3.60
2	2.80
5	1.42
8	0.61
10	0.21

Iguana, in Mexico.

a) Describe each of the steps allowing you to establish the regression equation of the logarithmic model that relates the variables in the experiment and allowing you to sketch its curve.

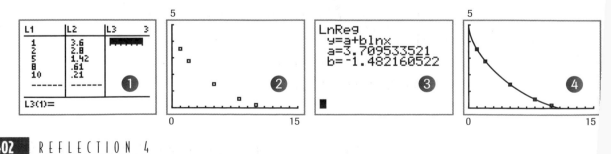

b) The experiment ended when the iguana's body temperature stopped increasing. How long did the experiment last?

Using a graphing calculator allows you to find, **by regression, the rule of a logarithmic function** based on a set of ordered pairs. The rule thus obtained is in the form $f(x) = a \ln x + k$.

SOLVING LOGARITHMIC EQUATIONS

Why some stars are brighter than others

The brightness of a star depends on its composition and its distance from the observer. Since the work of Norman Pogson in 1860, the brightness of a star has been measured as its magnitude. According to this system, the greater a star's magnitude, the less bright it is. Rule $M = -2.5 \log r + 1$ makes it possible to calculate the magnitude M of a star based on the ratio of its luminous intensity to that of the star Antares, which serves as a reference point for astronomers.

The Pleiades, a loose cluster of 400 to 500 stars, are about 4105 light-years from Earth in the constellation Taurus.

a) From Earth, Mars seems 27 times brighter than Antares. Find the magnitude of Mars.

b) State the equation that calculates the luminous intensity ratio:

1) Between a zero magnitude star and Antares.

2) Between the star Sirius, whose magnitude is -2.5 and Antares.

c) In this situation, can the ratio r be zero or negative? Explain your answer.

For many situations, we must solve **logarithmic equations algebraically** or find the **zero of logarithmic functions.**

d) Given that the magnitude of Venus is -4, you can find the ratio of its luminous intensity to that of Antares by solving the equation $-4 = -2.5 \log r + 1$. Interpret this result in this context.

$$-4 = -2.5 \log r + 1$$
$$-5 = -2.5 \log r$$
$$2 = \log r \implies r = 10^2$$
$$r = 100$$

e) The magnitude of the Sun is -26 and that of the Moon is -13. How much greater is the Sun's luminous intensity than the Moon's?

As a general rule, solving logarithmic equations in one variable consists of:

1. Finding the restrictions.
2. Writing the equation using a single logarithm.
3. Converting the equation into exponential form.
4. Finding the value or values of x.
5. Checking the solutions.

EXAMPLE 1

What is the zero of the function f defined by $f(x) = \ln(-3x + 13)$?

Restriction: $-3x + 13 > 0 \Rightarrow x < 13/3$

We have: $f(x) = 0 \Rightarrow \ln(-3x + 13) = 0$.

$\ln(-3x + 13) = 0$

$\Downarrow$ (By definition)

$-3x + 13 = e^0$

$-3x + 13 = 1$

$-3x = -12$

$x = 4$

Since $x = 4$ respects the restriction, 4 is the zero of the function f.

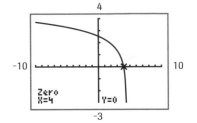

EXAMPLE 2

We want to solve the equation $2 \log_3(2(x + 5)) = 6$.

Restriction: $2(x + 5) > 0 \Rightarrow x > -5$

$2 \log_3(2(x + 5)) = 6$

$\log_3(2(x + 5)) = 3$

$\Downarrow$ (By definition)

$2(x + 5) = 3^3$

$2(x + 5) = 27$

$x + 5 = 13.5$

$x = 8.5$

The solution is 8.5, because it respects the restriction.

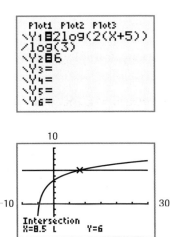

EXAMPLE 3

We want to solve the equation $\log (x + 2) = 1 - \log (x - 1)$.

Restrictions: $x + 2 > 0$ and $x - 1 > 0$

$\rightarrow x > $ -2 and $x > 1$

$\Rightarrow x > 1$

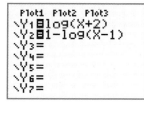

$$\log (x + 2) = 1 - \log (x - 1)$$

$$\log (x + 2) + \log (x - 1) = 1$$

$\Downarrow$ (The product law for logarithms)

$$\log ((x + 2)(x - 1)) = 1$$

$$\log (x^2 + x - 2) = 1$$

$\Downarrow$ (By definition)

$$x^2 + x - 2 = 10$$

$$x^2 + x - 12 = 0$$

$$(x - 3)(x + 4) = 0$$

$$x = 3 \text{ and } x = -4$$

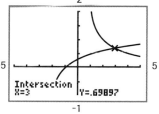

The root -4 is rejected because it does not respect the restriction. The solution set is therefore {3}.

f) Solve the following logarithmic equations:

1) $\log_2 (x - 3) = 4$

2) $\log_8 (2x - 7) = \log_8 (5 - x)$

3) $\log_3 (x + 4) - \log_3 x = 2$

Transformed logarithmic functions have the following **properties:**

Rule	$f(x) = a \log_c (b(x - h)) + k$ ($c > 0$, $c \neq 1$, $a \neq 0$ and $b \neq 0$)
Graph	The asymptote is a vertical line whose equation is $x = h$.
Domain	If $b < 0$: $]-\infty, h[$ If $b > 0$: $]h, +\infty[$
Range	IR
Zero	There is always one and only one.
Extremes	None
Sign	Dependent on the zero
Variation	Always decreasing or always increasing.
Inverse	The inverse is an exponential function.

SOLVING EXPONENTIAL EQUATIONS

Keep that freezer door shut!

The temperature inside a freezer is -15°C. When a power failure hits, avoid opening the freezer door so that the cold air does not escape. But even if you keep the door shut, the air inside your freezer starts to warm up. The graph below shows the relationship between the length of a power failure and the temperature inside a freezer.

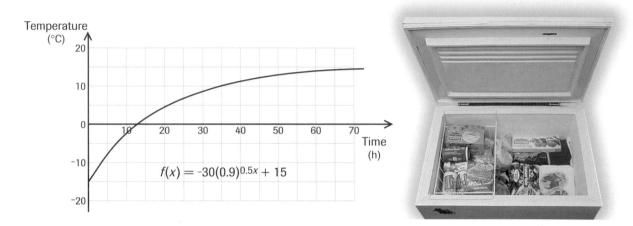

$$f(x) = -30(0.9)^{0.5x} + 15$$

a) What is the temperature inside the freezer after 24 h without power?

b) From the graph, estimate the solution to each of the following equations:

1) $-5 = -30(0.9)^{0.5x} + 15$ 2) $0 = -30(0.9)^{0.5x} + 15$ 3) $10 = -30(0.9)^{0.5x} + 15$

c) Is it possible to solve the previous equations by expressing both sides in the same base?

You can use logarithms to solve exponential equations, no matter what their form. The property of logarithms that makes this possible is:

For $m > 0$ and $n > 0$, we have $\boldsymbol{m = n} \Rightarrow \boldsymbol{\log_c m = \log_c n}$

d) Here is a solution of the equation $0 = -30(0.9)^{0.5x} + 15$ using logarithms. Justify steps (4) and (5).

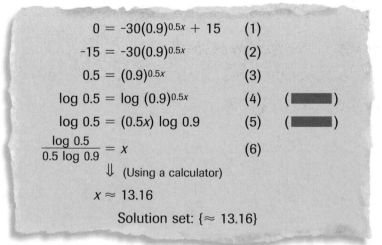

$$0 = -30(0.9)^{0.5x} + 15 \quad (1)$$
$$-15 = -30(0.9)^{0.5x} \quad (2)$$
$$0.5 = (0.9)^{0.5x} \quad (3)$$
$$\log 0.5 = \log (0.9)^{0.5x} \quad (4) \quad (\rule{1cm}{0.2cm})$$
$$\log 0.5 = (0.5x) \log 0.9 \quad (5) \quad (\rule{1cm}{0.2cm})$$
$$\frac{\log 0.5}{0.5 \log 0.9} = x \quad (6)$$
$$\Downarrow \text{ (Using a calculator)}$$
$$x \approx 13.16$$

Solution set: $\{\approx 13.16\}$

e) How do you interpret this result in this situation?

f) Can you solve this problem using natural logarithms? Justify your answer.

Here is another example of solving an exponential equation.

EXAMPLE

We want to solve $4^{(2x - 3)} = 5^x$.

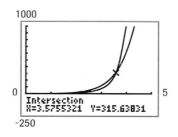

$$4^{(2x - 3)} = 5^x$$

⇓ (The logarithms on both sides are equal.)

$$\ln 4^{(2x - 3)} = \ln 5^x$$

⇓ (The power law for logarithms)

$$(2x - 3) \ln 4 = x \ln 5$$

$$2x \ln 4 - 3 \ln 4 = x \ln 5$$

$$2x \ln 4 - x \ln 5 = 3 \ln 4$$

$$x(2 \ln 4 - \ln 5) = 3 \ln 4$$

$$x = \frac{3 \ln 4}{2 \ln 4 - \ln 5}$$

⇓ (Using a calculator)

$$x \approx 3.58$$

Solution set: $\{\approx 3.58\}$

The steps required to **solve exponential equations in one variable** usually include the following:

1. Make both sides of the equation equal and strictly positive.

2. Apply the property:
$$m = n \implies \log_c m = \log_c n$$

3. Apply the laws of logarithms and equations to isolate the variable.

g) Solve the following equations algebraically:

1) $3^{(x + 2)} = 4^{5x}$

2) $6^{(3x - 1)} = 4^x$

INVESTMENT 7

1. Here are some rules for logarithmic functions:

$$f_1(x) = -\log_3 (2x) - 7 \qquad f_2(x) = 0.25 \log_3 (-x) \qquad f_3(x) = 5 \log_3 (3(x - 1))$$

a) For each function, find the values of the parameters **a, b, h** and **k**.

b) Indicate the transformations of the plane that associate the curve of the given function with the curve of the basic function defined by $f(x) = \log_3 x$.

2. By inspection, find the equation of the asymptote to the curve associated with each of the functions defined below:

a) $f(x) = 2 \log (x - 9)$

b) $g(x) = -\log (4(x + 3)) + 5$

c) $r(x) = \ln (2x) - 1$

d) $s(x) = 5 \log (2x + 8) - 6$

3. Here are graphical representations of the functions *p, q, r* and *s*. The rules for these functions are in the form $f(x) = \ln (b(x - h))$.

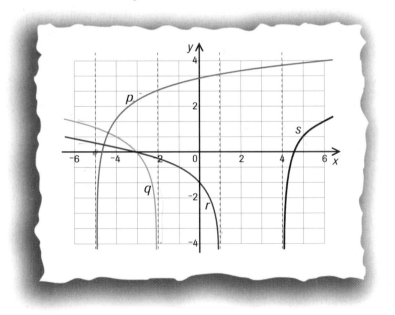

For each one, find:

a) The value of parameter **h**.

b) The sign of parameter **b**.

c) The domain.

4. By examining the parameters **b** and **h** of a function whose rule has the form $f(x) = a \log_c (b(x - h)) + k$, how can you tell if the curve intersects the *y*-axis?

5. The rule for a transformed logarithmic function is $f(x) = -\log_2 (3(x + 1)) - 5$.

a) What is the rule for its basic function?

b) Provide the three critical ordered pairs of the basic function's graph.

c) Find the three critical ordered pairs of the transformed function.

d) Find the equation of the asymptote of function f.

e) Graph function f.

6. Find the y-intercepts (if they exist) of the curves defined by:

a) $f(x) = -\log_3 (-2(x - 1.5))$ **b)** $g(x) = -2 \log (x - 5)$

c) $h(x) = -3 \log^{\frac{1}{2}} (0.5(x + 1)) - 6$

7. Examine the signs of the functions in question 6.

8. For each function shown on the screen on the right, determine:

a) The base.

b) The domain and range.

c) Whether it is increasing or decreasing.

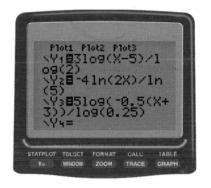

9. Graph the functions defined by:

a) $f_1(x) = \log_2 (x + 5) + 3$ **b)** $f_2(x) = -\log_5 2x + 7$

c) $f_3(x) = \log_3 (2(x - 4))$ **d)** $t_4(x) = 4 \log^{\frac{1}{2}} (x + 3) - 1$

10. The rule for a logarithmic function has the form $f(x) = a \log_c b(x - h) + k$. Indicate whether the following statements are true or false.

a) Only parameter **h** affects the position of the asymptote.

b) If $c \in\,]0, 1[$, then the function is decreasing.

c) A logarithmic function always has a zero.

d) The curve of this function always has a y-intercept.

e) The domain of f is $]-\infty, h]$ or $[h, +\infty[$ and its range is IR.

11. Functions f and g are defined by $f(x) = \log_2 (x + 3)$ and $g(x) = \log (5x) + 4$. Find the value of x if:

a) $f(x) = 4$ **b)** $f(x) = -2$ **c)** $g(x) = 3$ **d)** $g(x) = 7$

12. Solve the logarithmic equations and identify any restrictions.

a) $\log_3 x + \log_3 2 = 4$

b) $\log 2 + \log (x + 1) = 1$

c) $4 \log_{\frac{1}{2}} 16(x - 11) = \text{-}20$

d) $3 \log (0.5x + 2)^2 - 1 = 5$

e) $\log_6 (x + 3) + \log_6 (x - 2) = 1$

f) $\log_3 \left(\dfrac{x - 6}{x + 2}\right) = 2$

g) $\log_2 x + \log_2 \left(\dfrac{x - 3}{5}\right) = 3$

h) $\log_7 (14x) = \log_7 (x - 5) + 2$

13. A telescope's power and efficiency depend on the diameter of its lenses. Using telescopes with wide lenses, we can see very faint stars. The faintest star S we can see using a telescope with diameter d is defined by the rule $S = 7 + 5 \log d$, where S is expressed in magnitude and d is expressed in metres.

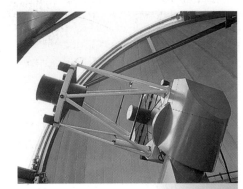

Located in Hawaii, Keck 1 is one of the largest telescopes in the world. Its diameter measures 4 m.

a) Graph this situation over the interval]0, 400].

b) Is this function increasing or decreasing?

c) What is the faintest star we can see using a 75 cm telescope?

Telescope at the observatory at Mt. Mégantic.

d) We wish to see stars with a magnitude of at least 15. What is the minimum diameter of the telescope we must use?

14. The law $\log_c m = \log_c n \Rightarrow m = n$ can be used to solve certain logarithmic equations. Prove this law.

15. Solve the equations using the property $\log_c m = \log_c n \Rightarrow m = n$.

a) $\log_7 20 = \log_7 2(x + 13)$

b) $\ln 6x = \ln (20 - 2x)$

c) $\log_2 (x^2 - 5x) = \log_2 14$

d) $2 \log_{\frac{1}{2}} (x + 1) = \log_{\frac{1}{2}} (x^2 - x + 7)$

e) $\dfrac{\ln 64}{2} + \ln x = \ln 18 - \ln x$

f) $\log (x + 2) + \log (x - 2) = 2 \log 3 - \log 0.9$

16. Here are the curves of the functions defined by $f(x) = 1$, $g(x) = 3 \log x$ and $h(x) = 2 \log (\sqrt{10x})$. Find the coordinates of points A, B and C.

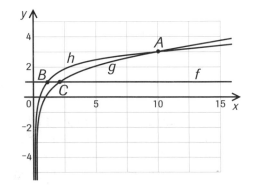

17. Atmospheric pollutants are responsible for acid rain. The acidity of a rainfall is measured on the pH scale, which ranges from 0 to 14. Rain is acidic when its pH is less than 7 and alkaline when its pH is greater than 7. The pH of acid rain is calculated using the formula pH = -log [H⁺], where [H⁺] is the concentration of hydrogen ions expressed in moles per litre of rain.

a) What is the pH of rainwater in which the concentration of hydrogen is 5×10^{-8} moles per litre?

b) Pure water has a pH of 7; that is, a neutral pH. What is the concentration of hydrogen ions in pure water?

c) Determine the concentration of hydrogen ions in:

1) Lemon juice whose pH is 2.5.   2) Milk that has a pH of 6.6.

d) An egg has a pH of 7.7. Find the pH of a substance whose concentration of hydrogen ions is twice that of an egg.

18. The rules for functions f_1 and f_2 graphed below have the form $f(x) = \log_c (x - h)$. Find the rules.

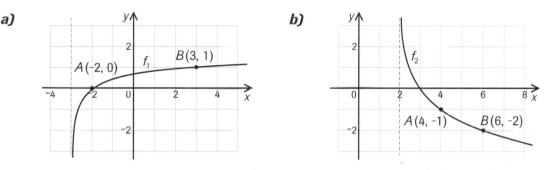

a)

b)

19. Solve the exponential equations below to the nearest hundredth.

a) $5^x = 10$

b) $3^{4x - 1} = 15$

c) $3\left(\dfrac{1}{2}\right)^{-2x + 5} = 21$

d) $3^{x + 5} = 4^{x + 3}$

e) $2^{x - 1} = 5(7^{3x})$

f) $2.5(10^x) = 6e^{4x - 3}$

20. The condenser in a camera stores the electric charge coming from the batteries. When you press the button to take a picture, the condenser releases the charge, which activates the flash. Some engineers are interested in the relationship between the time and the voltage of a condenser during discharge. They found the rule $v = 8.85e^{-0.05t}$, where v is expressed in volts and t is expressed in seconds.

a) What is the voltage of the condenser 3 s after its discharge?

b) How much time after the start of discharge does the condenser have a charge of:

1) 6 V?   2) 3.5 V?   3) 2.25 V?

c) How many seconds are required for the charge to drop by half?

21. The price of a new car is $20 000. After its purchase, the car depreciates in value, losing 20% each year. How many years after the purchase date will the car be worth:

a) $16 000?   **b)** $10 000?   **c)** $5 000?

22. Find the rule for the inverse function of each of the following exponential functions:

a) $f_1(x) = (5)^{2x} + 6$ **b)** $f_2(x) = (6)^{x + 10} - 4$ **c)** $f_3(x) = 3.3e^{x - 4} + 1$

23. Throughout our lives, we breathe in carbon dioxide, which contains a radioactive element called carbon 14, written as ^{14}C or C^{14}. The amount of C^{14} present in an organism remains constant for its entire life. After an organism's death, the amount of C^{14} decreases according to the function f defined by $Q = Q_0 e^{-0.000124t}$, where Q is the quantity in milligrams of C^{14} that remains after t years, and where Q_0 is the quantity of C^{14} that was present at the time of death.

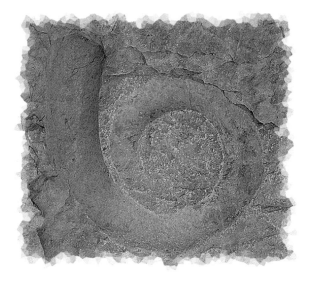

a) Archaeologists discovered a skeleton along the coast of the Mediterranean Sea. An analysis revealed that the quantity of C^{14} present in the bones was about 60% of that which is normally found in a living person of the same size. How old is the skeleton according to the C^{14} dating test?

b) Analysis of a fish fossil revealed the C^{14} content to be about 1/5 of what is normally found in a living fish of the same size. How old is this fossil?

c) The half-life of an element is the time required for the element to decay to half of the original amount. What is the half-life of C^{14}?

d) State the rule for the inverse function f^{-1} so that t is expressed as a function of Q.

24. In a village of 1000 people, a local store owner erects a billboard along the main road. After posting the sign, the owner conducts a monthly survey to see how many people have not yet noticed his sign. The results are shown in the table of values on the right.

Time (months)	Number of people who have not noticed the sign
1	900
2	700
4	500
6	400
8	300
10	250

a) Using a calculator, find the rule for the logarithmic function that defines this situation by regression.

b) According to this rule, determine:

1) The time between when the billboard was erected and the time it was seen by 800 people.

2) The time required for everybody in the village to see the billboard.

a) What is the value of parameter **a** in the rule $f(x) = a \ln x$, if its graph is identical to the graph of the function whose rule is $g(x) = 5 \log x$?

b) By examining the tables of values of the functions below, identify the relationship between their rules. Justify your answer.

1) $Y_1 = 0.5 \log (100(x - 5)) + 3$ 2) $Y_2 = 0.5 \log (x - 5) + 4$

3) $Y_3 = \log_{100} (x - 5) + 4$

c) Given $x = \left(1 - \dfrac{1}{2}\right)\left(1 - \dfrac{1}{3}\right)\left(1 - \dfrac{1}{4}\right) \dots \left(1 - \dfrac{1}{n}\right)$, show that $\log x + \log n = 0$ for every whole number greater than 2.

d) Which of the two expressions is larger: 1999^{2000} or 2000^{1999}? Explain your strategy.

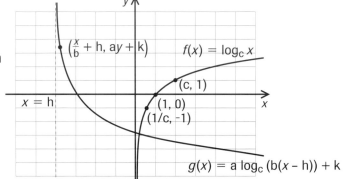

An exponent assigned to a base is a **logarithm.** In the expression $x = c^y$, y is the logarithm of x in base c. Symbolically, this is written:

$$x = c^y \iff y = \log_c x \quad \text{where } c > 0 \text{ and } c \neq 1$$

The equivalence of these two expressions allows us to identify the following properties:

$$c^{\log_c m} = m \qquad \log_c c^m = m \qquad \log_c 1 = 0 \qquad \log_c c = 1$$

Thus the **logarithm of m in base 10,** also called the common logarithm, is written **log m** and the **natural logarithm** of m is written **ln m.**

The **inverse** of an exponential function is a **logarithmic function,** and vice versa. The rule for a basic logarithmic function is $f(x) = \log_c x$. From the graph of a basic logarithmic function, you can **sketch the graph** of any transformed logarithmic function by including the parameters **a, b, h** and **k.**

Working with logarithmic equations is made easier by applying the laws of logarithms. For $c > 0$, $c \neq 1$, $s > 0$, $s \neq 1$, m and $n \in \mathbb{R}_+^*$, we have:

- Logarithm of a product: $\qquad \log_c mn = \log_c m + \log_c n$

- Logarithm of a quotient: $\qquad \log_c \left(\dfrac{m}{n} \right) = \log_c m - \log_c n$

- Logarithm of a power: $\qquad \log_c m^n = n \log_c m$

- Change of base: $\qquad \log_c m = \dfrac{\log_s m}{\log_s c}$

Solving a logarithmic equation consists of writing the equation using **one single logarithm** so that it can be **converted into the equivalent exponential form.** Once the solution(s) are found, you must **check their validity.**

Solving an exponential equation consists of making both sides of the equation equal and strictly positive; finding their logarithms; and applying the laws of logarithms and equations to isolate the variable. This method is based on the following equation:

$$m = n \iff \log_c m = \log_c n$$

This property can also be used to solve logarithmic equations.

1 Here are three different ways to get 10 by adding four natural numbers:

$$1 + 2 + 3 + 4 \qquad 0 + 3 + 3 + 4 \qquad 4 + 2 + 2 + 2$$

Find at least 10 ways to get 20 by adding 5 natural numbers.

2 Here is one method for getting 100 by using the same number 5 times:
$5 \times 5 \times 5 - 5 \times 5$. Find two other methods.

3 What operation will produce the same result as "multiplying by $\frac{3}{5}$ and dividing by $\frac{3}{4}$"?

A) Dividing by $\frac{4}{3}$ B) Dividing by $\frac{9}{20}$ C) Multiplying by $\frac{9}{20}$

D) Dividing by $\frac{5}{4}$ E) Multiplying by $\frac{5}{4}$

4 A person is said to have a "lucky" year when the product of the day and month of their birthday equals the last two digits in that year. Therefore, people born on December 8 celebrated their lucky year in 1996. Find the possible birthdays for a person whose lucky year is:

a) 1992   *b)* 1999   *c)* 2000   *d)* 2008

5 If $2^x = 15$ and $4^y = 32$, evaluate:

a) xy *b)* $\sqrt{xy}$ *c)* $\frac{x}{y}$ *d)* $\frac{x+y}{x-y}$

6 If $\log 2 \approx 0.30$, $\log 3 \approx 0.48$, $\log 5 \approx 0.70$ and $\log 7 \approx 0.85$, evaluate:

a) $2 \log 3 + \log 2$ *b)* $3 \log 2 - \log 7$ *c)* $\log 15$

d) $\log \left(\frac{3}{7}\right)$ *e)* $2 \log 20$ *f)* $2 (\log 7)^2$

7 Without using a calculator, arrange these logarithms in increasing order:

$$\log 10^{10} \qquad 100 \log 10 \qquad \log 100 + \log 100 \qquad -\log 10^{-3}$$

8 Solve the following equations in your head:

a) $\log_2 32 = x$ *b)* $\log_{\frac{1}{2}} x = -3$ *c)* $\log_5 x = -\frac{1}{2}$ *d)* $\log_x 27 = x$

9 For each of these pairs of logarithms, find the one that is larger:

a) $\log_2 3$ or $\log_3 2$ *b)* $\log_{0.5} 2$ or $\log_2 0.5$ *c)* $\log 1000$ or $\ln e^5$

10 Convert the exponential expressions into logarithmic form, and vice versa.

a) $2\log_3 m = n$

b) $m = e^n$

c) $r + 5 = \ln s$

d) $10^{2n-1} = m$

e) $\log_4 (5(m - 1)) = n^2$

f) $2 \log (n + 3) = m - 1$

11 Evaluate the following expressions. If this is not possible, explain why not.

a) $\log_\pi 1$

b) $\log (-1)$

c) $\ln 0$

d) $\log^{\frac{3}{17}} \left(\dfrac{3}{17}\right)$

12 Evaluate the following expressions.

a) $\log_{0.5} 0.5^{-2.3}$

b) $4^{\log_4 \sqrt{3}}$

c) $\log_{12} 10 + \log_{12} 14.4$

d) $\ln e^\pi$

e) $0.3 \log 1$

f) $\log_{0.5} 13 - \log_{0.5} 26$

13 Write the following statements in logarithmic form:

a) 12 is the exponent assigned to base x to obtain a power of 40.

b) x is the natural logarithm of 10.

c) The cube root of 50 is x.

d) The common logarithm of 15 is a.

14 The rule for a basic logarithmic function has the form $f(x) = \log_c x$.

a) What restrictions apply to the base c?

b) For what values of c will the function f be:

   1) Increasing?
   2) Decreasing?

c) What restrictions apply to x? Justify your answer.

15 Three basic logarithmic functions are defined by the rules below:

$$f(x) = \log_3 x \qquad g(x) = \log_5 x \qquad h(x) = \log_{\frac{1}{4}} x$$

a) For each, state the equation of its asymptote.

b) What value of x will result in $f(x) = g(x) = h(x)$?

c) For each rule, find the value of the x-coordinates for the points $(x_1, -1)$ and $(x_2, 1)$.

d) Graph the functions f, g and h.

e) Find the domain and range of each function.

f) Find the interval over which:

   1) $f(x) > g(x)$
   2) $f(x) < h(x)$

Here are the tables of values for the basic logarithmic functions f, g and h respectively.

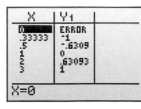

a) State the rule for each function.

b) Can we state that the curves of the functions g and h are symmetric about the x-axis? Explain your answer.

17 The rule $f(x) = \log_{\sqrt{3}} x$ enables us to calculate the elapsed time, in seconds, since a wound occurred, according to the number of bacteria found in the wound. The rule is valid for only the first 30 s following the wound.

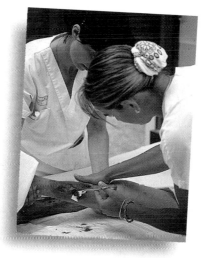

a) Calculate $f(2)$, $f(10)$ and $f(20)$.

b) Sketch the functions f and f^{-1} on the same axes.

c) Compare the domains and ranges of these functions.

18 We calculated the number 15^{100} using a computer. The result took up more than one entire line on the computer screen!

a) Calculate 15^{100} on your calculator. What result appears?

b) Using logarithms, express 15^{100} as a power of 10.

c) How many digits does the result on the computer screen have?

19 Each of the ordered pairs shown belongs to a logarithmic function whose rule has the form $f(x) = \log_c x$. Find the base of each one.

a) $(100, 2)$ **b)** $(16, -2)$ **c)** $(0.2, -1)$

d) $(81, 4)$ **e)** $\left(\dfrac{9}{16}, 2\right)$ **f)** $(4, -2)$

20 Which law of logarithms allows you to state that:

a) $5^{\log_5 18} = 18$ **b)** $\ln 1 = 0$ **c)** $\ln 81 = 4 \ln 3$ **d)** $\ln\left(\dfrac{3}{8}\right) + \ln\left(\dfrac{10}{11}\right) = \ln\left(\dfrac{15}{44}\right)$

e) $\log_{0.3} 0.3^6 = 6$ **f)** $\log 10 = 1$ **g)** $\log_7 8 = \dfrac{\ln 8}{\ln 7}$ **h)** $\log 4 = \log 8 - \log 2$

21 Rewrite each of these logarithms such that the exponent of each variable is 1.

a) $\log_2 m^{10}$ **b)** $2 \log_5 m^3 n^{-4}$ **c)** $\ln \sqrt{\dfrac{m^2}{n^3}}$

22 Reduce these expressions to a single logarithm.

a) $3 \log_2 m + 7 \log_2 n^4$

b) $2 \log_5 m - 2 \log_5 8 + 3 \log_5 n$

c) $\log_c (x^2 - 25) - \log_c (x + 5)$

d) $3 \log_c x - (0.5 \log_c x + 2 \log_c x)$

23 Using $\log_c 2 = x$, $\log_c 3 = y$ and $\log_c 5 = z$, simplify the expression $\log_c \left(\dfrac{4\sqrt{6}}{15} \right)$.

24 Show that: $2 \ln (2x + 4) - \ln x = \ln 4 + \ln \left(x + 4 + \dfrac{4}{x} \right)$.

25 The formula $F = \dfrac{1}{2L} \sqrt{\dfrac{T}{m}}$ is used to calculate the frequency F, in hertz, of a string of length L, from which a mass m is suspended, with tension T. Express $\ln F$ in terms of $\ln L$, $\ln T$ and $\ln m$.

26 Prove:

a) $\log_c \left(\dfrac{1}{m} \right) = -\log_c m$

b) $\log_{\frac{1}{c}} m = -\log_c m$

c) $\log_{\sqrt{c}} m = 2 \log_c m$

d) $(\log_m n)(\log_n m) = 1$

27 Here is the table of values of a logarithmic function. Complete this table using the laws of logarithms.

x	2	3	4	5	6	7	8	9	10
$\log_c x$	0.231	0.367	■	0.537	■	0.650	■	■	■

28 Here are the rules for six logarithmic functions. How many distinct curves can be observed? Justify your answer using the laws of logarithms.

```
Plot1 Plot2 Plot3
\Y1◻ln(X)
\Y2◻ln(5X)
\Y3◻5ln(X)
\Y4◻ln(X)+ln(5)
\Y5◻ln(X^5)
\Y6◻log(X)/log(e)
```

29 For the rule $f(x) = \log x^a$, what is the value of a if its curve coincides with that of the function $g(x) = \ln x$?

30 Using their basic functions, graph the following functions:

a) $g(x) = 3 \log_2 (x + 6)$

b) $h(x) = -\log_2 x - 5$

c) $i(x) = \log_2 (x - 5) + 3$

d) $j(x) = 2 \log_2 (0.5x)$

31 Given the rules $f(x) = \log_2 (b(x - h))$, $g(x) = -\log_2 (x - h) + k$ and $h(x) = \log_c (x - h)$, state the specific rule for each from the information provided in the graphs below.

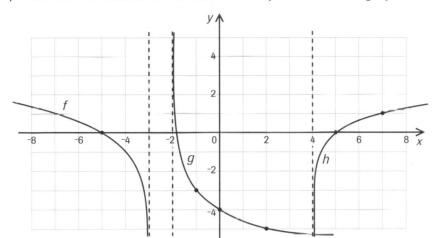

32 Find all the properties of the following functions:

$$f_1(x) = \log_3 (x + 5) - 2$$

$$f_2(x) = -\log_5 (2x)$$

$$f_3(x) = 2 \log_{0.25} x + 3$$

$$f_4(x) = \log (5(x - 1)) - 2$$

33 A student wants to display the following functions on her graphing calculator:

$$g_1(x) = 2 \log_3 x + 4 \qquad g_2(x) = -\log_3 (x + 5) \qquad g_3(x) = \log_{0.4} x - 1$$

For each function, provide a rule she can enter to obtain the desired result.

34 Most calculators only have keys for common and natural logarithms. Based on the following instructions, write a program that will execute a change of base.

1. Request the base of the logarithm to be calculated.

2. Input value C.

3. Request the power of the logarithm to be calculated.

4. Input value A.

5. Use the change of base law to calculate the log of A in base C.

6. Display the result.

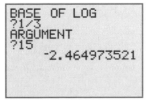

$\log_2 50 = $ ▬▬▬

```
BASE OF LOG
?2
ARGUMENT
?50
          5.64385619
```

$\log_{\frac{1}{3}} 15 = $ ▬▬▬

```
BASE OF LOG
?1/3
ARGUMENT
?15
         -2.464973521
```

35 Determine the zeros (if they exist) of each function algebraically.

a) $f(x) = \log_{0.5} x + 3$ **b)** $gf(x) = 8 \log_2 (x - 5) - 24$ **c)** $h(x) = -3 \log_5 (2x) + 6$

d) $i(x) = 3^{x-4} - 27$ **e)** $j(x) = 11(6)^{x-2}$ **f)** $k(x) = -2.5(4)^{2x+6} + 40$

36 Solve these logarithmic equations:

a) $\log_2 x^2 = 3$

b) $\log_{\sqrt{3}} x + \log_{\frac{2}{3}} \left(\frac{27}{8}\right) = 1$

c) $\ln (x - 2)^2 = 2 \ln (3 - x)$

d) $\log_8 (x - 2) + \log_8 (x + 1) = \frac{2}{3}$

e) $15 - \log_2 10 = \log_2 x + \log_2 3$

f) $\log_3 (\log_3 (\log_3 (\log_3 x))) = 0$

g) $2 \log x + 1 = \log (10x + 20)$

h) $\log (x + 1) + \log (x + 2) - \log (x - 0.8) = 1$

37 Find the domain and range of the following functions:

a) $f(x) = \log (x^2)$ **b)** $g(x) = \ln (x^2 + 3) + 10$ **c)** $h(x) = \log_3 (2x^2 - 5x)$

d) $i(x) = (\log x)^2$ **e)** $j(x) = \log (\log x)$ **f)** $k(x) = \log (\sqrt{x})$

g) $l(x) = \log_5 (\sqrt{x + 5})$ **h)** $m(x) = \log (|x|)$ **i)** $n(x) = \log \left(\frac{x + 1}{x - 1}\right)$

38 The demand for a product varies primarily according to the sales price. A bicycle company estimates that the number of teenagers willing to buy its new helmet follows the rule $C(x) = 30 - 8 \ln \left(\frac{x}{10}\right)$, where $C(x)$ is the number of customers in thousands, and x is the sales price in dollars.

a) How many customers would be willing to buy a helmet that costs $34?

b) By how much must the company lower its price to sell 1000 more helmets?

39 Write a logarithmic equation in one variable whose:

a) Root is 5.

b) Roots are -3 and 4, but only the first value is valid.

c) Roots are 2, 4 and 5, but only the last value is valid.

40 How many zeros can a logarithmic function have? Justify your answer.

41 Solve these inequalities using a graph:

a) $\log x - \log 2 > \log 3 - \log 4$

b) $\log x \leqslant x$

c) $\ln (3x - 8) < \ln (2 - x)$

d) $\log (x^2) > (\log x)^2$

42 Solve these equations and identify the restrictions of each.

a) $x - y = -4$
$\log x + \log y = 1$

b) $x - y = 3$
$2 \log_5 (x + 1) - \log_5 y = 2$

43 Solve these exponential equations to the nearest hundredth:

a) $10^x = e$

b) $2^{2x} = 5^x$

c) $5^{7-x} = 10^{3x-1}$

d) $\left(\dfrac{1}{3}\right)^{2x+5} = 11$

e) $3(2^{2x}) = 6^{4x+1}$

f) $-2(3^{2x}) = -5 \times 4^x$

44 A group of economists presented a study to their local Chamber of Commerce. Based on the study's results, they predicted that the price of a basket of groceries for a family with two children, which was $110 at the time of the study, would increase 1% each month for the next 3 years. According to this hypothesis, how many months after the study would a family with two children pay $140 for a basket of groceries?

45 For each function below, state the rule for the inverse.

a) $f(x) = -5(6)^{2x+7}$

b) $g(x) = 2(3)^{2.5x} - 10$

c) $h(x) = -1.5 e^{x-2} - 4$

d) $i(x) = 2 \log_5 3(x - 1)$

e) $j(x) = -\log 2x + 15$

f) $k(x) = \ln -(x + 3) - 10$

46 In which quadrants will the inverse f^{-1} be located if the logarithmic function f is located in:

a) The 1st and 4th quadrants?

b) The 2nd and 3rd quadrants?

47 A delivery company estimates that its road equipment depreciates by 30% each year. After 5 years one of its transport trucks was worth no more than $12 605.

a) How much did the company pay for this truck?

b) After how much time was the truck worth 10% of its original cost?

48 HEIGHT AND WEIGHT

A mathematical model exists that relates the height h and mass m of children aged 5 to 13. Algebraically, this model follows the formula $m = \ln 2.4 + 0.0184h$, where m is expressed in kilograms and h is expressed in centimetres.

a) State the rule that enables you to:

   1) Express the height of a child as a function of his/her mass by isolating h.

   2) Express the mass of a child as a function of his/her height by isolating m.

b) Use the formula to find:

   1) The height of a child whose mass is 30 kg.

   2) The mass of a child who is between 130 and 150 cm tall.

49 LIGHTNING STRIKES

During a storm, lightning is caused by electrical discharges between two clouds or between a cloud and the earth. The intensity of electrical discharges can be found using Kirchhoff's law. In an experiment where lightning was simulated using sparks, the rule for this law was found to be $I = I_0 e^{-1.4t}$, where I is the electromotive force of the current in volts, I_0 is the initial electromotive force of the current, and t is the duration of the discharge in seconds.

a) How much time after the start of the discharge was the electromotive force of the current reduced by half?

b) What rule expresses the duration of the discharge based on the electromotive force of the current?

50 RADIOACTIVE ELEMENTS

When radioactive elements emit radiation, their mass decreases. The term half-life is used to define the time required for the element to decay to one half of its original mass. The half-life of strontium-90 is 20 years. The half-life of polonium-218 is 3 min.

a) What rule can be used to calculate the mass of:

   1) 20 g of strontium-90 in x years?

   2) 1000 g of polonium-218 after n min?

b) How much time is required:

   1) For the mass of 20 g of strontium-90 to decay by 1/5?

   2) For the mass of 1000 g of polonium-218 to decay by 90%?

Marie Curie (1867–1934) discovered the radioactivity of thorium, polonium and radium. She was the first woman professor at the Sorbonne, and she received the Nobel Prize for Physics in 1903 and the Nobel Prize for Chemistry in 1911.

51 WALKING SPEED

Different studies suggest that the average walking speed of a pedestrian in a city depends on the city's population. The theory is that the higher the population, the higher the stress level, and this stress manifests itself in how fast people walk. A person's average walking speed is estimated by the function $v(x) - 0.01 + 0.46 \log x$, where x is the population and $v(x)$ is the average walking speed in metres per second.

Shibuya district, Tokyo

a) What is the average walking speed of pedestrians in a city of 10 000 people?

b) What can be said about the population of a city where the pedestrians walk faster than 2 m/s?

52 TEST YOUR MEMORY

For a particular TV game show, participants test their visual memories to win prizes. To win a mountain bike, the participants must observe 20 objects for 10 s. The objects are then hidden, and the participant has 15 s to name at least $\frac{3}{4}$ of the objects. The data, in the table below, show the average percentage of 20 objects that a person can memorize according to the time (in seconds) allowed to memorize them

a) By regression, find the logarithmic function that relates the time spent observing 20 objects to the percentage of objects remembered.

b) Explain why it is difficult to win at this game.

c) According to the model, how much time is needed to memorize all 20 objects?

Observation time (s)	Percentage of objects memorized
1	20
2	35
5	45
10	65
15	75
20	80

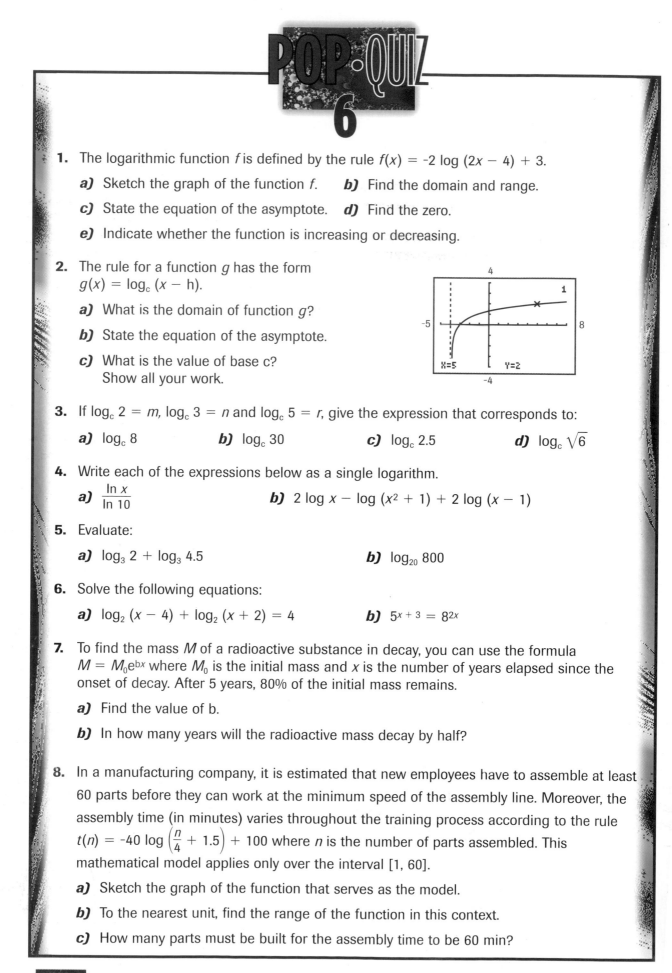

1. The logarithmic function f is defined by the rule $f(x) = -2 \log (2x - 4) + 3$.

    a) Sketch the graph of the function f.   **b)** Find the domain and range.

    c) State the equation of the asymptote.   **d)** Find the zero.

    e) Indicate whether the function is increasing or decreasing.

2. The rule for a function g has the form $g(x) = \log_c (x - h)$.

    a) What is the domain of function g?

    b) State the equation of the asymptote.

    c) What is the value of base c?
    Show all your work.

3. If $\log_c 2 = m$, $\log_c 3 = n$ and $\log_c 5 = r$, give the expression that corresponds to:

    a) $\log_c 8$ **b)** $\log_c 30$ **c)** $\log_c 2.5$ **d)** $\log_c \sqrt{6}$

4. Write each of the expressions below as a single logarithm.

    a) $\dfrac{\ln x}{\ln 10}$ **b)** $2 \log x - \log (x^2 + 1) + 2 \log (x - 1)$

5. Evaluate:

    a) $\log_3 2 + \log_3 4.5$ **b)** $\log_{20} 800$

6. Solve the following equations:

    a) $\log_2 (x - 4) + \log_2 (x + 2) = 4$ **b)** $5^{x + 3} = 8^{2x}$

7. To find the mass M of a radioactive substance in decay, you can use the formula $M = M_0 e^{bx}$ where M_0 is the initial mass and x is the number of years elapsed since the onset of decay. After 5 years, 80% of the initial mass remains.

    a) Find the value of b.

    b) In how many years will the radioactive mass decay by half?

8. In a manufacturing company, it is estimated that new employees have to assemble at least 60 parts before they can work at the minimum speed of the assembly line. Moreover, the assembly time (in minutes) varies throughout the training process according to the rule $t(n) = -40 \log \left(\dfrac{n}{4} + 1.5\right) + 100$ where n is the number of parts assembled. This mathematical model applies only over the interval [1, 60].

    a) Sketch the graph of the function that serves as the model.

    b) To the nearest unit, find the range of the function in this context.

    c) How many parts must be built for the assembly time to be 60 min?

Interview with...

Joseph Louis Lagrange
(1736-1813)

Mr. Lagrange, near the end of the 18th century, you set up the metric system that we currently use. Why did you set up this new measurement system?

At the time there were about 300 different measurement systems being used in Europe. In France alone, different regions were using different measures. As you can imagine, this made many things, including business, very cumbersome. So the government of France set up a commission to implement a common measurement system.

How did you come up with the idea for a measurement system using base 10?

Since the beginning of history, many measurement systems had used a base of 12. So when I suggested a base of 10, the committee members were initially quite skeptical. But then I gave them a brief demonstration and they agreed that a decimal system would make calculations much easier. The committee immediately agreed to use the metric system for measurements of length, mass and volume.

Is it true that both King Louis XVI and Queen Marie-Antoinette admired you very much?

That's what they say! I was in Berlin for about 20 years working at King Frederick's court when the monarchy in France invited me to rejoin them in Paris. I was welcomed with many honours and was offered a place to stay at the Louvre. I also worked as a professor at the French Academy of Sciences.

But there was a time when you lost your interest in mathematics. What happened?

I had been working very hard for 30 years in Berlin. In France, I found myself in a much different situation. The French Revolution really scared me. I tried to remain politically neutral and simply earn a living. It was the marriage to my second wife that rejuvenated me. What a happy marriage!

Joseph Louis Lagrange published numerous works on various subjects. His greatest work, *Mécanique Analytique*, was published in 1788 in Paris. Lagrange was one of the mathematicians who contributed most to the introduction of the analytical method in education. The French recognized his great talent to the extent that when he died, his remains were buried at the Pantheon.

In 1770 Lagrange proved Fermat's famous conjecture: "Every positive integer can be written as a sum of at most four squares." This statement is now called "Lagrange's Four Squares Theorem." Here are some examples:

$$3 = 1 + 1 + 1 \qquad 7 = 4 + 1 + 1 + 1 \qquad 22 = 16 + 4 + 1 + 1 \text{ or } 9 + 9 + 4$$

a) Express these numbers as the sums of four squares or fewer.

1) 12   2) 19   3) 23   4) 48   5) 114

b) Find those numbers from 1 to 20 that can be expressed as a sum of three perfect squares or fewer.

MY PROJECTS

PROJECT 1 The fatherless drone

Queen bees are able to lay eggs, some of which are fertilized and others not. The males, called drones, always come from unfertilized eggs, and the females always come from fertilized eggs. Beekeeper J. Dzierzon is credited with this discovery. It seems that this genetic peculiarity results in the most heart-wrenching situation: drones do not have fathers!

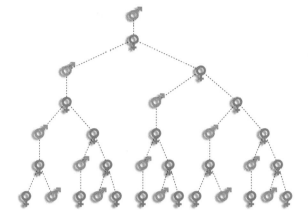

Accounting for the number of individuals in each successive generation, the following numerical series was found:

Generation	1	2	3	4	5	6	7	8	9	10	11
Number of individuals	1	1	2	3	5	8	13	21	34	55	89

a) By regression, define the exponential function that best describes this situation.

b) Using a mathematics dictionary, define the terms "arithmetic series," "geometric series" and "Fibonacci sequence."

c) Research Leonardo Fibonacci's contributions to mathematics.

PROJECT 2 Semi-logarithmic graph

One of the main characteristics of exponential functions is the rapid rate at which they increase or decrease. This makes it very difficult to graph an exponential function if the value of a base or parameter is very large. Using a graph on which the y-axis is scaled in logarithms can simplify graphical representations of exponential functions, such as $h(x) = 50(10)^x$.

a) On graph paper, construct a graph that has the following features:
   1. An x-axis graduated from 0 to 10.
   2. A y-axis graduated from 0 to 10, where each graduation represents the logarithm in base 10 of the powers of 10.

b) Sketch the graphs of functions $f(x) = 10^x$, $g(x) = 2^x$, $h(x) = 50(10)^x$ and $k(x) = 20(0.4)^x$.

c) Describe the type of curves obtained.

d) Research the various types of systems of axes used to represent different functions graphically.

I UNDERSTAND THE MEANING OF THE FOLLOWING EXPRESSIONS:

Base of a logarithm: The number used to define a logarithmic system.

Base of a power: A number to which an exponent has been assigned.

Change of base: The operation that enables you to change the number defining a logarithmic system.

Common logarithm: An exponent assigned to base 10 to obtain a given power x.
It is written $\log_{10} x$ or simply $\log x$.

Exponent: The number assigned to a base to obtain a power.

Exponential function: A function defined by a rule in which the independent variable is an exponent.

Logarithm: An exponent attributed to a base to obtain a given power x.
Thus $x = c^y \implies y = \log_c x$.

Logarithmic function: The inverse of an exponential function.

Natural base: Irrational number written as e and whose value is ≈ 2.718.

Natural logarithm: An exponent assigned to base e to obtain a given power x.
It is written $\log_e x$ or simply $\ln x$.

Power: The result of raising a base to an exponent.

Regression rule: A rule interpreting a mathematical model that gives the best possible representation of a set of points on a Cartesian plane.

INDEX

PHOTO CREDITS

We are grateful to the people, schools and organizations who kindly provided photographs. We also wish to thank the students who took part in the photo sessions.

p. 1   Fractal: Akuma Takegami/Int'l Stock/Réflexion Photothèque

p. 2   Airplane: Sylvain Grandadam/Publiphoto

p. 9   Teacher: Anne Gardon

p. 10   Teacher: Anne Gardon

p. 11   Teacher: Anne Gardon

p. 20   Freezing rain: Catherine Bisson

       Shelter: Publiphoto

p. 22   Celia, Irene, Joseph: Catherine Bisson; Mary, Bertha, Raoul: Scott Barrow/Int'l Stock/Réflexion Photothèque; Morris: Noble Stock/Int'l Stock/Réflexion Photothèque

p. 24   Mexico: Nawrocki Stock Photo/Réflexion Photothèque

p. 26   Teacher and students: Anne Gardon

p. 27   Ultrasound: Réflexion Photothèque

p. 28   Teacher and students: Anne Gardon

p. 29   Unicycle: Réflexion Photothèque

p. 30   Graduates: Catherine Bisson

p. 33   Camper on mountain top: Tony Denim/Réflexion Photothèque

p. 43   Olympic medalists: *La Presse* Newspaper

p. 44   Migraine headache sufferer: Réflexion Photothèque

p. 48   Students: Anne Gardon

p. 49   Montréal Exchange: Michel Gagné/Réflexion Photothèque

p. 51   Rollerblader: Sean O'Neill/Réflexion Photothèque

p. 60   Statue of Liberty: Valder/Torney/Int'l Stock/Réflexion Photothèque

       Pig: Stock Imagery/Réflexion Photothèque

p. 67   Saint-Lambert Lock: Tibor Bognar/Réflexion Photothèque

       Côte-Sainte-Catherine Locks: Catherine Bisson

p. 73   Teacher and students: Anne Gardon

p. 75   Raccoon: Réflexion Photothèque

p. 76   Apple orchard: Guy Schiele/Publiphoto

p. 83   Snowflake: Mehaw Kulyk/Science Photo Library/Publiphoto

p. 85   Sprinkler system: Guy Schiele/Publiphoto

p. 87   Adolescent: Catherine Bisson

p. 88   Adolescent: Catherine Bisson

p. 90   Beach: Tibor Bognar/Réflexion Photothèque

       Bay of Alma: B. Terry/Réflexion Photothèque

p. 91   Water purification plant: City of Montréal

p. 96   Child with kite: O. Plantey/Publiphoto

       Chinese kite: A. Grosclaude/Publiphoto

p. 100   Adolescent: Anne Gardon

p. 102   Supersonic jet: Marc Simon/Publiphoto

p. 105   Calculator: Anne Gardon

p. 107   Kennedy Space Center: Réflexion Photothèque

p. 111   Ship: Mauritius-Huhnholz/Réflexion Photothèque

p. 112   Evergreens: Wilson North/Int'l Stock/Réflexion Photothèque

p. 113   Water slides: J. Greenberg/Camerique/Réflexion Photothèque

p. 114   Electrical tower: Catherine Bisson

p. 115   Pendulum: Publiphoto

p. 117   Rescue operation: Ron Kokcis/Publiphoto

p. 118   Outboard: Catherine Bisson

p. 120   Adolescent: Catherine Bisson

       P. Roussel/Publiphoto

p. 131   Fakir: S. Grandadam/Publiphoto

p. 133   Chernobyl nuclear plant: Novosti/Science Photo Library/Publiphoto

       Danger of radioactivity sign: PonoPresse

NOTATION AND SYMBOLS

$\{...\}$: set

$\mathbb{N}$: set of natural numbers $= \{0, 1, 2, 3, ...\}$

$\mathbb{N}^*$: set of natural numbers excluding zero $= \{1, 2, 3, ...\}$

$\mathbb{Z}$: set of integers $= \{..., -3, -2, -1, 0, 1, 2, 3, ...\}$

$\mathbb{Z}_+$: set of positive integers $= \{0, 1, 2, 3, ...\}$

$\mathbb{Z}_-$: set of negative integers $= \{0, -1, -2, -3, ...\}$

$\mathbb{Q}$: set of rational numbers

$\mathbb{Q}'$: set of irrational numbers

$\mathbb{R}$: set of real numbers

$A \cup B$: A union B

$A \cap B$: A intersection B

A' : complement

$A \setminus B$: A less B or A minus B

$\varnothing$ or $\{\}$: empty set

∞ : infinity

$-\infty$: negative infinity

$+\infty$: positive infinity

$\forall$: for every

$\exists$: there exist(s)

$\exists!$: there exists one and only one

$\in$: . . . belongs to . . . or . . . is an element of . . .

$\notin$: . . . does not belong to . . . or . . . is not an element of

$\subseteq$: . . . is included in or equal to . . . is a subsct of . . .

$\subset$: . . . is a proper subset of . . .

$\not\subset$: . . . is not a proper subset of

$\dfrac{a}{b}$: fraction a, b or ratio a, b or quotient a, b

$a : b$: the ratio of a to b

$-a$: the opposite of number a

a^2 : a squared, a to the second power, or a to the power of two

$\dfrac{1}{a}$: the reciprocal of number a

a^x : a exponent x, or a to the power of x

$[x]$: greatest integer less than or equal to

$a!$: factorial a

$|a|$: absolute value of a

$\sqrt{a}$: the positive, or principal, square root of a

$-\sqrt{a}$: the negative square root of a

$\sqrt[3]{a}$: cube root of a

$\sqrt[n]{a}$: n^{th} root of a

$\log_c x$: logarithm of x to base c

$\log x$: logarithm of x to base 10

$\ln x$: logarithm of x to base e (or natural logarithm of x)

$\sin x$: sine x

$\cos x$: cosine x

$\tan x$: tangent x

$\bar{x}$: arithmetic mean of x

$\sum(x)$: sum of x

Med : median

Mo : mode

$a \cdot 10^n$: scientific notation, where $1 \leqslant a < 10$ and $n \in \mathbb{Z}$

(a, b) : ordered pair a, b

$[a, b]$: closed interval with endpoints a and b

$]a, b[$: open interval with endpoints a and b

$[a, b[$: interval open on the right with endpoints a and b

$]a, b]$: interval open on the left with endpoints a and b

f : function f

f^{-1} : inverse of f

$f(x)$: f of x, value of function f for x, image of x by f

dom f : domain of f

ran f : range of f

$x_1, x_2, \ldots$: specific values of x

$y_1, y_2, \ldots$: specific values of y

$\neq$: . . . is not equal to . . . or . . . is different from . . .

$<$: . . . is less than . . .

$>$: . . . is greater than . . .

$\leqslant$: . . . is less than or equal to . . .

$\geqslant$: . . . is greater than or equal to . . .

$\approx$: . . . is approximately equal to . . .

$\cong$: . . . is congruent to . . . or

. . . has the same measure as . . . or . . . is isometric to . . .

$\equiv$: . . . is identical to . . .

$\sim$: . . . is similar to . . .

$\triangleq$: . . . corresponds to . . .

$\wedge$: and

$\vee$: or

$\Rightarrow$: . . . implies that . . .

$\Leftrightarrow$: . . . is logically equivalent to . . .

$\mapsto$: . . . has as its image . . .

Ω : universe of possibilities or set of results

$P(A)$: probability of event A

$\overline{AB}$: line segment AB

m $\overline{AB}$ or meas $\overline{AB}$: length of line segment AB

$d(A, B)$: distance between A and B

AB : line AB

$\parallel$: . . . is parallel to . . .

$\nparallel$: . . . is not parallel to . . .

$\perp$: . . . is perpendicular to . . .

$\angle A$: angle A

$\overparen{AB}$: arc with endpoints A and B

$\overparen{AOB}$: arc passing through O and with endpoints A and B

m $\angle A$ or meas $\angle A$: measure of angle A

$n°$: n degrees

$\llcorner$: right angle

$\triangle ABC$: triangle ABC

t : translation t

t^1 : inverse of t

r : rotation r

$\wr$: reflection $\wr$

gr : glide reflection gr

h : dilatation

. . . o . . . : composite function

$\$k$: thousands of dollars

$\$M$: millions of dollars

$\$G$: billions of dollars

km/h : kilometres per hour

m/s : metres per second

°C : degrees Celsius

C : circumference, or perimeter, of a circle

P : perimeter

d : diameter

r : radius r

π : 3.141 59... or $\approx$ 3.14

A_l : lateral area

A_t : total area

V : volume

$P(x)$: polynomial in x

$P(x, y)$: polynomial in x, y

R_5 : quintile rank

R_{100} : centile rank

Q_1, Q_2, Q_3 : quartiles

EI : interquartile rank

A·N·S·W·E·R·S

R·E·F·L·E·C·T·I·O·N 1

Workout 1

1. $\frac{7}{13}$, since $\frac{1}{2} = \frac{52}{104}$, $\frac{7}{13} = \frac{56}{104}$ and $\frac{3}{8} = \frac{39}{104}$

3. An infinite number. Because there are an infinite number of numbers between 2 and 3, there are an infinite number of numbers between $\sqrt{2}$ and $\sqrt{3}$.

5. ≈ 300

7. An infinite number. Because there are an infinite number of numbers between 2 and 3, there are an infinite number of numbers between $\frac{2}{5}$ and $\frac{3}{5}$.

9. $72 \times 0.46 \approx 72 \times 0.5 \approx 36$

11. a) $\{-12.5, 12.5\}$ **b)** $\{-170, 170\}$

    c) $\{-8.4, 8.4\}$ **d)** $\{-7, 7\}$

    e) $\{-12, 2\}$ **f)** $\{-50, 20\}$

    g) $\left\{\frac{1}{4}, \frac{3}{4}\right\}$ **h)** $\{-4, 3.6\}$

    i) $\{-5.08, 5.08\}$ **j)** $\{-16, 16\}$

13. a) ≈ 7.0 **b)** ≈ 1.0 **c)** ≈ 3.2 **d)** ≈ 2.6

15. a) The cyclist increased his speed for 25 min, decreased his speed over the next 25 min, stopped for 10 min, accelerated for 25 min, then decreased his speed over the last 15 min.

    b) [0, 25] and [50, 85]

    c) Between 50 min and 60 min after his departure (the 6th 10 min period).

d)

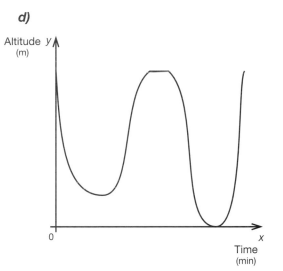

    e) Domain: [0, 100]
       Range: [0, 40]

17. a) $f(x) = 2|x + 2| - 3$

    b) $g(x) = 2|x - 6| + 1$

    c) $h(x) = -|x - 2| + 5$

19. a) $y = -|x - 2| + 4$

    b) Domain: $\mathbb{R}$
       Range: $]-\infty, 4]$

    c) Increasing over $]-\infty, 2]$
       Decreasing over $[2, +\infty[$

21. a) $\left\{-\frac{15}{2}, \frac{5}{2}\right\}$ **b)** $\{1, 2\}$

    c) $\left\{\frac{3}{4}, \frac{7}{4}\right\}$ **d)** $\mathbb{R}$

23. a) Function is positive for $x \in]-\infty, -6] \cup [0, +\infty[$
       Function is negative for $x \in [-6, 0]$

    b) Function is positive for $x \in [-4.5, -3.5]$
       Function is negative for $x \in]-\infty, -4.5] \cup [-3.5, +\infty[$

    c) Function is positive for $x \in \mathbb{R}$
       Function is never negative.

25. a) $\left[\frac{2}{3}, 8\right]$ **b)** $]1.5, +\infty[$

27. a) $V(t) = 2.5|x - 5| + 3.5$

b) $21

c) After 10 months.

d) $5 (or 31.5%) over a 12–month period.

29. a) {-2, 10}   **b)**]-2, +∞[

c) {-4, 8}   **d)**]-4, 8[

31. a) It must be vertical, or parallel to the y-axis.

b) $x = a$

33. a) Graph: semi-parabola

Domain:]-∞, 3]

Range: [-1, +∞[

Zero: 2

Minimum: -1

Decreasing over]-∞, 3]

Positive over]-∞, 2]

Negative over [2, 3]

Inverse: is a function

$$y = -(x + 1)^2 + 3 \text{ where } x \geq -1$$

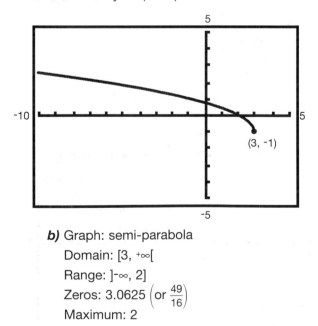

b) Graph: semi-parabola

Domain: [3, +∞[

Range:]-∞, 2]

Zeros: 3.0625 $\left(\text{or } \frac{49}{16}\right)$

Maximum: 2

Decreasing over [3, +∞[

Positive over [3, 3.0625]

Negative over [3.0625, +∞[

Inverse: is a function

$$y = \frac{1}{64}(x - 2)^2 + 3 \text{ where } x \leq 2$$

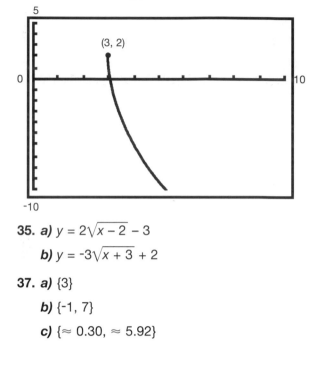

35. a) $y = 2\sqrt{x - 2} - 3$

b) $y = -3\sqrt{x + 3} + 2$

37. a) {3}

b) {-1, 7}

c) {≈ 0.30, ≈ 5.92}

39. a) $f^{-1}(x) = 2\sqrt{x - 2} + 4$

b) $(6 + 2\sqrt{3}, 6 + 2\sqrt{3})$

41. a) ≈ 25.3 mm

b) Rule: $y = 8\sqrt{x}$

Graph: semi-parabola

Domain: [0, 10]

Range: [0, $8\sqrt{10}$]

Zero: 0

Maximum: $8\sqrt{10}$

Minimum: 0

Function increasing over [0, 10]

Function is positive over [0, 10]

Function is negative over {0}

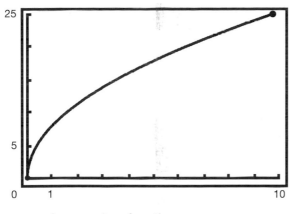

Inverse: is a function
$$y = \frac{x^2}{64} \text{ for } x \in [0, 8\sqrt{10}]$$

43. Yes, since the level in the vase rises with time; but this increase is progressively slower as the vase is filled.

page 150

45.

$$f(h + 1) - f(h) = a\sqrt{h + 1 - h} + k - (a\sqrt{h - h} + k)$$
$$= a\sqrt{1} + k - k$$
$$= a$$

$$f(h - 1) - f(h) = a\sqrt{-(h - 1 - h)} + k - (a\sqrt{-(h - h)} + k)$$
$$= a\sqrt{1} + k - k$$
$$= a$$

47. a) For f_1: There is a vertical scale change of factor 1/3 followed by a translation of 4 units to the right.

For f_2: There is a horizontal scale change of factor 1/3 followed by a vertical translation of 7 units down.

For f_3: There is a vertical scale change of factor 5, followed by a horizontal scale change of factor 1/3, followed by a reflection across the y-axis.

b) For f_1: 1 unit.
For f_2: 1/3 unit.
For f_3: 1/3 unit.

c) For f_1: 1/3 unit.
For f_2: 1 unit.
For f_3: 5 units.

49. a) $\frac{1}{5}$ unit

b) 3 units

c) 3 units

page 151

d) 1 unit

e) 1 unit

51. a) Consider $f(x) - \sqrt{x}$ and $g(x) - [x]$
$$h(x) = (g \circ f)(x) = [\sqrt{x}]$$
$$i(x) = -(f \circ g)(x) = -\sqrt{[x]}$$

b)

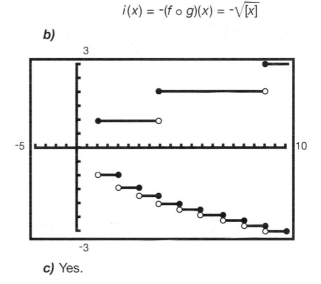

c) Yes.

d) No.

53. a) 34 s

b) A truncation.

c) From 0 m to $\approx$ 13.9 m.

page 152

55. a)

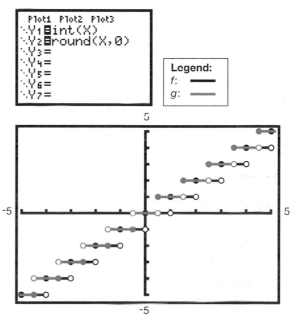

b) No known simple transformation.

c) $g(x) = [x + 0.5]$ for $x \geq 0$
$\quad\quad -[-(x + 0.5)] - 1$ for $x < 0$

57. a) (Other answers are possible.)

For function f, the segments are 2 units apart and the length of each segment is 3 units.

For function g, the segments are 3 units apart and the length of each segment is 2 units.

b) The result is the graph of function f under a reflection across the x-axis of the basic function $y = [x]$. The function is decreasing over IR and the segments are closed-open.

The graph of function g is obtained following a reflection across the y-axis of the basic function $y = [x]$. The function is also decreasing over IR, but the segments are open-closed.

c) Function f is increasing over IR, but the segments are closed-open.

Function g is increasing over IR, but the segments are open-closed.

59. a) $f_1(x) = \dfrac{2}{x - 1} + 3$ for $x \neq 1$

b) $f_2(x) = 3x - 1$ for $x \neq 1$ (impossible)

c) $f_3(x) = \dfrac{9}{2(x - 3.5)}$ for $x \neq 3.5$

d) $f_4(x) = \dfrac{4}{x + 4} - 1$ for $x \neq -4$

e) $f_5(x) = \dfrac{-1.5}{4(x - 0.5)} - 1.25$ for $x \neq 0.5$

f) $f_6(x) = \dfrac{3}{2(x + 2)}$ for $x \neq -2$ and $x \neq 2$

page 153

61. a) Homographic rational function.

b)

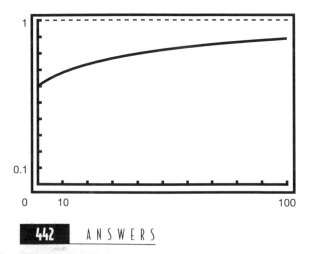

c) 24 consecutive baskets.

d) It represents a success rate of 100%.

63. a) $C(h, k)$ and $y = x + (k - h)$
$\quad\quad\quad\quad\quad y = -x + (k + h)$

b) Yes.

65. $f(x) = \dfrac{2}{3(x - 10)} - 9$

page 154

67. a) $R(x) = \dfrac{400\ 000 + 100x}{x + 20\ 000}$

b) More than 44 000 m².

69. a) $f^{-1}(x) = \dfrac{4x + 6}{4 - 3x}$

b) Homographic rational function.

c) $x = \dfrac{4}{3}$ $y = -\dfrac{4}{3}$

71. Domain $(f_1 \bullet f_2) = $ IR $\setminus \{-2, 3\}$
Range $(f_1 \bullet f_2) = \left\{\dfrac{15}{16}\right\}$
Zero: none

73. $(f \circ f)(x) = \sqrt{\sqrt{x}} = (x^{1/2})^{1/2} = x^{1/4} = \sqrt[4]{x}$

page 155

75. (Other answers are possible.)
$h(x) = \sqrt{x^2 - 1}$ et $j(x) = \left(\dfrac{h}{g}\right)(x)$

77. a) Minimum: 6; function is increasing over $[-4, {}^+\infty[$ and decreasing over $]-\infty, 2]$.

b) Minimum: -6; function is increasing over IR and decreasing over $]-\infty, 4]$ and $[2, {}^+\infty[$.

c) Minimum: 0; function is increasing over $[-4, -1]$ and $[2, {}^+\infty[$ and decreasing over $]-\infty, -4]$ and $[-1, 2]$.

d) Minimum: 0; function is increasing over $[-4, 2[$ and decreasing over $]-\infty, -4]$ and $]2, {}^+\infty[$.

79. a) $y = 2\sqrt{(x - 4)} + 3$

b) $y = 2(x - 1)^2 + 3$

c) $y = -1.5x + 3$

d) $y = 3|x - 1| + 2$

e) $y = \dfrac{2x - 1}{x + 2}$

f) $y = 2\left[\dfrac{x}{2}\right] - 1$

81. *a)*

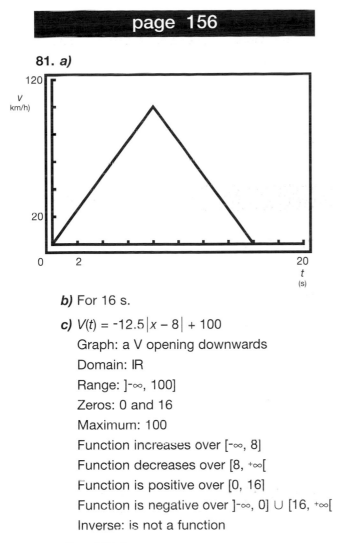

b) For 16 s.

c) $V(t) = -12.5|x - 8| + 100$

Graph: a V opening downwards

Domain: IR

Range: $]-\infty, 100]$

Zeros: 0 and 16

Maximum: 100

Function increases over $[-\infty, 8]$

Function decreases over $[8, {}^+\infty[$

Function is positive over $[0, 16]$

Function is negative over $]-\infty, 0] \cup [16, {}^+\infty[$

Inverse: is not a function

d) ≈ 222.2 m

83. *a)* $y = \dfrac{3000}{x - 200} + 2$

b) ≈ 307.14 m

c) 90 mm

page 192

Workout 2

1.

5	-9	-8	2
-6	0	-1	-3
-2	-4	-5	1
-7	3	4	-10

3. **a)** $\frac{2}{6} + \frac{4}{8}$ **b)** $\frac{4}{6} - \frac{8}{2}$

   c) $\frac{2}{6} \times \frac{4}{8}$ or $\frac{2}{8} \times \frac{4}{6}$ **d)** $\frac{2}{6} \div \frac{8}{4}$ or $\frac{2}{8} \div \frac{6}{4}$

5. C

7. **a)** 288

   b) 288

   c) 2484

   d) 3596

9. **a)** $y = 2x + 3$

   b) $y = 4 - 4x$

   c) $y = 4x - 2$

page 193

11. **a)** The difference between the x-coordinate and the y-coordinate must be less than 6.

   b) (Other answers are possible.)
     (8, 0) and (12, 0)

   c) No, because the difference is 6.

13. (5, 11)

page 194

15. **a)** Yes; $x - 4y > -8$.

   b) $2x + y > 4$:   1) No.   2) No.   3) Yes.
     $x - 4y > 8$:   1) Yes.   2) No.   3) Yes.
     $y < 2x + 0.25$: 1) No.   2) No.   3) Yes.
     $y < x^2 + 2$:   1) Yes.   2) No.   3) Yes.

17. **a)** $y \geq 3x + 10$

   b) $y = 3x + 10$

   c) Above.

page 195

19. **a)** x: number of in–ground pools
     y: number of above–ground pools
$$x \geq 0$$
$$y \geq 0$$
$$10x + 12y \geq 120$$
$$x > 4$$
$$y \leq 6$$
$$x + y \leq 12$$

   b)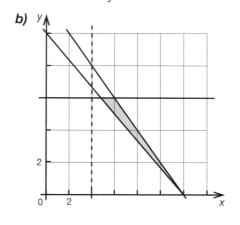

   c) (6, 6), (12, 0) and (4.8, 6)

21. (Other answers are possible.)

   a) You have to be older than 18 to enter a bar.

   b) Deannah has some money in her wallet. She pays $33 for a pair of running shoes and has at least $50 left.

   c) The temperature in the refrigerator must be greater than -4°C but not greater than 10°C.

   d) Peter and Petra own 56.5 ha of land.

page 196

23. **a)** 1) Yes.   2) Yes.   3) Yes.

43. a)

Decay of technetium

t (h)	Q (g)
0	5
1	≈ 4.5242
2	≈ 4.0937
3	≈ 3.7041
4	≈ 3.3516
5	≈ 3.0327
6	≈ 2.7441
7	≈ 2.4829
8	≈ 2.2466
9	≈ 2.0328
10	≈ 1.8394

b) ≈ 6.93 h

c)

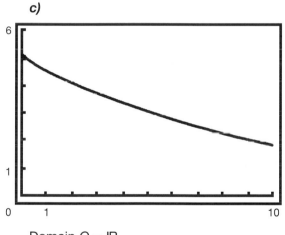

Domain Q = IR
Range Q =]0, +∞[
Value at x = 0: 5
No zero.
Function decreasing over IR
Function positive over IR
Extremes: none
Asymptote: $y = 0$

page 379

45. a) Curve A.

b) -3

c) (Other answers are possible.)
{(-3, 0), (-4, 1), (-1, -1)}

d) (-5, -5)

47. a) ≈ 1.648 437 5

b) e ^ 0.5 ≈ 1.648 721 271
There is a difference of about 0.000 283 77.

page 380

49. a) (Other answers are possible.)
Column Y_1 represents the powers of 3.

b) Each number in column Y_2 is equal to the sum of the number beside it in column Y_1 and the previous values of Y_1.

c) (Calculator work.)

d) 55 987

51. a) $f(x) = 6(3)^x$ **b)** $f(x) = (0.8)^x$

c) $f(x) = -4(1.25)^x$

page 381

53. $s(x) = 4(1.5)^x$
$r(x) = 4(1.5)^{-x+4}$ or $r(x) = 4\left(\frac{2}{3}\right)^{x-4}$

55. a) $x > 3$

b) $x > -4$

c) $x > -\frac{1}{2}$

57. a) 1) $f \circ g\ (x) = 3(2)^{-2x+8} + 2$
2) $g \circ f\ (x) = -6(2)^{x+5} - 1$

b) Domain $(f \circ g)$ = IR
Range $(f \circ g)$ =]2, +∞[

Domain $(g \circ f)$ = IR
Range $(g \circ f)$ =]-∞, -1[

page 382

59. a) ≈ 7.68 billion people.

b) In 2078.

61. a) Daily: $V = 1 \left(1 + \frac{1}{365}\right)^{365}$; $2.714\ 57

Hourly: 8 760; $V = 1 \left(1 + \frac{1}{8760}\right)^{8\ 760}$;
$2.718\ 127

Each second: 31 536 000;
$V = 1 \left(1 + \frac{1}{31\ 536\ 000}\right)^{31\ 536\ 000}$;
$2.718\ 282

b) The value increases as the number of capitalization periods increases.

c) Towards e ($\approx$ 2.72).

d) $\approx$ $1.98

e) 1) $6 468.57
2) $6 411.22

63. a) 10^6 times.

b) 10^{12} times.

c) $\approx$ 105 699 years

65. a) $(T_1 - T_2) \approx 49.2668(0.9843)^t$

b) $T_1 \approx 49.2668(0.9843)^t + 28$

c)

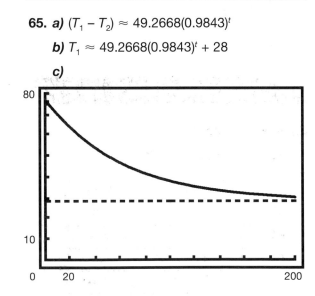

Workout 6

1. (Other answers are possible.)

2 + 3 + 4 + 5 + 6	1 + 2 + 3 + 7 + 7
0 + 1 + 1 + 9 + 9	1 + 4 + 4 + 5 + 6
0 + 1 + 5 + 5 + 9	2 + 2 + 5 + 5 + 6
0 + 2 + 4 + 6 + 8	3 + 3 + 3 + 5 + 6
1 + 1 + 2 + 8 + 8	3 + 4 + 1 + 3 + 9

3. D

5. (Other answers are possible.)
$x \approx 4$ and $y \approx 2.5$

a) $\approx$ 10 **b)** $\approx$ 3 **c)** $\approx$ 1.6 **d)** $\approx$ 4

7. $-\log 10^{-3}$, $\log 100 + \log 100$, $\log 10^{10}$, $100 \log 10$

9. a) $\log_2 3$ **b)** $\log_{0.5} 2 = \log_2 0.5$ **c)** $\ln e^5$

11. a) 0

b) Impossible, because the argument is negative.

c) Impossible, because the argument is negative.

d) 1

13. a) $\log_x 40 = 12$ **b)** $\ln 10 = x$

c) $\log_{50} x = \frac{1}{3}$ **d)** $\log 15 = a$

15. a) $x = 0$

b) $x = 1$

c)

	x_1	x_2
f	$\frac{1}{3}$	3
g	$\frac{1}{5}$	5
h	4	$\frac{1}{4}$

d)

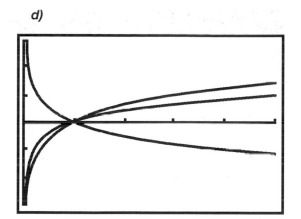

e) For all the functions, the domain is $]0, {}^{+}\infty[$.

For all the functions, the domain is IR.

f) 1) $]1, {}^{+}\infty[$ 2) $]0, 1[$

17. a) $f(2) \approx 1.26$ s

$f(10) \approx 4.19$ s

$f(20) \approx 5.45$ s

b)

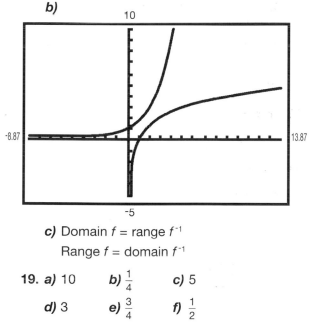

c) Domain f = range f^{-1}

Range f = domain f^{-1}

19. a) 10   **b)** $\frac{1}{4}$ **c)** 5

d) 3   **e)** $\frac{3}{4}$ **f)** $\frac{1}{2}$

21. a) $10 \log_2 m$ **b)** $6 \log_5 m - 8 \log_5 n$

c) $\ln m - \frac{3}{2} \ln n$

23. $2.5x - 0.5y - z$ or $\frac{5x - y - 2z}{2}$

25. $\ln F = \ln \left(\frac{1}{2L} \sqrt{\frac{T}{m}} \right)$

$= \frac{1}{2} \ln T - \left(\ln 2 + \ln L + \frac{1}{2} \ln m \right)$

27.

x	$\log_c x$
4	0.462
6	0.598
8	0.693
9	0.734
10	0.768

29. $\frac{1}{\log e}$ or $\ln 10$

31. $f(x) = \log \left(-\frac{1}{2}(x + 3) \right)$

$g(x) = -\log_2 (x + 2) - 3$

$h(x) = \log_3 (x - 4)$

33.

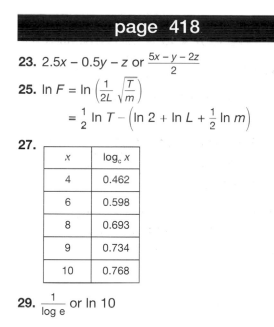

35. a) 8   **b)** 13   **c)** 12.5

d) 7   **e)** None.   **f)** -2

37.

		Domain	Range
a)	f	IR*	IR
b)	g	IR	$[11.099, {}^{+}\infty[$
c)	h	IR \ [0, 2.5]	IR
d)	i	$]0, {}^{+}\infty[$	$[0, {}^{+}\infty[$
e)	j	$]1, {}^{+}\infty[$	IR
f)	k	$]0, {}^{+}\infty[$	IR
g)	l	$]-5, {}^{+}\infty[$	IR
h)	m	IR*	IR
i)	n	$]-\infty, -1[\cup]1, {}^{+}\infty[$ IR	IR \ {0}

39. (Other answers are possible.)

a) $\log_5 x = 1$

b) $\left(\dfrac{1}{x-4}\right) \log(x^2 - x - 11) = 0$

c) $(x-2)(x-4)\log(x-4) = 0$

page 421

41. a) $x \in]1.5, {}^+\infty[$ **b)** $x \in]0, {}^+\infty[$

    c) No solution.   **d)** $]1, 100[$

43. a) ≈ 0.43 **b)** 0

    c) ≈ 1.59 **d)** ≈ -3.59

    e) ≈ -0.12 **f)** ≈ 1.13

45. a) $f^{-1}(x) = 0.5 \log_6\left(\dfrac{-x}{5}\right) - 3.5$

    b) $g^{-1}(x) = 0.4 \log_3\left(\dfrac{x+10}{2}\right)$

    c) $h^{-1}(x) = \ln\left(\dfrac{x+4}{-1.5}\right) + 2$ or

       $h^{-1}(x) = \ln\left(\dfrac{-2(x+4)}{3}\right) + 2$

    d) $i^{-1}(x) = \dfrac{5^{\frac{x}{2}}}{3} + 1$

    e) $j^{-1}(x) = \dfrac{10^{15-x}}{2}$

    f) $k^{-1}(x) = -e^{x+10} - 3$

47. a) About $75 000.

    b) ≈ 6.46 years

page 422

49. a) ≈ 0.5 s

    b) $t = \dfrac{\ln\left(\frac{I}{I_0}\right)}{-1.4}$ or $t = \dfrac{\ln I_0 - \ln I_0}{4}$

page 423

51. a) 1.85 m/s

    b) $\approx 21\ 188$ people